GEOMETRY

AND THE

IMAGINATION

BY

D. HILBERT

AND

S. COHN-VOSSEN

TRANSLATED BY
P. NEMENYI

CHELSEA PUBLISHING COMPANY
NEW YORK
1956

THIS WORK IS A TRANSLATION INTO ENGLISH
OF THE FAMOUS *ANSCHAULICHE GEOMETRIE*
BY DAVID HILBERT AND S. COHN-VOSSEN

PREFACE

In mathematics, as in any scientific research, we find two tendencies present. On the one hand, the tendency toward *abstraction* seeks to crystallize the *logical* relations inherent in the maze of material that is being studied, and to correlate the material in a systematic and orderly manner. On the other hand, the tendency toward *intuitive understanding* fosters a more immediate grasp of the objects one studies, a live *rapport* with them, so to speak, which stresses the concrete meaning of their relations.

As to geometry, in particular, the abstract tendency has here led to the magnificent systematic theories of Algebraic Geometry, of Riemannian Geometry, and of Topology; these theories make extensive use of abstract reasoning and symbolic calculation in the sense of algebra. Notwithstanding this, it is still as true today as it ever was that *intuitive* understanding plays a major role in geometry. And such concrete intuition is of great value not only for the research worker, but also for anyone who wishes to study and appreciate the results of research in geometry.

In this book, it is our purpose to give a presentation of geometry, as it stands today, in its visual, intuitive aspects. With the aid of visual imagination we can illuminate the manifold facts and problems of geometry, and beyond this, it is possible in many cases to depict the geometric outline of the methods of investigation and proof, without necessarily entering into the details connected with the strict definitions of concepts and with the actual calculations. For example, the proof of the fact that a sphere with a hole can always be bent—no matter how small the hole—or of the fact that two different toroidal surfaces can not in general be wrapped onto each other conformally, can be treated in such a fashion that even one who does not wish to follow the details of the analytical arguments, may still gain an insight into how and why the proof works.

In this manner, geometry being as many-faceted as it is and being related to the most diverse branches of mathematics, we may even obtain a summarizing survey of mathematics as a whole, and a valid idea of the variety of its problems and the wealth of ideas it contains. Thus a presentation of geometry in large brushstrokes, so to speak, and based on the approach through visual intuition, should contribute to a more just appreciation of mathematics by a wider range of people than just the specialists. For it is true, generally speaking, that mathematics is not a popular subject, even though its importance may be generally conceded. The reason for this is to be found in the common superstition that mathematics is but a continuation, a further development, of the fine art of arithmetic, of juggling with numbers. Our book aims to combat that superstition, by offering, instead of formulas, figures that may be looked at and that may easily be supplemented by models which the reader can construct. This book was written to bring about a greater enjoyment of mathematics, by making it easier for the reader to penetrate to the essence of mathematics without having to weight himself down under a laborious course of studies.

With aims like these to strive after, there could be no question of strict systematic arrangement or of completeness, nor was it possible to treat individual topics exhaustively. Also, it was impossible to assume the same amount of mathematical training on the reader's part as a prerequisite for all sections of the book; while the presentation is for the most part quite elementary, there are nevertheless some beautiful geometric investigations which can be fully explained only to those with a certain amount of training if tiresome length of presentation is to be avoided.

The appendices to the various chapters all assume a certain amount of knowledge for their understanding; they are throughout supplements to, and not explanations of, the main text.

The various branches of geometry are all interrelated closely and quite often unexpectedly. This shows up in many places in this book. Even so, because of the great diversity of the material treated, it was necessary to make each chapter more or less self-contained, and to avoid making the later chapters dependent for their understanding on a complete acquaintance with the earlier ones. We hope that, by making a few minor repetitions, we have rendered each chapter taken by itself—occasionally even an individual section taken by itself—understandable and interesting. We want to take the reader on a leisurely walk, as it were, in the big garden that is geometry, so that each may pick for himself a bouquet to his liking.

The basis for this book was a course of lectures, given four times weekly, called *Anschauliche Geometrie*, which I gave at Göttingen in the winter of 1920-21 and for which W. Rosemann worked out notes. In essence, the outline and contents of that course have been retained for this book, but S. Cohn-Vossen has re-worked many details, and has supplemented the material in quite a few places.

The line diagrams have all been drawn by K. H. Naumann and H. Bödeker (Göttingen). The photographic pictures were taken by W. Jentzsch (Göttingen), and the models he photographed belong to the collection of the Göttingen Mathematical Institute. The following have read the manuscript and proofs and made many valuable suggestions: W. Fenchel, H. Lewy, H. Schwerdtfeger, H. Heesch, and especially A. Schmidt. The final arrangement of the book has been S. Cohn-Vossen's responsibility.

DAVID HILBERT

Göttingen, June 1932

CONTENTS

CHAPTER III
PROJECTIVE CONFIGURATIONS

CHAPTER IV
DIFFERENTIAL GEOMETRY

CHAPTER V
KINEMATICS

CHAPTER VI
TOPOLOGY

APPENDICES TO CHAPTER VI

CHAPTER I

THE SIMPLEST CURVES AND SURFACES

§ 1. Plane Curves

The simplest surface is the plane. The simplest curves are the plane curves, and of these the simplest is the straight line. The straight line can be defined as the shortest path between two points, or as the intersection of two planes, or as an axis of rotation.

The next simplest curve is the circle. Even so simple a figure as this has given rise to so many and such profound investigations that they could constitute a course all by themselves. We define the circle as the curve whose points are of constant distance from a given point. We generate it by means of the well-known construction using a thread or a compass. From this construction it is evident that the circle is a closed curve that is everywhere convex. Hence a definite straight line—the tangent—can be drawn through any point of the circle so as to have only this one point —the point of contact—in common with the circle while remaining outside the circle everywhere else (see Fig. 1). If B is the point of contact, the radius MB must be the shortest path joining the center M to the tangent t. For, all other points of t, being outside the circle, must be farther from M than the point of contact. From this it follows that the radius MB is perpendicular to the tangent. To prove this, we reflect the center M in the tangent t, i.e. we drop the perpendicular from M onto t and extend it by its own length to M'; M' is called the image of M. Now since MB is the shortest path from M to t, it follows because of symmetry that $M'B$ is the shortest path from M' to t. Consequently the polygonal path MBM' must be the shortest path from M to M' and is thus not bent at B; that is, MB is indeed perpendicular to t.

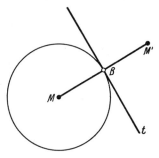

Fig. 1

Let us consider a generalization suggested by the construction of the circle. In constructing the circle by means of a thread, we had to hook the closed thread around a fixed point, the center, and keep it stretched while drawing the circle. We obtain a similar curve if we keep the closed thread stretched around two fixed points. This curve is called an ellipse, and the two fixed points are called its foci. The thread construction characterizes the ellipse as the curve with the property that the sum of the distances from two given points to any point on the curve is constant. If the distance between the two points is diminished until the points coincide, we obtain the circle as a limiting case of the ellipse. There is a simple property of the ellipse corresponding to each of the properties of the circle mentioned above. The ellipse is a closed curve that is convex every-

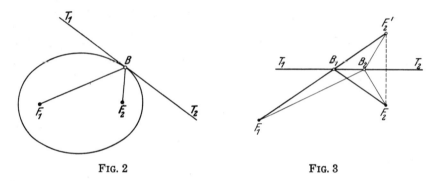

FIG. 2 FIG. 3

where, and at each point it has a tangent that remains outside the ellipse everywhere except at the point of contact. Corresponding to the radius of a circle are the two line-segments connecting a point of the ellipse with the foci; these are called the focal radii of the point on the ellipse. In analogy to the fact that any tangent to a circle is perpendicular to the radius at the point of contact, every tangent to an ellipse forms equal angles with the focal radii at the point of contact. In the notation of Fig. 2, this statement reads as follows: $\angle F_1 B T_1 = \angle F_2 B T_2$. To prove this, we reflect F_2 in the tangent (Fig. 3), and call the image F_2'. The straight line $F_1 F_2'$ is the shortest path joining F_1 and F_2'. Let it intersect the tangent at B_1. Then $F_1 B_1 F_2$ is the shortest path from F_1 via a point of the tangent to F_2; for if B_2 is any other point on the tangent, $F_1 B_2 F_2 = F_1 B_2 F_2'$ is longer than $F_1 B_1 F_2 = F_1 B_1 F_2'$. But the shortest path from F_1 to F_2 meeting the tangent is formed by the focal radii of B, the point of contact. For since every other point of the tangent lies outside the ellipse, the sum of the distances from the foci to such a point must always exceed the sum of the distances to the point B on the ellipse. Hence B coincides with B_1. Now F_2 and F_2' are symmetrical with respect to the straight line $T_1 T_2$, so that $\angle F_2' B_1 T_2 = \angle F_2 B_1 T_2$. Also the vertical angles $F_2' B_1 T_2$ and $F_1 B_1 T_1$ are equal, and it follows that our assertion is true.

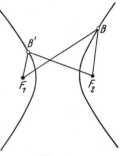

This property of the tangent to an ellipse admits of an application to optics to which the terms focus and focal radius owe their origin:[1] if a source of light is located at one of the foci of a mirror having the form of an ellipse, the reflected light will converge at the other focus.

FIG. 4

Another construction, which is not quite as easily carried out as the construction of the ellipse but is just as simple in principle, generates a curve with the property that the *difference* of the distances from two fixed points to any point on the curve is constant. The curve is called a hyperbola, and the two fixed points are called its foci. It is thus required that $F_1 B - F_2 B = \text{const.} = a$ or

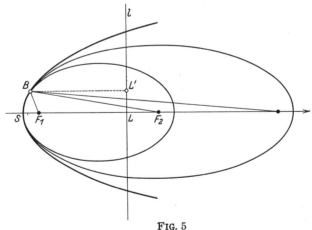

FIG. 5

$F_2 B' - F_1 B' = \text{const.} = a$ for every point B or B' on the curve (see Fig. 4). The hyperbola consists, accordingly, of two separate

---

[1] The literal meaning of the Latin word focus is "fireplace." The German term for focus is *Brennpunkt* or "burning point." [*Trans.*]

branches. Intuitively it is clear that the hyperbola is everywhere convex and has a tangent at every point. Later on we shall prove (see footnote 3, p. 9) that here, as in the case of the ellipse and the circle, the tangent has no point in common with the curve other than the point of contact. By a method analogous to that used in proving the corresponding property for the ellipse, it can be proved that the tangent to a hyperbola bisects the angle between the focal radii at the point of contact (see Fig. 6).

Another curve, the parabola, can be obtained from the ellipse by a limiting process (Fig. 5). To this end, we fix one focus, say F_1, and the vertex S nearest to this focus (where the vertices of the ellipse are defined to be the two points of intersection of the ellipse with the line joining the foci). Let us consider the ellipses that result when the second focus F_2 keeps moving further and further away from F_1 on the extension of the line SF_1. These ellipses approach a limiting curve, and this is the parabola. From this limiting process we can derive a simple definition of the parabola. If in the thread construction of the ellipse the distance F_1F_2 is large, then the thread from F_2 is approximately parallel to SF_1 as long as the pencil is near S (see Fig. 5). If a perpendicular l is now erected at any point L on F_1F_2 and if L' is the foot of the perpendicular dropped from B onto l, it follows that the equation

$$F_1B + BF_2 = F_1B + BL' + LF_2 = \text{const.}$$

is approximately true. If a new constant is introduced in place of

$$\text{const.} - LF_2,$$

we get

$$F_1B + BL' = \text{const.}$$

(for, LF_2 is constant for a fixed curve). Thus the last equation becomes more and more nearly correct as the distance F_1F_2 is increased, and for the limiting curve it is strictly true. Hence the parabola is a curve with the property that the sum of the distances of any point on it from a fixed point and a fixed straight line is a constant. This comes to the same thing as saying that the distance of any point on the curve from a fixed point is equal to the distance from a certain fixed straight line, namely the line, known as the directrix of the parabola, that is parallel to l and is on the other side of S at a distance from S equal to SF_1.

If a ray of light parallel to SF_1 strikes a parabolic mirror, the reflected ray will converge at F_1. This is another consequence of the above limiting process.

We have considered the "family" of all ellipses that have a vertex and the nearest focus in common. Let us now consider the family of all ellipses having both foci in common. This family of "confocal" ellipses "covers the whole plane simply"; i.e. given any point of the plane there is exactly one curve of the family passing through it. For, the sum of the distances from the two foci to the given point has a definite value, so that the point lies on the ellipse the sum of whose focal distances has that particular value.[2]

Let us now add the family of all hyperbolas having the same pair of foci as the ellipses we have just been considering. This family also covers the plane simply.[3] Thus there are exactly two curves of the system of confocal ellipses and hyperbolas passing through every point of the plane (see Fig. 6). At every given point, except at the foci, the tangent to the ellipse and the tangent to the hyperbola bisect the two supplementary angles formed by the focal radii at the point and are therefore perpendicular to each other.

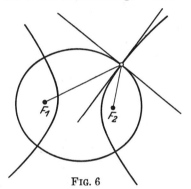

FIG. 6

Thus the confocal ellipses and hyperbolas form an "orthogonal net of curves" (two families being called orthogonal if every curve of one family intersects every curve of the other at right angles, where the angle between two curves at their point of intersection is defined to be the angle between their tangents at this point). In order to obtain an over-all view of this system of curves, we begin with the perpendicular bisector of $F_1 F_2$ (see Fig. 7) and then pass through the family of hyperbolas. These flatten out until we arrive

[2] The straight-line segment joining the foci is a (degenerate) ellipse: the sum of the focal distances of any point on this ellipse is equal to the distance between the foci.

[3] The part of the line joining the foci that is not between the foci is a degenerate hyperbola, and so is the perpendicular bisector of the segment joining the foci. In the latter case the difference of the focal distances has the constant value zero.

at the pair of half-lines that continue $F_1 F_2$ on either side. The plane has now been completely covered once. We then jump over to the line segment $F_1 F_2$. This broadens first into very flat ellipses

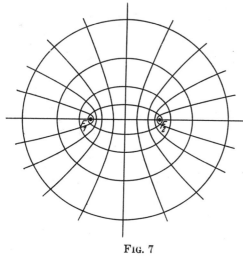

which gradually become more and more like circles as they grow indefinitely in size. We have now covered the plane for a second time.

Another particularly simple example of orthogonal families of curves are concentric circles and the straight lines passing through their common center. This figure is obtained as a limiting case from the above when the foci approach each other until they coincide; the ellipses become

Fig. 7

circles, and the hyperbolas become pairs of straight lines.

The contour lines and lines of maximum slope on a map constitute another example of orthogonal nets of curves.

In conclusion, let us mention another thread construction that

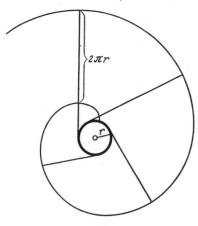

leads to an orthogonal net of curves. A thread is wound around a closed curve, say a circle. We consider the path traced by the free end when the stretched thread is unwound (see Fig. 8). The curve obtained in this way is called an "involute" of the circle, and is seen to be a spiral. It is apparent from the construction that the curve is always perpendicular to one of the two tangents from any of its points to the circle. All the other coils of the spiral also cut this tangent at right angles, and the seg-

Fig. 8

ment of the tangent that is cut off by two successive coils has a constant length which is equal to the circumference of the generating circle.

We can draw any number of other involutes of the same circle by starting to unwind the thread at different points of the circumference. On the other hand, this whole family of involutes can also be obtained by rotating one member of the family about the center of the circle. The family covers the whole plane simply, except for the interior of the circle. It is orthogonal to one of the two families of half-tangents of the circle.

For any other family of straight lines, the orthogonal family of curves also consists of involutes; they are always generated by the curve (in our example the circle) that the given straight lines envelop. We shall return to this phenomenon in the study of differential geometry (p. 178) and of kinematics (pp. 276, 277).

§ 2. The Cylinder, the Cone, the Conic Sections and Their Surfaces of Revolution

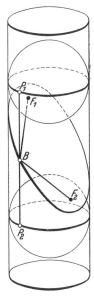

The circular cylinder is the simplest curved surface. It can be obtained from the simplest curves —the straight line and the circle—by moving a straight line around the circumference of a circle while keeping it perpendicular to the plane of the circle. Another way to get the cylinder is by rotating a straight line about an axis parallel to it. Thus the circular cylinder is a *surface of revolution*. The surfaces of revolution are an important class of surfaces, characterized by the property that

FIG. 9

they can be generated by rotating a plane curve about an axis lying in the plane of the curve. We meet them in the course of everyday living in the guise of drinking glasses, bottles, etc.

A circular cylinder intersects every plane at right angles to its axis in a circle. A plane not at right angles to the axis nor parallel to it intersects the cylinder in a curve that looks like an ellipse. We shall prove this this curve really is an ellipse. To this end, we take a sphere that just fits into the cylinder, and move it within the cylinder until it touches the intersecting plane (Fig. 9). We then take another such sphere and do the same thing with it on the other side of the plane. The spheres touch the cylinder in two circles and touch the intersecting plane at two points, F_1 and F_2. Let B be any point on the curve of intersection of the plane with the cylinder. Consider the straight line through B lying on the cylinder (i.e. parallel to the axis). It meets the circles of contact of the spheres at two points, P_1 and P_2. BF_1 and BP_1 are tangents to a fixed sphere through a fixed point B, and all such tangents must be equal, because of the rotational symmetry of the sphere. Thus $BF_1 = BP_1$; and similarly $BF_2 = BP_2$. It follows that

$$BF_1 + BF_2 = BP_1 + BP_2 = P_1 P_2.$$

But by the rotational symmetry of our figure, the distance $P_1 P_2$ is independent of the point B on the curve. Therefore $BF_1 + BF_2$ is constant for all points B of the section; i.e. the curve is an ellipse with foci at F_1 and F_2.

The fact that we have just proved can also be formulated in terms of the theory of projections as follows: The shadow that a circle throws onto an oblique plane is an ellipse if the light rays are perpendicular to the plane of the circle.

The circular cone is, next to the circular cylinder, the simplest surface of revolution. It is obtained by rotating a straight line about an axis that intersects it. Thus the tangents from a fixed point to a fixed sphere form a circular cone, and so do the rays passing through the circumference of a circle from a fixed point on its axis.

A plane perpendicular to the axis of a circular cone intersects the cone in a circle. When the plane is slightly inclined, the section becomes an ellipse. This is proved with the aid of two auxiliary spheres in exactly the same way as in the case of the cylinder.

As the intersecting plane is inclined more towards the axis, the ellipse becomes more elongated. Finally the plane becomes parallel to a generating line of the cone, and the section ceases to be a closed curve. A limiting process that we have carried out before (see Fig. 5, p. 3) shows that the section has become a parabola.

If the intersecting plane is inclined still nearer to the axis of the cone, it meets both branches of the cone (which it did not do in the previous cases). Now the curve of intersection looks like a hyperbola, (see Fig. 10). In order to prove that it really is a hyperbola, we consider the two inscribed spheres that touch both the cone and the intersecting plane. This time the spheres occupy different branches of the cone but lie on the same side of the plane (whereas in the first case both spheres were in the same branch of the cone but on opposite sides of the plane). In analogy to the proof on pages 7 and 8, we have (See Fig. 10).

$$BF_1 = BP_1, \quad BF_2 = BP_2, \quad BF_2 - BF_1 = BP_2 - BP_1 = P_1 P_2 = \text{const.}$$

We have thus seen that every plane that does not contain the vertex intersects a cone either in an ellipse[1] or in a parabola or in a hyperbola. There is, accordingly, a relation between these curves that justifies applying the common term *conic section*[2] to all of them.[3] Apart from the three types of "proper" conics mentioned above, there are the limiting cases obtained from them by letting the intersecting plane pass through the vertex of the cone or letting the cone degenerate into a cylinder. Thus the following configurations may be considered as degenerate conics: a single point, a straight line "counted twice," two intersecting straight lines, two parallel straight lines, and the empty plane. The conics are also known as the *curves of the second order* because they are represented by equations of second degree in Cartesian coordinates. The property of being a curve of second order cannot be directly expressed in visual terms. It is true that it implies another property that is easily accessible to visual perception: a second-order

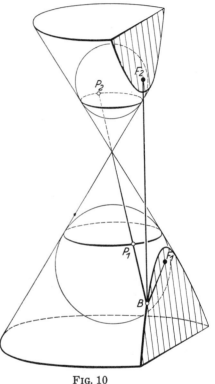

Fig. 10

expressed in visual terms. It is true that it implies another property that is easily accessible to visual perception: a second-order

---

[1] The circle being considered as a limiting case of an ellipse.

[2] Or simply *conic*. [*Trans.*]

[3] Thus the shadow of a circle on any plane is a conic if the light comes from a point on the axis of the circle. We can see that the curves obtained in this way include the hyperbola, for the cone of light coming from an automobile headlight illuminates the inside of a branch of a hyperbola on the highway. From the fact that every tangent to a hyperbola can be considered as the shadow of a tangent to a circle, it follows that the point of contact is the only point that any tangent has in common with a hyperbola, as we stated on page 4.

curve cannot intersect a straight line in more than two points. But there are many other curves besides the conics that share this latter property.

In the appendices to this chapter we shall discuss two other geometrical phenomena which, like the construction by use of the foci, characterize the non-degenerate conics. They are the pedal-point construction of the conics and the properties of the directrices.

Now that we have seen how the cylinder and the cone are generated by rotating a straight line about an axis, it would appear reasonable to consider the surfaces of revolution obtained by rotating a conic section. Let us choose an axis of symmetry as the axis of rotation; for then a half-turn merely interchanges the parts of the curve lying on either side of the axis, so that we obtain a single

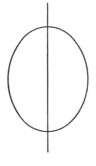

FIG. 11

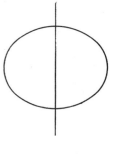

FIG. 12

surface, whereas we would obtain a more complicated configuration on rotating the curve about any other axis.

Let us begin with an ellipse. It has two axes of symmetry, giving rise to two different surfaces of revolution. We obtain a prolate spheroid (see Fig. 11) or an oblate spheroid (see Fig. 12) depending on whether we rotate the ellipse about its major axis or about its minor axis. The egg is an approximation to the former type of spheroid, while the earth is a familiar example of the latter type.

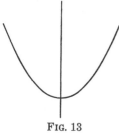

FIG. 13

We get the transitional case between the two types of spheroids by letting the difference between the major and minor axes of the ellipse approach zero. In the limit, the ellipse becomes a circle, and our surface of revolution becomes a sphere. Since the circle is symmetrical about every diameter, the sphere can be generated by rotation in infinitely many ways. This property is characteristic of the sphere; it is the only surface that can be generated by rotation in more than one way.

The parabola has only one axis of symmetry. Thus it gives rise to only one surface of revolution, the paraboloid of revolution (Fig. 13).

The hyperbola, on the other hand, gives rise to two different surfaces of revolution. According to whether we rotate a hyperbola about the line connecting the foci or about the perpendicular bisector of that line, we obtain the hyperboloid of revolution of two sheets (Fig. 14) or the hyperboloid of revolution of one sheet (Fig. 15). Now it is a surprising fact that there are infinitely many straight lines on the hyperboloid of one sheet. Indeed, this sur-

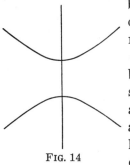

FIG. 14

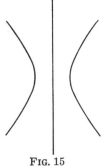

FIG. 15

face can also be generated by rotating a straight line about a skew axis. (So far we have have only considered surfaces obtained by rotating a curve about an axis in its own plane.) The proof of this fact can only be given analytically. It is visually apparent, however, that the construction indicated must generate the surface in two different

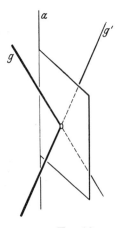

FIG. 16

FIG. 17

ways; for if the straight line g' (in Fig. 16) and the original generating line g are symmetrical with respect to a plane through the axis a, then g' must generate by rotation the same surface as g. Accordingly, there are two families of straight lines on the hyperboloid of revolution of one sheet, and each family covers the surface completely. Every straight line of one family intersects every straight line of the other (or is parallel to it), but any two lines of the same family are mutually skew (see Fig. 17).

§ 3. The Second-Order Surfaces

The surfaces obtained by rotating conics are special types of a broader class of surfaces which are called, for analytical reasons, "surfaces of second order"; these are the surfaces satisfying equations of the second degree in three-dimensional Cartesian coordinates. The second-order surfaces are also known as "quadrics." It is easy to show analytically that the quadrics have the property of intersecting every plane in a (proper or degenerate) conic. Furthermore, the cone consisting of all the tangents from a fixed point to a quadric cuts every plane in a conic, and the points of

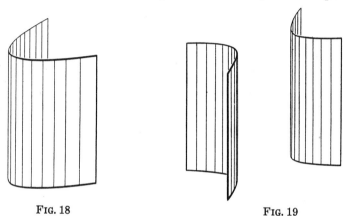

FIG. 18   FIG. 19

contact of this cone with the surface form a conic. Moreover, the quadrics are the only surfaces having any one of these properties.[1] Let us consider the different types of quadrics.

By generalization of the circular cylinder we obtain the elliptic cylinder; it is generated by a straight line moved along an ellipse in such a way as to be always perpendicular to the plane of the curve. We get the parabolic and the hyperbolic cylinder from the parabola and the hyperbola by the same procedure. (See Figs. 18 and 19.)

An analogous generalization of the circular cone produces the general cone of the second order; it consists of the lines joining the points of any non-degenerate conic to a fixed point outside the plane of the curve. We must bear in mind, however, that we do not get

---

[1] A consequence of the first of these properties is that a straight line that does not have a whole segment on the surface cannot have more than two points in common with it. However, there are many other surfaces that share this property with the second-order surfaces—the surface of a cube, for example.

different types of cones by starting variously with an ellipse, a parabola, or a hyperbola, although there were three distinct classes of
cylinders corresponding to these curves. Indeed, we have seen that a
variable plane intersects a fixed cone in all three types of second-
order curves, which is not the case with a fixed cylindrical surface.

The most general cone and the elliptical cylinder can also be
obtained from the corresponding surfaces of revolution by a
deformation called *dilatation*. This is achieved by holding fixed
all the points of some arbitrary plane containing the axis of rotation and moving all other points in a fixed direction toward the
plane or away from it in such a way that the distances from
the plane of all points in space change in a fixed ratio. It can be
proved that such a transformation changes all circles into ellipses
(or circles), straight lines into
straight lines, planes into planes,[2]
and all second-order curves and
surfaces into second-order curves
and surfaces respectively.

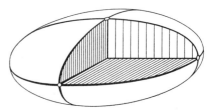

By dilatation of a spheroid
(either prolate or oblate), we get
the most general ellipsoid. While

FIG. 20

a spheroid is symmetrical about every plane through the axis, the
general ellipsoid has only three planes of symmetry. They are
called the principal planes of the ellipsoid. They are mutually
perpendicular, and the segments of their lines of intersection cut
off by the surface are three unequal axes, called the *major, mean,*
and *minor* axes of the ellipsoid (Fig. 20). The general ellipsoid
can be transformed back into an oblate or a prolate spheroid by
dilatations that make the major and the mean axes or the mean
and the minor axes, respectively, equal.

The ellipsoidal shape can often be recognized in stones that are
exposed to the waves of the ocean. A stone of any shape becomes
increasingly similar to an ellipsoid as the water wears away at it.
The mathematical study of this phenomenon involves problems of
the theory of probability.

The hyperboloids of one and of two sheets and the elliptic paraboloid are the most general surfaces that can be obtained from

---

[2] A dilatation subjects the figures of a plane to the same changes as does a
parallel projection of this plane onto an intersecting plane.

the hyperboloids of revolution and the paraboloid of revolution by dilatations. Both types of hyperboloids have three principal planes; the elliptic paraboloid has two.

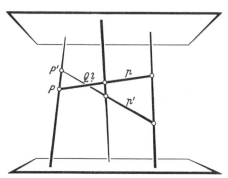

Like the corresponding surface of revolution, the general hyperboloid of one sheet contains two families of straight lines, since a dilatation always transforms straight lines into straight lines. Again the lines are arranged in such a way that every line of one family has a point in common with every line of the other family and any two lines of the same family are skew.

Fig. 21

This gives rise to the following construction of the hyperboloid of one sheet (see Fig. 21). We start with any three straight lines

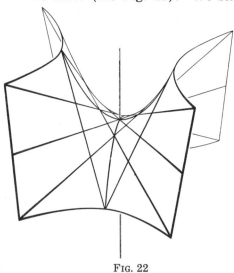

of one family. Since no two of them have a plane in common, every point P on one of them is on one and only one straight line p meeting the other two given lines, namely the intersection of the plane containing P and the second line with the plane containing P and the third line. p has three points in common with the hyperboloid. But no straight line can intersect a quadric in more than two points. Consequently p must be one of the lines on the hyperboloid. If the point P

Fig. 22

traverses the first line, the corresponding line p will take on the positions of all the straight lines of that family on the hyperboloid to which the first line does not belong. If we choose any three straight lines of this family, we can get the other family by the same procedure, and of course this will also include the three lines with which we started originally. The construction shows that every pair of straight lines of the same family must be skew, provided it is at all possible to find three non-coplanar straight lines in one of the families. For, if we could find three skew straight lines with which to carry out our construction, while p and p' were to meet at a point Q, (Fig. 21), then the original lines would all have to lie in the plane $PP'Q$, in contradiction to one of the assumptions. On the other hand, it is clear that our surface would be not a hyperboloid, but a plane, if three lines of the same family always turned out to be coplanar.

Thus three skew straight lines always define a hyperboloid of one sheet, except in the case where they are all parallel to one plane (but not to each other). In this case they determine a new type of second-order surface, called the hyperbolic paraboloid, which does not include any surface of revolution as a special case. The hyperbolic paraboloid looks somewhat like a saddle (see Fig. 22). It has two mutually perpendicular planes of symmetry which it intersects in parabolas. Like the three straight lines that we started with in the construction of the surface, all straight lines belonging to a given one of the two families are parallel to a fixed plane. It is apparent on inspection that every plane intersects our surface in a curve that extends to infinity, so that the intersection can never be an ellipse. Consequently the hyperbolic paraboloid cannot be obtained from any surface of revolution by a dilatation, for there are circles on every surface of revolution, and these would be transformed into ellipses by a dilatation.

We have thus learned a new method for generating surfaces. It consists of fixing a certain course in space along which we move a straight line. A surface that can be generated in this manner is called a *ruled surface*. Thus of the nine different types of quadrics, six are ruled surfaces, namely the three kinds of cylinders, the cone, the hyperboloid of one sheet, and the hyperbolic paraboloid. Of these, the last two are distinguished by the special property that each point of the surface is on more than one of the straight lines. A surface that contains two families of straight lines or "rulings" is called a *doubly ruled* surface. The plane and the two last-mentioned quadrics are the only doubly ruled surfaces.

The remaining three types of quadrics—the ellipsoid, the elliptic paraboloid, and the hyperboloid of two sheets—cannot contain any straight lines, as is immediately evident from the fact that none of these surfaces extends uninterruptedly to infinity in any two opposite directions.

The two families of straight lines that lie on the hyperboloid of one sheet and on the hyperbolic paraboloid have a surprising property. Let us imagine all these straight lines to be made of a rigid material and fastened together at all the intersections in a way that permits of rotation but not of sliding. It would seem reasonable to think that the straight lines fastened in this way must form a rigid framework. But as a matter of fact, the framework is

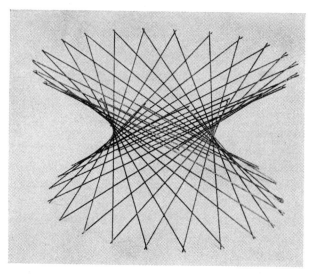

Fig. 23a

movable (see Figs. 23a and 23b). In order to get a picture of the way in which the model of the hyperboloid can change its form, we shall keep in a fixed horizontal position the principal plane whose intersection with the surface is an ellipse, and try to deform the framework in such a way that this plane always continues to be a principal plane. Since the hyperboloid and the hyperbolic paraboloid are the only doubly ruled surfaces (except for the plane), it is clear that the configuration obtained by deforming the rod model of the hyperboloid must either stay a hyperboloid or become a hyperbolic paraboloid, and it can be proved that the latter cannot occur. We may now try to raise the framework up in such a way as to keep making the rods more and more nearly perpendicular to the principal plane. Then the surface becomes progressively less curved. The intersection with the principal plane traverses the family of confocal ellipses described in § 1 which become more and more narrow. In the limit, the framework folds up in a vertical plane, and the rods are tangents to a hyperbola in this plane, while the horizontal ellipse degenerates into a double straight-line segment. In much the same way, we can deform the framework in the opposite direction by inclining the rods more closely to the horizontal plane. In this process the constriction of the surface near the principal plane becomes more pronounced, and in the limit the structure folds up in a horizontal plane in which the rods now envelop an ellipse. We shall give an analytic proof for the movability of the rod model in one of the appendices to this chapter.

We can proceed analogously for the hyperbolic paraboloid. Here the framework always retains the form of a paraboloid, folding up to form the envelope of a plane parabola in both limiting cases.

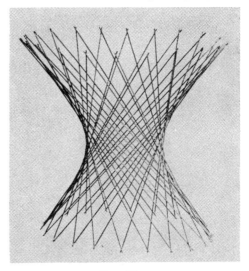

Fig. 23b

There is yet another criterion for classifying the quadrics into two types. Three of them—the hyperbolic and parabolic cylinders and the hyperbolic paraboloid—do not intersect any plane in a circle; for, any plane section of any one of these surfaces extends to infinity. On each of the six other types of surface, however, there are infinitely many circles, which is also connected with the fact that these six surfaces include surfaces of revolution as special cases, in contrast to the three types mentioned first.

We shall use the ellipsoid to illustrate the proof of the existence of circular sections (see Fig. 24). Every plane through the mean axis b cuts the ellipsoid in an ellipse having one axis equal to b. Beginning with the plane containing b and the minor axis c of the ellipsoid and rotating about b until the plane containing b and the major axis a of the ellipsoid is reached, the section is at first an ellipse with its other axis shorter than b, but in the final position is an ellipse with its other axis longer than b. Somewhere in between there must be a position of the intersecting plane where the second axis is equal to b, so that the section is a circle. Because of the symmetry of the ellipsoid, there is a second plane through b—obtained by reflection of the first one in the plane (b, c)—which also intersects the surface in a circle. Furthermore, it can be proved that every plane parallel to a circular section also intersects the ellipsoid in a circle. Thus there are two families of parallel circles on every ellipsoid (see Fig. 25). On the ellipsoid of revolution, the two families coincide.

The same considerations can be applied to other second-order surfaces whose intersections with some planes are closed curves.

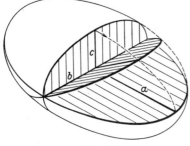

FIG. 24

A theorem similar to the one considered above, concerning the straight lines on the hyperboloid, applies to the two families of circular sections. Let all the circles be fastened together at their points of intersection in such a way that they can rotate without sliding. The resulting framework is not rigid, but movable. (In Figs. 25a and 25b, circular disks made of cardboard are attached in mutually intersecting positions by means of suitably chosen slits. The reader will be satisfied that this model does not differ essentially from the one described above.) The families of surfaces obtained by changing the form of such movable models of circular disks are not the same as the families obtained from the rod models. The conics in the principal planes of the present model do not in general form a confocal family. For example, a model of circular disks forming a general ellipsoid can always be changed into the form of a sphere; here every section by a plane of symmetry is a circle, although a circle cannot appear in a family of confocal ellipses. Like the rod model, the model of circles is movable to such an extent that it can be folded up into a plane.

Although the two kinds of models are very different, they are related by a transitional case. This is the movable rod model of the hyperbolic paraboloid, which may also be regarded as a limiting case of a circle model in which the radii of the circles have become infinite, i.e. in which the circles have become straight lines. If we have a family of hyperboloids of one sheet approaching the form

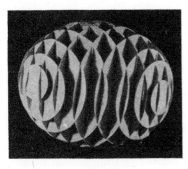

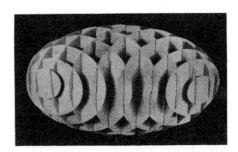

Fig. 25a   Fig. 25b

of a hyperbolic paraboloid, both the circles and the straight lines on the hyperboloid become straight lines on the paraboloid.

§ 4. The Thread Construction of the Ellipsoid, and Confocal Quadrics

Since the quadrics play a role in space which is analogous to that of the conics in the plane, it is not unreasonable to investigate the possibility of adapting the thread construction of the ellipse to these surfaces. The problem was solved by Staude, who in 1882 found a thread construction for the ellipsoid. His construction makes use of a fixed framework consisting of an ellipse and a hyperbola (see Fig. 26). The plane of the hyperbola is perpendicular to the plane of the ellipse and passes through the major axis of the ellipse. The hyperbola has its vertices at the foci F_1 and F_2 of the ellipse and has its foci at the vertices S_1 and S_2 of the ellipse; the hyperbola is thus uniquely determined once the ellipse is given.

One end of a thread is now attached to a vertex, say S_1, of the ellipse. The other end of the thread is then passed behind the nearest branch of the hyperbola and in front of the ellipse and finally attached to F_2. If we stretch the part of the thread that is between the hyperbola and the ellipse, the thread will occupy the polygonal path S_1HBEF_2, where the part BHS_1 is the shortest path from B to S_1 via a point on the hyperbola, and BEF_2 has a corresponding property. *If the point B now changes its position in such*

a way as to keep the thread stretched, it will move on an ellipsoid.
When the thread is arranged as in Fig. 26, the possible positions

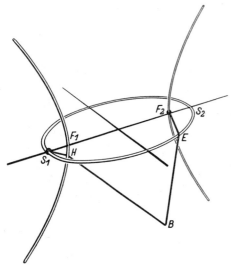

taken on by B cover a quarter
of the ellipsoid, namely the
front part of the lower half.
The other quarters can be obtained by passing the thread
through the framework according to different schemes before
attaching the second end to F_2.[1]

The part played by the
framework of two conics in the
construction of the ellipsoid is
analogous to that played by the
foci in the construction of an
ellipse. For this reason we call
them focal curves (focal ellipse
and focal hyperbola) of an
ellipsoid. In general, we say

FIG. 26

of any quadric that two given conics are its focal curves if their
planes are principal planes of the surface and intersect it in conics

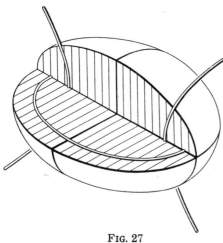

that are confocal with the focal
curves. Since each of the sections must be an ellipse or a
hyperbola, we have to consider
four possible cases. If both sections are ellipses, we get an
ellipsoid (Fig. 27). If both are
hyperbolas, we get a hyperboloid of two sheets (Fig. 28).
If the surface cuts the plane of
the focal hyperbola in a hyperbola and that of the focal ellipse
in an ellipse, it is a hyperboloid
of one sheet (Fig. 29). The

FIG. 27

[1] The ends of the thread may also be attached to the ellipse and the hyperbola
at any other points, instead of at S_1 and F_2, the only requirement being that the
relative positions of the ends do not make it impossible to stretch the thread
as prescribed.

fourth possibility— where the surface cuts the plane of the focal hyperbola in an ellipse and that of the focal ellipse in a hyperbola—is ruled out; for, here the ellipse and the hyperbola would have to intersect the straight line F_1F_2 (in Fig. 30) in four distinct points E_1, E_2, H_1, and H_2, and therefore the plane of the focal hyperbola would have an ellipse and two points H_1, H_2 not on the ellipse in common with the surface, and this would contradict the definition of a second-order surface.

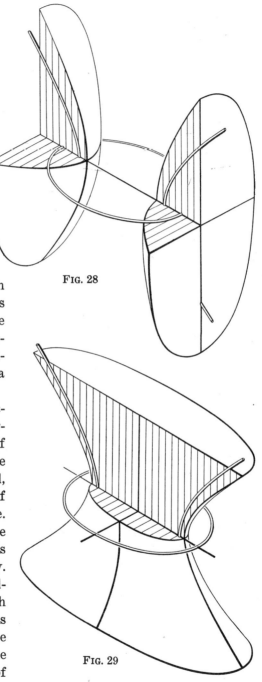

Fig. 28

If the thread construction of the ellipsoid is performed with threads of different lengths, while the focal curves are fixed, there results a family of "confocal ellipsoids" (i.e. ellipsoids having the same focal curves) which fills the whole space simply. The family of hyperboloids of two sheets with the same focal curves also fills the whole space simply, and so does the corresponding family of

Fig. 29

hyperboloids of one sheet, thus one ellipsoid, one hyperboloid of one sheet, and one hyperboloid of two sheets pass through any given point in space (see Fig. 31). Now it is true, just as in the case of confocal conics in the plane, that the confocal quadrics in space intersect each other at right angles, i.e. the tangent planes of the three surfaces passing through any given point in space are mutually perpendicular.[2] Such systems of three mutually orthogonal families of surfaces—the systems of confocal quadrics being the outstanding example—occur in many mathematical and physical considerations.

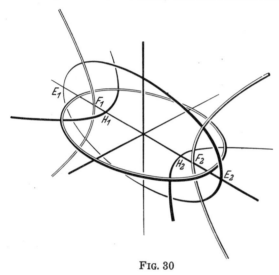

FIG. 30

Thus the analytic representation of these surfaces leads to "elliptic coordinates," which have proved very effective in the treatment of numerous problems, among them problems in astronomy.

We can get an overall picture of the way in which a system of confocal quadrics is built up, by going over the different surfaces in a certain order. Let us start with the very large almost spherical surfaces of the family of ellipsoids and then gradually make the major axes shorter. Since the surfaces are subjected to unequal compressions in the directions of the three axes, they must become flatter and lose their resemblance to spheres as the process continues. As a limiting case of the ellipsoids we finally get the inside of the focal ellipse, covered twice. In the plane of this focal ellipse, we now jump over to the part that is outside the curve; if we also imagine this part of the plane doubly covered, it serves as the limiting case of a flattened hyperboloid of one sheet. Beginning with this limiting surface, we pass through the family of hyperboloids of one sheet which get progressively steeper and approach the plane of the focal hyperbola

---

[2] The points of the focal curves are exceptional; here two of the three planes are indeterminate. Cf. the following paragraph.

from both sides. Meanwhile the ellipses in the plane where the hyperboloids are narrowest become more slender as they pass through a confocal family, until they become "infinitely thin," i.e. fold up to form a double straight-line segment. The surfaces have collapsed to form a double cover for the plane strip bounded by the two branches of the focal hyperbola.[3] Now we make a discontinuous transition once more in going over to the other side of the focal hyperbola, which must again be thought of as being doubly covered; here we have the limiting case of a flat hyperboloid of two sheets. Let us gradually inflate the two shells of the hyperboloid. The surface will approach both sides of that plane through the center of the two focal curves that is perpendicular to the planes of both curves, and in the limiting position we get a double cover for this plane.

FIG. 31

Now we have gone through the complete system of confocal quadrics and have seen the way in which each separate family fills up the whole space simply.

There is another property that characterizes the way in which the focal curves are related to each other and to the quadrics generated by them. If from any point on the focal hyperbola we look along the tangent toward the focal ellipse, that curve looks like a circle with its center on the line of sight. Thus the focal hyperbola

---

[3] It is precisely this family of hyperboloids, including the limiting positions in a plane, that is described by the movable rod model considered earlier.

is the locus of the vertices of all circular cones that pass through the focal ellipse, and the axis of rotation of each such cone is tangent to the hyperbola at the vertex of the cone. Moreover, the cones consisting of tangents from an exterior point lying on the hyperbola to any ellipsoid having the given focal curves, is also circular, and furthermore, it always has the same axis as the cone considered before. More generally, we have the theorem that every surface of the confocal system when viewed from a point lying on a focal curve and not enclosed by the surface, looks like a circle with its center on the line of sight, provided the line of sight is tangent to the focal curve. (But the points at which a tangent cone touches the surface do not by any means generally form a circle; they may form any conic, including even a hyperbola.) [4]

Now that we have discussed the focal curves, it is not out of place to consider also the other curves in which pairs of unlike surfaces of a confocal system intersect. In terms of differential geometry these curves have a simple property which we shall discuss later (cf. p. 188). Also they afford us a first example of curves that are not in a plane. It is easy to see that a curve in which two arbitrary quadrics in arbitrary positions intersect cannot meet any plane in more than four points, unless the curve has a whole arc in common with the plane. For, the plane intersects the surfaces in two conics; and it is easy to prove analytically that two conics that do not coincide or have a whole straight line in common cannot meet at more than four points (cf. p. 160)—a theorem which is intuitively evident as well.

This property of the points of intersection is connected with the analytic basis for classifying the curves as curves of the fourth order. (Curves of the n-th order have the corresponding property that they have either at most n points or a whole arc in common with any plane.) But there also exist curves of the fourth order that do not form the intersection of two second-order surfaces. [5] The space

---

[4] The following is another property of the confocal system, which, incidentally, includes the property just mentioned as a limiting case: The planes of symmetry of the tangent cone from any point P in space to any surface of the system which does not enclose P are the tangent planes at P to the three surfaces of the system that pass through P.

[5] But for any curve of intersection of two quadrics it can be proved analytically that there are infinitely many additional quadrics passing through it, including four cones some of which may coincide or degenerate into cylinders.

curves of higher orders would be difficult to study without the aid of analytic methods; so we shall not go into them here.

APPENDICES TO CHAPTER I

1. The Pedal-Point Construction of the Conics

Let a curve K and a point F_1 be given (see Fig. 32). If we drop perpendiculars from F_1 onto all the tangents t of K, the feet of these perpendiculars trace out a second curve k which is called the pedal curve of K with respect to F_1. Conversely, we can obtain K if we are given F_1 and k. For this purpose we connect F_1 with the points of k and at these points draw the perpendiculars t to the connecting lines.

FIG. 32

Then the straight lines t envelop K. We shall call this second construction a *pedal-point construction* and say that K is generated by a pedal-point construction on k (with respect to F_1). We note that the pedal-point construction on a single curve k can give rise to a variety of different curves K, depending on the choice of F_1.

We shall prove the following: The pedal-point construction on the circle and the straight line always gives rise to conics. If the center of the circle is at M, and F_1 is inside the circle, then we obtain an ellipse with one focus at F_1 and the other at the point F_2, where F_2 is the point on F_1M produced such that $MF_2 = F_1M$. If F_1 is outside the generating circle we get a hyperbola with the foci F_1 and F_2 defined as before. Starting with a straight line g instead of the circle, we get a parabola. Here the focus is at F_1 and the directrix is that straight line h which is parallel to g and such that h and F_1 are equally distant from g and on opposite sides of it.

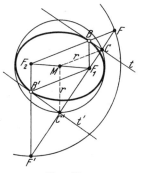

FIG. 33

To begin with, we shall prove this for the case of the ellipse (Fig. 33). We draw any straight line through F_1 and denote by C and C' its points of intersection with the circle. Let F and F' be the points on this straight line defined by the relations $F_1C = CF$ and $F_1C' = C'F'$. Let t and t' be the perpendiculars to CC' erected at C and C' respectively. Now we define the point F_2 as indicated above, so that M bisects the segment F_1F_2. If F_2F intersects t at B and F_2F' intersects t' at B', then $F_1B = FB$ and therefore $F_1B + BF_2 = FF_2$. But M and C bisect the segments F_1F_2 and F_1F, so that $FF_2 = 2CM$. This

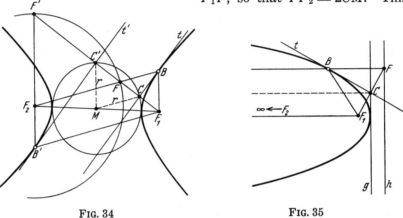

FIG. 34   FIG. 35

yields the equation $BF_1 + BF_2 = 2r$, where r is the radius of the circle. Hence B lies on the ellipse whose foci are at F_1 and F_2 and whose major axis has length $2r$. Now it only remains to prove that t is tangent to the ellipse at B. This follows from the fact,

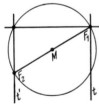

FIG. 36

demonstrated on page 2, that any tangent to an ellipse makes equal angles with the focal chords at its point of contact; for, according to our construction, $\angle CBF_1 = \angle CBF$. The proof for the line t' is completely analogous, using the points B', C', and F'.

The proof for the hyperbola follows from Fig. 34. This is exactly the same as Fig. 33 except for the fact that F_1 is now assumed to be outside the circle. In this case B and B' trace out the two separate branches of the hyperbola; for, $FF_2 = 2r = BF_2 - BF_1$ and $F'F_2 = 2r = B'F_1 - B'F_2$.

For the parabola, the proof has to be modified slightly. If the points C and F and the straight line t are constructed in the same way as before, it is necessary in this case to drop the perpendicular from F onto g (see Fig. 35). If this perpendicular intersects t at the point B, we have $BF_1 = BF$. But F moves on the straight line h

defined above.[1] Hence B actually does trace out a parabola having F_1 as focus and h as directrix. Here again t is tangent to the parabola at B because of the fact that t bisects the angle FBF_1.[2]

If F_1 is on the circumference of the circle (as in Fig. 36), the lines t and t' rotate about F_1 and F_2, and we obtain a pair of pencils of lines. This is a well-known degenerate case of the second-order curves, which occurs quite naturally when they are regarded as configurations consisting of tangents.

2. The Directrices of the Conics

The parabola was defined in the first chapter as the locus of all points whose distance from a fixed point F, the focus, is equal to their distance from a fixed straight line g, the directrix. A similar definition can be given for the ellipse and the hyperbola. Consider all points whose distance from a fixed point F is in a constant ratio v to their distance from a fixed line g. If $v = 1$ we obtain a parabola. We shall prove the following statement: If $v < 1$, the locus is an ellipse; if $v > 1$, it is a hyperbola. In each case F is a focus of the conic. Conversely, there are two straight lines g_1 and

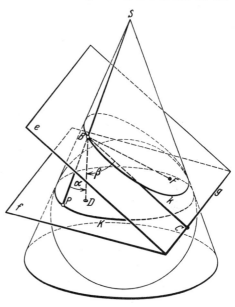

FIG. 37

g_2 defined by every ellipse or hyperbola, such that for all points of the curve the distance from F_1 (or F_2) is in a fixed ratio to the distance from g_1 (or g_2, respectively).

---

[1] In the pedal-point construction of the ellipse and hyperbola, F describes a circle with center at F_2 and with radius equal to twice the radius of the original circle, since $FF_2 = 2CM$. Moreover, it follows from $FF_1 = 2CF_1$ that F_1 is the center of the magnification by which the two circles are related.

[2] Of course we can derive Fig. 35 from Fig. 33 by the same limiting process by which we got the parabola from the ellipse on page 4.

The proof is based on Fig. 37. Consider a circular cone intersecting a plane e in an ellipse k. We shall prove the statement for this ellipse. As in Fig. 10, we make use of a sphere which touches the cone in a circle K and the plane at a point F. Then we know that F is a focus of k. Let f be the plane of K and g the line in which f intersects e. Take any point B on the ellipse and drop the perpendiculars BC and BD onto g and f respectively. Now consider the lines BF and BS, where S is the vertex of the cone, and let BS intersect K at the point P. Set $\angle DBP = \alpha$ and $\angle DBC = \beta$. Then $BC = \dfrac{BD}{\cos\beta}$ and $BP = \dfrac{BD}{\cos\alpha}$. Also $BF = BP$, because both lines are tangents to the same sphere from the same point B. Hence

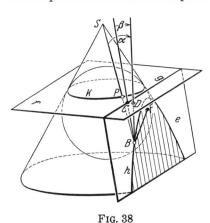

$$\frac{BF}{BC} = \frac{BP}{BC} = \frac{\cos\beta}{\cos\alpha}.$$

But the angles α and β are independent of the choice of B, since α is equal to half the angle of aperture of the cone and β is equal to the angle at which the plane e in inclined to the axis of the cone. Hence, setting $\dfrac{\cos\beta}{\cos\alpha} = v$, we have proved our assertion for the ellipse k and have at the same time found a construction for the

Fig. 38

directrix g. A second directrix, associated with the second focus, is immediately evident if we consider the symmetry of the ellipse about its minor axis.

If, as in Fig. 38, e intersects the cone in a hyperbola rather than in an ellipse, the proof is exactly the same as before; only we must note that $\alpha < \beta$ in the first case and $\alpha > \beta$ in the second, so that $v < 1$ for the ellipse k but $v > 1$ for the hyperbola h.

So far our considerations have only proved the existence of the directrix for given ellipses and hyperbolas, whereas we have set out to do the converse, i.e. given a number v, a point F, and a straight line g, to find the corresponding curve. But clearly the form of the desired curve depends only on the value of v, and since we can arrange the construction so that α and β and therefore v assume any values we please, it follows that our construction produces all the possible forms of the desired curve; thus the curve must indeed be a conic section.

The parabola is characterized by $a = \beta$, i.e. $v = 1$ (if we retain the notation used above), which leads us back to the original definition of the parabola. On the other hand, if e intersects the cone in a circle the construction is impossible, because in this (and only this) case the planes e and f do not have a line of intersection but are parallel. Every non-degenerate conic can be regarded as a section of a circular cone and is thus, except for the circle, subject to our construction. Hence the property of having directrices is shared by all non-degenerate conics other than the circle.

Incidentally, the Greek names of the conics are based on the way they are related to their directrices; thus the names indicate that v falls short of the number 1 in the case of the ellipse (ἐλλείπειν), exceeds it in the case of the hyperbola (ὑπερβάλλειν) and exactly reaches it in the case of the parabola (παραβάλλειν).

3. The Movable Rod Model of the Hyperboloid

We shall prove the statement, made on page 16, that the rod model of the hyperboloid of one sheet is movable. (In this proof some knowledge of three-dimensional analytic geometry is presupposed.) We shall prove at the same time that as the framework changes shape it runs through a family of confocal hyperboloids of one sheet.

Let x_1, x_2, x_3 and y_1, y_2, y_3 be the Cartesian coordinates in three dimensions of the points P and Q respectively. Let us consider the confocal quadrics

$$(1) \qquad \frac{x_1^2}{a_1 - \lambda} + \frac{x_2^2}{a_2 - \lambda} + \frac{x_3^2}{a_3 - \lambda} = \sum_1^3 \frac{x_i^2}{a_i - \lambda} = 1 \,.$$

Let us choose a value of λ such that (1) represents a hyperboloid of one sheet. P is supposed to be a point of this surface, as (1) indicates. Let Q be another point of the surface satisfying the additional condition that it is on one of the straight lines of the surface that pass through P. These conditions are equivalent to the equations

$$(2) \qquad \sum_1^3 \frac{y_i^2}{a_i - \lambda} = 1 \,,$$

$$(3) \qquad \sum_1^3 \frac{x_i y_i}{a_i - \lambda} = 1 \,.$$

For, the midpoint M of the segment PQ must certainly be on the surface, and M has the coordinates $\frac{1}{2}(x_i + y_i)$. Thus

$$\sum \frac{1}{4} \frac{(x_i + y_i)^2}{a_i - \lambda} = \frac{1}{4} + \frac{1}{4} + \frac{1}{2} \sum \frac{x_i y_i}{a_i - \lambda} = 1,$$

which amounts to the same thing as (3). Conversely, the whole straight line PQ lies on the surface if it has the three points P, Q, M in common with the surface, i.e. if (1), (2), and (3) are true.

Let us calculate the distance $PQ = r$. We have

$$r^2 = \sum_1^3 (x_i - y_i)^2 = \sum x_i^2 + \sum y_i^2 - 2 \sum x_i y_i$$

$$= \sum (a_i - \lambda) \frac{x_i^2}{a_i - \lambda} + \sum (a_i - \lambda) \frac{y_i^2}{a_i - \lambda} - 2 \sum (a_i - \lambda) \frac{x_i y_i}{a_i - \lambda}$$

$$= \sum a_i \left[\frac{x_i^2}{a_i - \lambda} + \frac{y_i^2}{a_i - \lambda} - 2 \frac{x_i y_i}{a_i - \lambda} \right]$$

$$- \lambda \left[\sum \frac{x_i^2}{a_i - \lambda} + \sum \frac{y_i^2}{a_i - \lambda} - 2 \sum \frac{x_i y_i}{a_i - \lambda} \right].$$

Because of (1), (2), (3), the expression in the last pair of brackets vanishes, so that we obtain

(4) $$r^2 = \sum a_i \frac{(x_i - y_i)^2}{a_i - \lambda}.$$

Now let λ' be a value such that (1) gives us another hyperboloid of one sheet if we substitute λ' for λ. This is the case if and only if $a_i - \lambda'$ has the same sign as $a_i - \lambda$ for each i. Accordingly the relations

(5) $$x_i' = x_i \sqrt{\frac{a_i - \lambda'}{a_i - \lambda}} \qquad (i = 1, 2, 3)$$

define a real affine transformation. Evidently (5) transforms the surface (1) into another hyperboloid of one sheet which is confocal with (1). We shall call this hyperboloid (1'). If $P'(x_i')$ and $Q'(y_i')$ are the images of P and Q under the transformation (5), then the whole straight line $P'Q'$, being the image of PQ, is on (1'). Our result will be proved as soon as we can prove that the distance $P'Q' = r'$ is equal to PQ, i.e. that $r' = r$. For r' we have the formula

(4') $$r'^2 = \sum a_i \frac{(x_i' - y_i')^2}{a_i - \lambda'},$$

analogous to (4). From (5) it follows that

$$\frac{(x_i' - y_i')^2}{a_i - \lambda'} = \frac{(x_i - y_i)^2}{a_i - \lambda} \qquad (i = 1, 2, 3),$$

and hence, because of (4) and (4'), the equality $r = r'$ holds.

If we fix λ and vary λ', then (5) represents the paths along which the points of the rod model move when the model is deformed in such a way that the principal planes are held fixed, as we have always stipulated. An easy calculation shows that these paths are the curves of intersection of the ellipsoids and hyperboloids of two sheets confocal with (1).

CHAPTER II

REGULAR SYSTEMS OF POINTS

In this chapter we shall consider the metric properties of space from a new point of view. We have till now been concerned with curves and surfaces—that is, with continuous entities. Now we shall turn to systems consisting of discrete elements. Such systems are frequently found also in other branches of mathematics, especially in the Theory of Numbers, in the Theory of Functions and in Crystallography.[1]

§ 5. Plane Lattices

A particularly simple structure consisting of discrete parts is the square lattice in the plane (Fig. 39). In order to construct it, we begin by marking out four corners of a unit square in a plane. Then we move the square through one unit of length in a direction parallel to one of its sides and mark the positions of the two new corners. We now imagine this process to be repeated indefinitely, first in the same direction and then in the opposite direction. We obtain in this way a strip consisting of two rows of equidistant points in the plane. We now move this strip through one unit of length in a direction perpendicular to itself, mark the newly generated points, and imagine that this process as well is repeated indefinitely in both directions. The totality of points so marked constitutes the square lattice; it can also be defined as the set of all points of the plane whose Cartesian coordinates are integers.

In this lattice we may of course form figures other than squares from four points—parallelograms, for example. Now it is easy to see that the whole square lattice can be generated from any such

---

[1] Where the subject of crystallography is touched upon in the following sections, we shall not always adapt our notation to the usual terminology of crystallography; in the simple geometrical considerations to which we shall confine our attention, other names are often found to be briefer and more suggestive.

parallelogram as well as from a square, provided the parallelogram does not have any lattice points in its interior or on its boundary other than its vertices (for otherwise, the generating process could not give us all the points of the lattice). Also, consideration of any such parallelogram shows that it must have the same area as the generating square (see Fig.

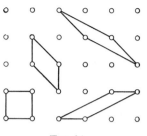

FIG. 39

39); we shall give a rigorous proof of this on page 34.

Even this simple lattice has given rise to important mathematical investigations. The first of these was made by Gauss. He tried to determine the number $f(r)$ of lattice points in the interior and on the boundary of a circle of radius r, where the center of the circle is a lattice point and r is an integer. Gauss found the value of this number empirically for many values of r. For example:

$r = 10$ $f(r) = 317$
$r = 20$ $f(r) = 1257$
$r = 30$ $f(r) = 2821$
$r = 100$ $f(r) = 31417$
$r = 200$ $f(r) = 125629$
$r = 300$ $f(r) = 282697.$

His interest was prompted by the fact that an investigation of this function yields a method for approximat-

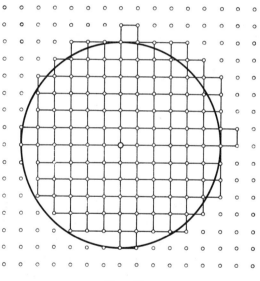

FIG. 40

ing the value of π. For since every generating square has unit area, $f(r)$ is equal to the area of the region F covered by all the squares whose lower left-hand corners are inside or on the boundary of the circle (see Fig. 40). Thus the difference between $f(r)$ and the area πr^2 of the circle is at most equal to the combined area $A(r)$ of those squares (the counted as well as the omitted ones) that are cut by the boundary of the circle;

$$|f(r) - r^2\pi| \leq A(r),$$

$$\left|\frac{f(r)}{r^2} - \pi\right| \leq \frac{A(r)}{r^2}.$$

Now it takes only a simple argument to get an estimate of $A(r)$. The maximum distance between any two points of a unit square is $\sqrt{2}$. Hence all the squares cut by the boundary of the circle are contained in an annulus of width $2\sqrt{2}$ bounded by circles of radii $r + \sqrt{2}$ and $r - \sqrt{2}$. The area of this annulus is equal to

$$B(r) = \left[(r + \sqrt{2})^2 - (r - \sqrt{2})^2\right]\pi = 4\sqrt{2}\pi r.$$

But $A(r) < B(r)$; therefore

$$\left|\frac{f(r)}{r^2} - \pi\right| < \frac{4\sqrt{2}\pi}{r}.$$

From this, a limiting process yields the formula

(1) $$\lim_{r \to \infty} \frac{f(r)}{r^2} = \pi,$$

which is what we were looking for. Inserting in this equation the values found by Gauss of the function $f(r)$, we get the following approximations to the value of $\pi = 3.14159$:

$r = 10$	$= 3.17$
20	3.1425
30	3.134
100	3.1417
200	3.140725
300	3.14107.

We give, as an application of equation (1), a proof of the assertion, made on page 33, that the area of any parallelogram that generates the square lattice is equal to unity. To this end, we consider every lattice point of the circular region as a vertex of a generating parallelogram, letting all of these vertices have like positions on the parallelograms assigned to them, and we compare the region F covered by the parallelograms, with the circle. Here again, the difference of the areas is less than the area $B(r)$ of a circular annulus of radii $r + c$ and $r - c$, where c is the maximum distance between two points of a generating parallelogram (and is independent of r). If the area of the generating parallelogram is a, then the area of F is $a \cdot f(r)$, and we obtain the formula

$$|af(r) - r^2\pi| < B(r) = 4rc\pi,$$

i.e.

$$\left|\frac{a f(r)}{r^2} - \pi\right| < \frac{4 c \pi}{r},$$

$$\lim_{r \to \infty} \frac{f(r)}{r^2} = \frac{\pi}{a}.$$

But we have proved above that

$$\lim_{r \to \infty} \frac{f(r)}{r^2} = \pi.$$

Hence[2] the assertion that $a = 1$ follows.

We shall now turn to the study of general "unit lattices," i.e. lattices that can be constructed from an arbitrary parallelogram of unit area in the same way as the square lattice was constructed from the unit square. Once again, different parallelograms can generate the same lattice, but again they must be of unit area, which is proved in the same way as it was in the case of the square lattice.

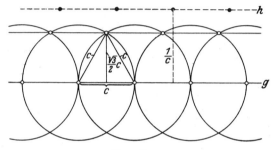

For any such unit lattices, the minimum distance c between two lattice points is a characteristic quantity. There are unit lattices

Fig. 41

for which c is arbitrarily small, e.g. the lattices generated by a rectangle with sides c and $1/c$. On the other hand it is obvious that c can not be arbitrarily large, for then the lattice could not be a unit lattice. Thus c must have an upper bound. We shall determine this bound.

In any given unit lattice, choose any pair of lattice points the distance between which is the minimum distance c (Fig. 41). On the straight line g passing through these two points there must, according to the definition of the lattice, be infinitely many more lattice points spaced at intervals of length c. The straight line h that is parallel to g and at a distance $1/c$ from it must also contain infinitely many lattice points, but the strip between g and h cannot

[2] We could have used, instead of the circle, any other region whose boundary can be covered by a strip of arbitrarily small width relative to the total area of the region.

contain any. Both of these facts follow from the unit property of the lattice. We now draw circles of radius c about all the lattice points on g. The totality of circles covers a strip of the plane bounded by circular arcs. Every interior point of this strip is less than c distant from at least one lattice point and therefore, by the definition of c, is not itself a lattice point. Hence $1/c$ is greater than or equal to the shortest distance between the boundary of the strip and g. Evidently this distance is the altitude of an equilateral triangle of side c. Thus we have

$$\frac{1}{c} \geqq \frac{c}{2}\sqrt{3},$$

$$c \leqq \sqrt{\frac{2}{\sqrt{3}}}.$$

The number $\sqrt{\dfrac{2}{\sqrt{3}}}$ is the desired upper bound for c. Moreover, there is a lattice in which c actually attains this maximal value; for, as can be seen from Fig. 41, this is the case in a lattice generated by a parallelogram that is composed of two equilateral triangles.

By expansion or contraction, any lattice can be obtained from a unit lattice. Hence if a^2 is the area of a generating parallelogram in a lattice and if C is the minimum distance between two lattice points, then

$$C \leqq a\sqrt{\frac{2}{\sqrt{3}}}.$$

Once again equality holds if and only if the lattice is built up of equilateral triangles. For a *given* minimum distance, this lattice therefore has the smallest possible generating parallelogram. But as we have already seen on page 34, the area of large regions is asymptotically equal to the number of lattice points in the region multiplied by the area of the generating parallelogram. Of all lattices with a given minimum distance, the lattice composed of equilateral triangles therefore has the greatest number of points in a given large region.

If we draw circles of radius equal to half the minimum distance of a lattice about all the points of the lattice, we get a system of circles no two of which overlap, but in which tangencies occur. A system constructed in this way is known as a regular packing of circles. One packing of circles is called closer than another if a (sufficiently large) prescribed region accommodates more circles of the first packing than of the other. Accordingly, the lattice of equilateral triangles gives rise to the closest packing of circles (see Fig. 42).

As a measure of the density of a packing of circles we choose the total area of the circles contained in a given region divided by the area of the region. For sufficiently large regions, this value obviously approaches the ratio of the area of a single circle of the packing to that of the generating parallelogram. The lattice of equilateral triangles gives us the optimum value for the density,

$$D = \frac{1}{2\sqrt{3}} \pi = 0.289\,\pi.$$

§ 6. Plane Lattices in the Theory of Numbers

The theory of lattices enters into many problems of Number Theory. We shall give some examples of this. However, in order to avoid lengthy explanations, it will be necessary to presuppose a little more mathematical background in this section than elsewhere in the book.

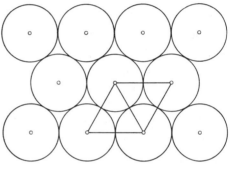

Fig. 42

1. Leibniz' series: $\frac{\pi}{4} = 1 - \frac{1}{3} + \frac{1}{5} - \frac{1}{7} + - \cdots$. As in § 5, let $f(r)$ denote the number of points of the square unit lattice in the interior and on the circumference of a circle of radius r whose center is a lattice point. Let us introduce Cartesian coordinates with the origin at the center of the circle, in such a way that the lattice points are the points with integer coordinates. Then $f(r)$ is the number of pairs of integers x, y for which $x^2 + y^2 \leq r^2$. But $x^2 + y^2$ is always an integer n. Hence we can obtain $f(r)$ by taking each integer $n \leq r^2$, counting the number of ways in which it can be represented as the sum of the squares of two integers, and then adding up the number of possible representations of this kind for all the different values of n. We shall now make use of the following theorem of Number Theory: The number of representations of an integer n as the sum of the squares of two integers is equal to four times the excess of the number of factors of n having the form $4k + 1$ over the number of factors of the form $4k + 3$. In this connection, representations like $n = a^2 + b^2$, $n = b^2 + a^2$, $n = (-a)^2 + b^2$, etc., corresponding to different points of our lattice, are to be regarded as distinct, so that every representation (except some special cases like $a = \pm b$, $a = 0$, $b = 0$) gives rise to a set of eight representations. To illustrate the theorem, let us consider the number $n = 65$. Its factors are 1, 5, 13, and 65, all of the form $4k + 1$; there are no factors of the form $4k + 3$. Thus the excess in which we are interested has the value 4, and it follows from our theorem that there must be 16 different ways of writing the number 65 as the sum of two squares (or, what amounts to the same thing, the circle of radius $\sqrt{65}$ about the origin passes through 16 lattice points). And indeed, we have $65 = 1^2 + 8^2$ and $65 = 4^2 + 7^2$, and each of these representations has to be counted eight times.

According to this theorem, we get the number $\frac{1}{4}(f(r) - 1)$ by subtracting the number of factors of the form $4k + 3$ from the number of factors of the form $4k + 1$ for each positive integer $n \leq r^2$ and adding up these differences. It is much simpler, however, to perform these additions and subtractions in a different order. We shall first add the number of factors of the form $4k + 1$ for all $n \leq r^2$ and then subtract the total number of factors of the form $4k + 3$. In order to determine the first sum, we write the numbers of the form $4k + 1$ in order thus, 1, 5, 9, 13, ..., omitting all numbers greater than r^2. Each of these numbers appears as many times as a factor as there are multiples of it that do not exceed r^2; thus 1 must be counted $[r^2]$ times but 5 only $[r^2/5]$ times, where $[a]$ denotes, in general, the largest integer that does not exceed a. Hence the total number of factors of the form $4k + 1$ in which we are interested is $[r^2] + \left[\frac{r^2}{5}\right] + \left[\frac{r^2}{9}\right] + \left[\frac{r^2}{13}\right] + \cdots$. By definition of the symbol $[a]$, this series breaks off as soon as the denominator in a bracketed expression exceed the numerator. The same argument can be applied to the factors $4k + 3$, giving rise to the expression $\left[\frac{r^2}{3}\right] + \left[\frac{r^2}{7}\right] + \left[\frac{r^2}{11}\right] + \cdots$ for the total number of factors of this form. We have to subtract this second sum from the first sum. Since both sums have a finite number of terms, it is again permissible to change the order of the terms at will; we shall find it expedient to do this in the subsequent passage to the limit in which $r \to \infty$. Let us write the result in the form

$$\frac{1}{4}\left(f(r) - 1\right) = [r^2] - \left[\frac{r^2}{3}\right] + \left[\frac{r^2}{5}\right] - \left[\frac{r^2}{7}\right] + \left[\frac{r^2}{9}\right] - \left[\frac{r^2}{11}\right] + \cdots .$$

To get a better idea as to when the series breaks off, we shall suppose r odd; the series then has $(r^2 + 1)/2$ terms. The terms alternate in sign, and their absolute values are non-increasing. The error committed in breaking off after the term $[r^2/r] = [r] = r$ is therefore at most equal to the last term r, so that we can write this error as ϑr, where ϑ is a proper fraction. If we omit the brackets on the $\frac{1}{2}(r + 1)$ terms that we retained, the resulting error in each term is less than unity, and therefore the total resulting error can be written as $\vartheta' r$, where ϑ' is a proper fraction. Accordingly we have

$$\frac{1}{4}\left(f(r) - 1\right) = r^2 - \frac{r^2}{3} + \frac{r^2}{5} - \frac{r^2}{7} + \cdots \pm r \pm \vartheta r \pm \vartheta' r ,$$

or, dividing through by r^2,

$$\frac{1}{4}\left(\frac{f(r)}{r^2} - \frac{1}{r^2}\right) = 1 - \frac{1}{3} + \frac{1}{5} - \frac{1}{7} + \cdots \pm \frac{1}{r} \pm \frac{\vartheta + \vartheta'}{r} .$$

If r now increases indefinitely (taking on all odd integral values), $f(r)/r^2$ approaches π, as we have proved in § 5. Thus we have arrived at Leibniz' series

$$\tfrac{1}{4}\pi = 1 - \tfrac{1}{3} + \tfrac{1}{5} - \tfrac{1}{7} + \cdots .$$

2. The minimal value of quadratic forms. Let

$$f(m, n) = am^2 + 2bmn + cn^2$$

be a quadratic form with real coefficients a, b, c and with determinant $D = ac - b^2 = 1$. Then a cannot vanish. Let us assume $a > 0$. It is a well-known fact that the form $f(m, n)$ satisfying these conditions is positive definite, i.e. positive for all pairs of real numbers m, n except $m = n = 0$. We shall prove the following: There are two integers m, n, not both equal to zero, such that $f(m, n) \leq \frac{2}{\sqrt{3}}$ for all values of the coefficients a, b, c satisfying our conditions $ac - b^2 = 1$ and $a > 0$.

The truth of this proves to be a consequence of our discussion on the minimal distance between two points of a unit lattice. By completing the square in the customary manner and using the equation $D = 1$, we get

$$f(m, n) = \left(\sqrt{a}\,m + \frac{b}{\sqrt{a}}\,n\right)^2 + \left(\sqrt{\frac{1}{a}}\,n\right)^2 .$$

Now we consider the points with coordinates

$$x = \sqrt{a}\,m + \frac{b}{\sqrt{a}}\,n\,,$$

$$y = \qquad \sqrt{\frac{1}{a}}\,n\,,$$

in a system of plane Cartesian coordinates, where m and n assume all integral values. It follows from elementary theorems of analytic geometry that these points form a unit lattice; for, they are obtained from the points of the square unit lattice $x = m$, $y = n$ by the affine transformation

$$x = \sqrt{a}\,\xi + \frac{b}{\sqrt{a}}\,\eta\,,$$

$$y = \qquad \sqrt{\frac{1}{a}}\,\eta$$

whose determinant is unity. But now $f(m, n) = x^2 + y^2$, and thus $\sqrt{f(m, n)}$ represents the distances from the origin of the lattice points obtained when m and n take on all integral values. According to the theorem mentioned above, there is a point P of the lattice for which this distance does not exceed $\sqrt{\frac{2}{\sqrt{3}}}$. For the pair of integers m, n that are the coordinates of P, we therefore have

$$f(m, n) \leqq \frac{2}{\sqrt{3}}\,,$$

as was to be proved.

This result can be applied to the problem of approximating real numbers by rational numbers. Let a be any given real number. Let us consider the form

$$f(m, n) = \left(\frac{\alpha n - m}{\varepsilon}\right)^2 + \varepsilon^2 n^2 = \frac{1}{\varepsilon^2}\,m^2 - 2\frac{\alpha}{\varepsilon^2}\,mn + \left(\frac{\alpha^2}{\varepsilon^2} + \varepsilon^2\right)n^2$$

with determinant

$$D = \frac{1}{\varepsilon^2}\left(\frac{\alpha^2}{\varepsilon^2} + \varepsilon^2\right) - \frac{\alpha^2}{\varepsilon^4} = 1\,,$$

where ε is an arbitrary positive number. By the result proved above, we can always find two integers m, n satisfying the inequality

$$\left(\frac{\alpha n - m}{\varepsilon}\right)^2 + \varepsilon^2 n^2 \leqq \frac{2}{\sqrt{3}}\,,$$

from which it follows *a fortiori* that the two inequalities

$$\left|\frac{\alpha n - m}{\varepsilon}\right| \leqq \sqrt{\frac{2}{\sqrt{3}}}\,, \qquad |\varepsilon n| \leqq \sqrt{\frac{2}{\sqrt{3}}}$$

are valid. From these we get the inequalities[1]

$$\left| \alpha - \frac{m}{n} \right| \leq \frac{\varepsilon}{|n|} \sqrt{\frac{2}{\sqrt{3}}}, \qquad |n| \leq \frac{1}{\varepsilon} \sqrt{\frac{2}{\sqrt{3}}}.$$

If α is not rational, the left-hand side of the first inequality must differ from zero. Hence we must necessarily obtain infinitely many such number pairs m, n by assigning smaller and smaller values to ε; for $\left| \alpha - \frac{m}{n} \right|$ has to approach zero in the process. We obtain in this way a sequence of rational numbers m/n approximating the irrational number α as close as we please. On the other hand, we can eliminate ε by means of the second inequality, getting

$$\left| \alpha - \frac{m}{n} \right| \leq \frac{2}{\sqrt{3}} \cdot \frac{1}{n^2}.$$

We thus have a sequence of approximating fractions in which the degree of approximation is proportional to the square of the denominator, so that a rather good approximation is obtained with comparatively small denominators.

3. Minkowski's Theorem. Minkowski succeeded in proving a theorem on lattices which has, despite its simplicity, resolved many problems of Number Theory that could not be treated by other methods. For the sake of clarity we shall not state the theorem here in its most general form but shall content ourselves with a special case which, although particularly simple to formulate, contains all that is essential for the method. The theorem is as follows:

If a square of side 2 is superimposed on any given unit lattice in the plane in such a way that the center of the square coincides with a lattice point, then there is bound to be another lattice point inside the square or on its boundary.

To prove the theorem, we consider any large region defined in the plane of the lattice, say the interior and circumference of a large circle c of radius r with center at a lattice point. For every lattice point in this region, construct a square of side s with center at the lattice point (see Fig. 43). Let us now require that no two of these squares overlap, no matter how large a value of r we

---

[1] Division by n is permissible for sufficiently small ε since the inequality

$$|\alpha n - m| \leq \varepsilon \sqrt{\frac{2}{\sqrt{3}}} \qquad \text{could not hold if } n \text{ were equal to zero.}$$

choose, and let us estimate the length of the sides s subject to this condition. There are, in our previous notation, $f(r)$ lattice points in the region; the total area of the non-overlapping squares is therefore $s^2 f(r)$. On the other hand, all the squares are certainly con-- tained in the interior of the circle concentric with c but of larger radius $r + 2s$. Therefore we have the inequality

$$s^2 f(r) \leqq \pi (r + 2s)^2 ,$$

or

$$s^2 \leqq \frac{\pi r^2}{f(r)} \left(1 + \frac{2s}{r} \right)^2 .$$

If s is kept fixed while r increases without bound, we see from our previous discussion of $f(r)$

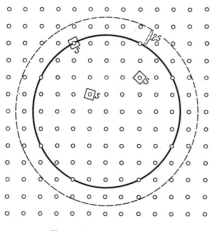

that the right-hand side of the inequality approaches unity. Hence we have the condition

$$s \leqq 1.$$

Since there are only two possibilities, either that the squares overlap, or that they do not, it follows that there must be over- lapping for every positive ε no matter how small, if we start with squares of side $1 + \varepsilon$. We have made no assumptions con- cerning the positions of the

FIG. 43

squares with respect to each other, and so we may rotate the squares at will about their centers. Let us think of all the squares as being parallel. If we now pick out two overlapping squares a, b with centers at A, B (which, according to our assumption, are lattice points), then the mid-point M of the segment AB must also be situated in the interior of both squares (see Fig. 44).

For brevity we shall use the term "bisecting point" of the lattice for all points which, like M, bisect a segment joining two lattice points. We can derive the following: Every square of side $1 + \varepsilon$ whose center is a lattice point contains a bisecting point in its interior. For, if we draw squares of the same size and orientation as a with centers at all the other lattice points, there must be some overlapping; and since all the squares are equivalent in this figure,

a must itself be partly covered by another square b and must therefore contain a bisecting point constructed like the point M in
Fig. 44. This established, we can easily complete an indirect proof
of the theorem. If a square of side 2 with a lattice point A at its
center could be placed so that no additional lattice point is inside
the square or on its boundary, then it could be slightly enlarged
to a parallel and concentric square a' of side $2(1 + \varepsilon)$ containing
in its interior no lattice point other than the center A. On the
other hand, we can shrink this square to a
parallel and concentric square a of half the
linear dimensions which, having a lattice point
at its center and being of side $1 + \varepsilon$, must
contain a bisecting point, by what we have just
proved. Here we have a contradiction; for
if AM is extended its own length to the point B,

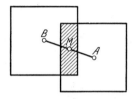

Fig. 44

B must be a lattice point, and from the relative positions of a
and a' it would follow that this lattice point would be inside a'
(see Fig. 45).

A particularly effective application of Minkowski's theorem
relates to the problem of approximating real numbers by rational
numbers, a problem which was already mentioned in the last subsection. Our method will be quite similar to that used before, but
the result will be a little stronger. Using the given irrational
number a, we construct the lattice consisting of the points with
Cartesian coordinates

$$x = \frac{\alpha n - m}{\varepsilon}, \qquad y = \varepsilon n,$$

Fig. 45

where m and n assume all integral values and ε is an
arbitrary positive number. We can see in the same
way as before that this is a unit lattice. A generating
parallelogram of the lattice is exhibited in Fig. 46; in
this figure it is assumed that $0 < a < 1$. Let us draw a square of
side 2 with center at the origin and with sides parallel to the coordinate axes. By Minkowski's theorem, this square must contain
another lattice point, and this point is characterized by a certain
pair of integers m, n, not both equal to zero. On the other hand, the
coordinates of the points inside and on the boundary of the square
are given by the inequalities $|x| \leqq 1$, $|y| \leqq 1$. Thus the numbers

m, n satisfy the inequalities

$$\frac{|\alpha n - m|}{\varepsilon} \leqq 1 , \qquad |\varepsilon n| \leqq 1$$

or

$$\left| \alpha - \frac{m}{n} \right| \leqq \frac{\varepsilon}{|n|} , \quad |n| \leqq \frac{1}{\varepsilon} .$$

This gives rise to another sequence of fractions m/n approximating α to any desired degree of accuracy. By eliminating ε we get

$$\left| \alpha - \frac{m}{n} \right| \leqq \frac{1}{n^2} .$$

Thus Minkowski's theorem proves the existence of a sequence of

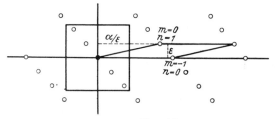

fractions that approximate to α even better than the sequence of fractions constructed in the preceding subsection could be proved to do. For there we had only obtained the

Fig. 46

approximations

$$\left| \alpha - \frac{m}{n} \right| \leqq \frac{2}{\sqrt{3}} \frac{1}{n^2}$$

and these are weaker, since $\dfrac{2}{\sqrt{3}} > 1$.

Of course, the methods described in this section can be applied not only in the plane but also in spaces of any number of dimensions, where they give rise to much more general number-theoretical results.

§ 7. Lattices in Three and More than Three Dimensions

A space lattice is constructed from a parallelepiped by using in three-dimensional space the same process by which the plane lattice was constructed in two dimensions from a parallelogram. Here again, the same lattice can be generated by parallelepipeds of different forms, but all the generating parallelepipeds must have the same volume. Furthermore, every generating parallelepiped must have its corners at points of the lattice but must not contain any additional lattice points in its interior or on its surface. If a generating parallelepiped has unit volume we refer to it as a unit lattice.

For the same reason as in the plane, the minimum distance between two points of a space lattice does not have a positive lower bound but does have an upper bound. The determination of the bound is accomplished by the same method as in the plane and will therefore be omitted. In this connection, the regular tetrahedron plays the same part in space as the equilateral triangle does in the plane. But whereas the generating parallelogram in the plane is composed of two equilateral triangles, the regular parallelepiped corresponding to it in space—the regular rhombohedron—consists of two regular tetrahedra and one regular octahedron (see Fig. 49, p. 48).[1] The volume of this parallelepiped is equal to $c^3/\sqrt{2}$, where c is the length of an edge of the tetrahedron. But since it is required that this volume be equal to unity, we have $c^3/\sqrt{2}=1$, or $c=\sqrt[6]{2}$. Thus we have the result, for three-dimensional unit lattices, that every lattice point has at least one other lattice point closer than $\sqrt[6]{2}$.

In the same way as in the plane, our result at the same time provides the solution for the problem of finding the closest regular packing of spheres, for this packing is realized when the centers of the spheres form the rhombohedral lattice. If the spheres have unit radius, the length of the edges of the tetrahedra is 2, so that the volume of the unit cell is equal to

$$\frac{2^3}{\sqrt{2}} = 4\sqrt{2}.$$

Accordingly, a region of volume J contains approximately $\dfrac{J}{4\sqrt{2}}$ lattice points and the same number of spheres of the corresponding packing; the approximation, as in the plane, becomes more nearly exact as J increases.

We shall now give a more detailed description of this packing of spheres. To begin with, let us imagine a flat layer of unit spheres arranged so that the centers form the lattice corresponding to the closest packing of circles in the plane. Evidently this gives us the

---

[1] In the plane the closest packing of circles leads to a tiling of the whole plane by congruent equilateral triangles. It might be expected that the analogous problem in space leads to a system of congruent regular tetrahedra filling the space. It can be proved, however, that space can not be tiled by congruent regular tetrahedra at all.

closest packing of spheres in a plane layer. Let us now take **a** second layer of the same kind and try to place it on top of the first

FIG. 47a

FIG. 47b

layer in such a way as to make room for the two layers between two parallel planes that are the smallest possible distance apart. To this end, we must place the spheres of the second layer so that they will just fit into the hollows of the first layer. However, there is not sufficient room to fit a sphere into every hollow, so that we must alternate, leaving every other hollow empty (see Fig. 42, p. 37). If a third layer is now to be placed on top of the first two in the same manner, this condition does not uniquely determine the position of the three layers relative to each other. We may place the spheres of the third layer into the hollows of the second in such a way that the first and third layers are symmetric with respect to the second (Fig. 47a). On the other hand, we may also place the spheres of the third layer over those hollows that were left free in the arrangement just mentioned (Fig. 47b, c) ; then the same translation that moves the first layer into the position of the second layer will move the second layer into the position of the third. In this case the repeated application of the same translation in both directions gives rise to the packing corresponding to the rhombohedral lattice. Thus we have seen that whereas in the plane the maximum density is attained by only one packing of circles, the same prob-

FIG. 47c

lem in space leads to two entirely different arrangements of spheres.[2] The centers of the spheres need not by any means form a figure that

---

[2] Both arrangements actually occur in nature. The first case is realized in the hexagonal crystals of the type of magnesium, the second in the face-centered cubic crystals. Cf § 8.

is regular throughout space, for in passing from one layer to the next we can change from one of the possible arrangements to the other at will. But there is one property that is characteristic of all the packings under consideration: Every sphere touches exactly twelve other spheres, namely six spheres in the same layer and three in each of the two adjacent layers.

The problem of finding the closest regular packing of spheres has also been studied in four-dimensional and five-dimensional space. Strangely enough, it has been found that the lattices in higher dimensional space corresponding to the triangular and rhombohedral lattices no longer generate the closest packing of spheres. The results are summarized in the following table:

	$c =$ minimum distance between two points	Density of the packing
Plane	$\sqrt{\dfrac{2}{\sqrt{3}}} = 1.075$	$0.289\,\pi = 0.907$
Ordinary Space	$\sqrt[6]{2} = 1.122$	$\dfrac{\sqrt{2}}{8} \cdot \dfrac{4}{3}\,\pi = 0.740$
Four-dimensional Space . . .	$\sqrt[4]{2} = 1.189$	$\dfrac{\pi^2}{16} = 0.617$
Five-dimensional Space . . .	$\sqrt[10]{2} = 1.074$	$\dfrac{\sqrt{2}}{60}\,\pi^2 = 0.465$

(The volume of the sphere of unit radius is equal to $\pi^2/2$ in four dimensions and $8\pi^2/15$ in five dimensions.)

Now there are numerous other regular packings that are of interest besides those of maximum density. As an example we note the cubic packing, where the centers of the unit spheres form the lattice generated by a cube of side 2. Here every sphere is in contact with exactly six neighboring spheres; it should therefore be expected that the density of this packing will be considerably less than that of the rhombohedral packing, in which every sphere touches twelve other spheres. To prove that this is so, we move the cubic lattice into such a position that every cube encloses exactly one sphere. The cube with edge of length 2 has a volume of 8; hence the number of spheres contained in a large region of volume $8x$ is asymptotically equal to x. Since the volume of a unit sphere is $\frac{4}{3}\pi$, it follows that the density of the cubic packing is

$$D = \frac{1}{8} \cdot \frac{4}{3}\,\pi = \frac{\pi}{6} = 0.524 \,.$$

It is now natural to investigate the problem, suggested by the one above, of finding the loosest of all the packings in space that

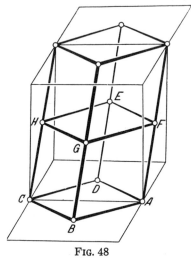

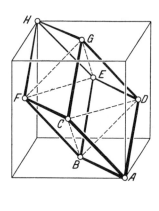

Fig. 48   Fig. 49

hold the spheres fixed in position. It is necessary here that every sphere touch at least four other spheres with centers not all in

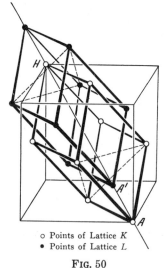

o Points of Lattice K
• Points of Lattice L

Fig. 50

one plane nor all on one hemisphere; for if this condition were not satisfied, the sphere would not be held fixed by its neighbors. Now it might perhaps be expected that every sphere in the loosest packing touches exactly four other spheres and that their centers form the vertices of a regular tetrahedron. We shall proceed to construct a system of points arranged in this way, leaving aside for the moment the question of whether the corresponding packing is really the loosest.

To the points of a cubic lattice we add the centers of the faces of the cubes. The resulting set of points also forms a lattice (the face-centered cubic lattice), for it can be generated by parallel translation from the parallelepiped $ABCDEFGH$ of Figs. 48 and 49. (These figures illustrate the fact mentioned before, that the same point lattice can be constructed from various, and quite different, unit cells.) From Fig. 49

it is apparent that we are dealing with the same lattice we encountered before as the lattice corresponding to the closest packing of spheres. For, in the plane ABD, the parallelogram $ABDE$ defines the lattice of equilateral triangles; the next parallel plane containing lattice points is CFG, and the position of the lattice points in this plane relative to those in the first plane is such as to form regular tetrahedra, such as $ABCD$ in Fig. 49.

To this lattice K we add a congruent lattice L obtained from K by a translation in the direction of the diagonal AH of the cube through a distance equal to one fourth of its length (Fig. 50). We

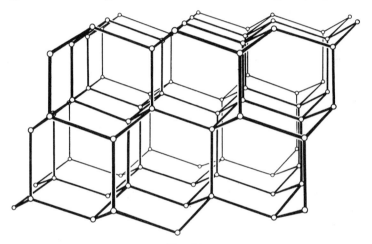

Fig. 51

shall see that the points of L together with those of K make up the centers of the desired "tetrahedral" packing of spheres, and furthermore that the radius of the spheres must be equal to $\frac{1}{2} AA'$, where A' is the point of L obtained from A. For, it is evident from the construction that the distances from A' to the points labelled A, B, C, D in Fig. 49 are all equal; therefore the sphere with center at A' just touches the spheres having their centers at the vertices of the tetrahedron $ABCD$. For reasons of symmetry, the corresponding statement must be true for all spheres with center at points of L. But the same also applies to the spheres with center at points of K (e.g. H in Fig. 50), since the positions of K and L relative to each other are the same except for the sense of the translation that moves one into the other. Figs. 51 and 52 illustrate the arrangement of the centers of the spheres forming the tetrahedral packing; the centers of contiguous spheres are connected by straight lines.[3]

We shall now compute the density of the tetrahedral packing. It is clear that there are four spheres of the lattice L for every cube; for in the translation that transforms K into L, the points E, F, G, H (in Fig. 49) and the spheres with centers at these points are moved completely out of the cube, while the spheres with centers at A, B, C, D are moved into its interior. Since K has the same density as L, there are exactly eight spheres of the packing in each cube. As usual, let us set the radius $\frac{1}{2}AA'$ of the spheres equal to unity, and let us denote the length of the edges of the cubes by a and that of the diagonals by b. Then $b = 4AA' = 8 = a\sqrt{3}$. Hence the volume of the cube is $a^3 = \dfrac{8^3}{3\sqrt{3}}$.

The density D that we wished to find is

$$D = \frac{8}{a^3} \cdot \frac{4}{3}\pi = \frac{\sqrt{3}}{16}\pi = 0.340$$

by the same type of argument used before.

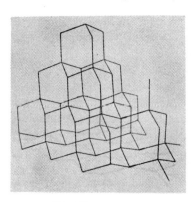

Fig. 52

We shall show (by a method due to H. Heesch and F. Laves, Göttingen[4]) that the tetrahedral packing is by no means the loosest packing but can be used as the starting point of a simple construction that gives rise to a substantially looser packing, in which each sphere still touches four other spheres and all the spheres are equivalent. It should be mentioned, however, that the centers of the four spheres contiguous to any given sphere in the new arrangement will form the vertices not of a regular tetrahedron as before, but of another kind of tetrahedron, with an equilateral triangle as its base and isosceles triangles as its faces.

To construct this packing, we begin with a sphere K of the tetrahedral packing and inscribe four smaller spheres k_1 to k_4, of equal

---

[3] The locus of the centers in this packing is not a lattice; it does not, for example, contain the point A'' defined in Fig. 50 as the point on AA' produced for which $A'A'' = AA'$, whereas a lattice containing A and A' would also have to contain A'' as one of its points. The structure with which we are dealing is called a system of points. The systems of points are characterized by more general properties of symmetry than are the lattices. They will be defined in § 9.

[4] Cf. *Zeitschrift für Kristallographie*, Vol. 82, p. 10, Fig. 7.

radius, touching K from inside at the same points at which K touches the neighboring spheres of the tetrahedral packing. Since these four points of contact are the vertices of a regular tetrahedron, so are the centers of the small spheres. The radius of the small spheres k_1 to k_4 may be chosen so as to make each pair of spheres tangent; each sphere thus touches the other three. We may now carry out the corresponding construction for all the other spheres of the tetrahedral packing. Then k_1 not only touches the spheres k_2, k_3, and k_4 inside K, but also touches another small sphere k_5 situated outside K, the point of contact being the point at which k_1 touches K from inside. For at this point K is in contact with a sphere K' of the tetrahedral packing, and at this point K' is touched, in its interior, by a small sphere which we shall call k_5. Of course the property we have demonstrated for k_1 applies equally to all the other congruent spheres of our construction, so that they still form a packing in which each sphere is held fixed by its neighbors. To see how the density d of our new packing compares with D, the density of the tetrahedral packing, it is clear that we need only compare the combined volume of k_1, k_2, k_3, and k_4 with the volume of K. If the radii of k_1 and K are r and R respectively, then

$$\frac{d}{D} = \frac{4 \cdot \frac{4}{3}\pi r^3}{\frac{4}{3}\pi R^3} = 4\,\frac{r^3}{R^3};$$

by elementary reasoning, it follows from our construction that $R = (\sqrt{3}/2 + 1)r$, whence $d = \dfrac{4}{(\sqrt{\frac{3}{4}} + 1)^3} D = 0.3633\,D$. Accordingly, the packing is considerably less close than the tetrahedral packing. There are reasons for believing that it is the loosest possible packing. The following table shows the characteristic constants for the four packings of spheres that we have discussed.

Closest Packing	$D = \dfrac{\sqrt{2}}{8} \cdot \dfrac{4}{3}\pi = 0.740$		12	
Cubic Packing	$D = \dfrac{1}{8} \cdot \dfrac{4}{3}\pi = 0.513$	Every Sphere touches	6	others
Tetrahedral Packing	$D = \dfrac{3 \cdot \sqrt{3}}{64} \cdot \dfrac{4}{3}\pi = 0.340$		4	
Loosest (?) Packing	$D = 0.123$		4	

We could drop the requirement that the arrangement of the circles or spheres be regular, and replace it by a weaker condition, say that every sufficiently extended region of the plane (or space) contain as many circles (or spheres) of a fixed size as possible. The problem then has to be treated by different methods. In the case of the plane it has been proved that the centers of the circles satisfying the new condition will of necessity form a lattice. In spaces of three and higher dimensions the problem has not yet been solved.

§ 8. Crystals as Regular Systems of Points

The most important application of the theory of discontinuous regular systems of points is in crystallography. Judging by the regular exterior form of crystals and their cleavability, it is to be expected that the individual atoms or molecules of this structure, when considered as points, form a figure that can be continued congruent to itself so as to fill all of space. Any figure obtained by such an extension is called a system of points. Later on we shall make this concept more precise and show that there is only a finite number of essentially different systems of points. There now arise two problems, partly of a mathematical and partly of a physical nature. First of all there is the problem of determining the system of points corresponding to each type of crystal. And then there is the problem of explaining the physical behavior of the different types of crystal in terms of the geometrical properties of the corresponding systems of points.

The first attempts to achieve a definite point of view on the structure of crystals by means of this approach date back to Bravais (1848). But his theory was not given a firm empirical basis until Laue's method using the diffraction of X-rays by crystals (1913) had made it possible to establish empirically not only the existence of crystal lattices but also their precise structure.

Obviously the crudest picture we may form of an atom is as a point with a number of "arms" equal to the valence of the atom. In this model we assume that the arms representing the valence bonds are arranged in space as symmetrically as possible, as long as no special reason exists for them to deviate from this symmetry. The combination of individual atoms to form a molecule is then represented by letting two arms of different atoms coincide.

Hydrogen (H), oxygen (O), nitrogen (N), and carbon (C), for example, have the valences one, two, three, and four respectively. Accordingly we may represent these atoms by points with one, two, three, or four arms as the case may be (Fig. 53). In the case of H, O, and N, symmetry demands that all the arms lie in one plane. For the same reason, we are led to expect that the four arms of a carbon atom point towards the four corners of a regular tetrahedron having the atom at its center.

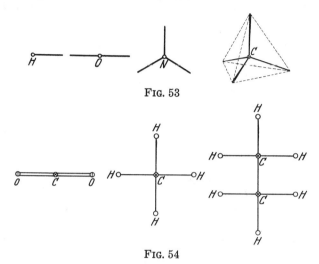

Fig. 53

Fig. 54

As examples of molecules, we may consider the molecules of carbon dioxide (CO_2), methane (CH_4), and ethane (C_2H_6). Fig. 54 shows a schematic representation of the way the atoms are connected (the "structural formula") without regard to the actual relative positions in space. Possible spatial arrangements for the molecules of methane and ethane which, according to recent investigations, are probably the correct arrangements, are illustrated in Fig. 55 (Van t'Hoff, 1874). In the model of ethane we have to think of the line connecting the C atoms as an axis about which the two tetrahedra can be rotated relative to each other.

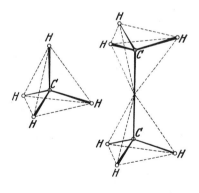

Fig. 55

Now the question arises whether it would not be possible for whole crystals to be generated like molecules by the attachment of more and more atoms. The possibility of such a construction will first of all be demonstrated for the simplest case, where the crystal consists of a single element. We choose as an example the diamond, which, as is well known, consists of pure carbon. Thus the problem is to arrange a great many C atoms, each consisting of a point with four arms, as symmetrically as possible in such a way that each point is connected with four others by pairs of coinciding arms. Whether such a structure exists is a purely geometrical question. In point of fact it does exist; the atoms are arranged like the centers of spheres forming a tetrahedral packing. For, by the construction considered in § 7, every point in this arrangement has four neighboring points that form the vertices of a regular tetrahedron

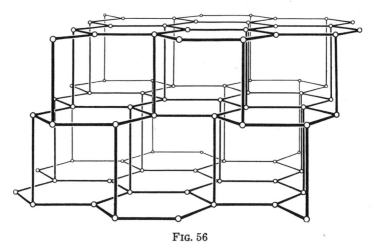

Fig. 56

with the original point at the center (cf. Figs. 50 to 52, pp. 48 to 50). Measurements due to Braggs reveal that this pattern, which we arrived at by purely geometrical methods, is the pattern in which the diamond crystal is actually built up from its atoms. These measurements also revealed that the distance between neighboring points in the diamond crystal is 1.53×10^{-8} cm.[1]

There is, besides the diamond, another crystal that consists of C atoms only, namely graphite. Measurements disclose that the arms of the C atoms in graphite are not symmetrically arranged and that they are in fact not even equal in length. Thus one of

---

[1] The crystals of zinc-blende (ZnS) also have this atomic structure, which corresponds to the tetrahedral packing. Here the Zn atoms and the S atoms separately constitute the two lattices from which we constructed the tetrahedral point system on p. 48 (Fig. 50).

the arms is lengthened to 3.41 × 10⁻⁸ cm. while the others are only
1.45 × 10⁻⁸ cm. in length. The latter three are approximately in
a plane. The experimental evidence is not yet adequate to tell us
whether they deviate from the plane position at all, and to what
extent, but for the present discussion it will suffice to assume that
they are exactly coplanar. With this assumption we can describe
the structure of graphite as follows. In the plane we construct a
system of regular hexagons with one atom at each corner (Fig. 56) ;
this accounts for three of the valence bonds of each atom. In order
to connect the layer above the plane with the one below, the valence
bonds that are still free—exactly one for each atom—must be connected alternately with atoms of the upper layer and atoms of the
lower layer. Then all three
layers are indeed congruent,
and the points of the middle
layer are alternately vertically
below a point of the upper
layer and vertically above a
point of the lower layer. In the
same way the structure can be
extended indefinitely in all
directions.

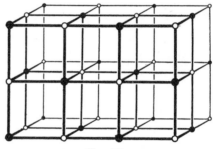

FIG. 57

The systems of points we have constructed as models for the
diamond and for graphite explain some of the physical differences
between the two crystals, such as the fact that graphite has far
greater cleavability and compressibility than the diamond. On the
other hand, the explanation of some other differences involves
considerable difficulties.

As an example of a crystal composed of more than one kind of
atom, we may mention common table salt (NaCl). The salt crystal
is a cubic lattice with its points occupied alternately by a Cl atom
and a Na atom (Fig. 57). The distance between neighboring lattice
points is 2 × 10⁻⁸ cm. and is thus greater than the length of the
short arms and smaller than that of the long arm of the C atom
in graphite. In the salt crystal every lattice point has six neighboring points. But the Na and Cl atoms are univalent. Hence
this crystal is not arranged in accordance with the theory of valences described above. In the general case too, there is no direct
connection between the valences of the atoms forming a crystal

and the number of neighboring points of any point in the structure. The diamond, where the two numbers coincide, is an exception.

Of particular interest is the fact that in the lattice of table salt there are no pairs of points distinguished that might correspond to the NaCl molecule. Thus the lattice is composed simply of the two types of atoms. On the other hand, there are crystals in which molecules—or at least complexes of atoms—have a fairly distinct identity. In the space lattice of calcite ($CaCO_3$) the radical CO_3 can be clearly recognized as a coherent unit.

While the diamond exemplifies the tetrahedral packing, there is a large number of crystals, represented by the "face-centered cubic" lattice, that corresponds to that closest packing of spheres in which the relative positions of two consecutive layers are always the same (see Figs. 47b and 47c, p. 46). The other form of closest packing, where alternate layers fill alternate sets of hollows (Fig. 47a, p. 46), is exemplified by the magnesium crystal. This arrangement is known as the "hexagonal closest packing of spheres."

§ 9. Regular Systems of Points and Discontinuous Groups of Motions

The study of crystallography leads to the purely geometrical problem of determining all the possible regular arrangements of objects, e.g. of atoms. Since it is sufficient for many purposes to visualize these objects as points, such an arrangement is called a regular system of points. In accordance with the earlier discussion we shall therefore define a regular system of points by the following three properties:

1. A regular system of points in the plane or in space is to contain infinitely many points; moreover the number of points of the system contained in a circle in the plane, or in a sphere in space, is to go to infinity as the square of the radius, or the cube of the radius, respectively.

2. Any finite region is to contain only a finite number of points of a regular system.

3. Each point of a regular point system is to have the same position relative to the remaining points as has any other point of the system.

The first two defining properties are clear without further explanation. The third can be elaborated on as follows. Let us draw the lines connecting some fixed point of a regular system with all the other points of the system and then do the same for a second fixed point; then the third defining property states that the two configurations of straight-line segments obtained in this way are congruent, i.e. that there is a well-defined motion of the plane that brings one of these two figures into coincidence with the other. Thus a person situated at some particular point of the system could not determine by any measurements which point of the system he is at, since the position of every point relative to the other points is the same. However, to satisfy the third condition it is not necessary to refer to the lines connecting points of the system; all that is required is that it be possible to bring any point of the system into coincidence with any other point of the system by some definite motion of the plane, or of space, which is such that every position occupied by a point of the system before the motion is also occupied after the motion by a point of the system, and vice versa. Such a motion is said to leave the point system unchanged, or invariant, and is called a *symmetry operation* of the system. Using this concept, we may express the third defining property for regular point systems in the following form:

3. It is possible to move any point of the regular system to any of the other points of the system by a symmetry operation of the system.

From our definition it follows that the lattices, which we had defined by generating them from a parallelogram or a parallelepiped in plane and space respectively, are regular systems of points. The introduction of the new concept of regular systems, which generalizes that of lattices, is justified by the existence of regular systems of points, such as the structure of the diamond, that are not lattices.

Let us now construct the totality of all possible regular point systems. We shall find that the only regular point systems there are, besides the lattices, are those that consist of several congruent lattices interlocking in parallel positions, like the structure of the diamond. At first sight it might appear that the notion of regular point systems as defined by our three conditions is so general as to rule out the possibility of obtaining a complete geometrical classification of these systems. Nevertheless such a classification can actually be made; it will be based on a study of the symmetry operations of the systems.

The totality of all symmetry operations of a system of points is characterized by two properties that substantially simplify the study of such systems. First, the resultant of two consecutive symmetry operations is always another symmetry operation, and second, the motion that reverses any symmetry operation of the system is always another symmetry operation. In mathematics, any set of transformations satisfying these two conditions is called a *group* of transformations. For the sake of easy algebraic manipulation we shall denote each transformation by a letter, such as a, b, etc.; the transformation resulting when a is carried out first and b second, will always be denoted by the symbol ab. The transformation that reverses a is denoted by a^{-1}, and is called the *inverse* transformation of a. Using the two defining properties of a group in combination, we are led to the transformation aa^{-1}. This operation evidently leaves all points unchanged. But it is convenient nevertheless to consider it as a special case of a transformation; we shall call it the identity transformation, or identity, and denote it by the letter e. The role of e in the symbolic combination of transformations is the same as that of the number one in the multiplication of numbers. $ae = ea = a$ always holds.

If a point of a regular system is subjected to all the symmetry operations of the system, it follows from the third defining property of regular systems that all the other points of the system are obtained from this one point. On the other hand, it follows from the definition of a symmetry operation that none of the points of the system can be transformed into a point not belonging to the system, since the motion would otherwise not leave the system invariant. In general, two points are called *equivalent* under a given group of transformations if one of the points can be obtained from the other by a transformation belonging to the group. The regular system of points accordingly consists of all the points that are equivalent to a given fixed point under the group of symmetry operations. Hence, by the second defining property of regular systems, there is only a finite number of equivalent points in any finite region. Any group of transformations having the property that in a finite region only finitely many points are equivalent to any given point under these transformations, is called *discontinuous*. Thus the symmetry operations of a system of points always form a discontinuous group. It is, to be sure, conceivable that there is a point not belonging to the system that has, in a finite region, infinitely many points equivalent to it under a group leaving the system invariant. However, it is intuitively clear, and easy to prove rigorously, that this would also imply the existence in a finite region of infinitely many points equivalent to a point of the regular system and would thus involve a contradiction.

All the groups of symmetry operations of a point system are thus to be found among the discontinuous groups of motions of the plane and space, and all the regular systems of points are to be found in turn among the sets of points equivalent to some point under such a group.

This apparent detour actually provides the easiest approach to the study of point systems. For, it is found that there are only finitely many discontinuous groups of motions in the plane and in space that are essentially distinct.

Consideration of the sets of points equivalent to a given point under any group from this finite class of groups shows that the second and third defining conditions for point systems are always satisfied. But there are groups giving rise to point sets that do not satisfy the first condition; we shall have to exclude such groups. The remaining groups give rise to the regular point systems, and no other groups do so. These groups are called the crystallographic groups of motions because of the important role played by regular point systems in crystallography.

We shall now proceed to construct the discontinuous groups of motions. But we shall confine our attention to the case of the plane, as the corresponding problem for space would involve too lengthy a study to fit into the framework of this book. Even the study of discontinuous groups of motions in the plane involves rather lengthy considerations. Nevertheless, we shall carry it out in full, because the methods it will teach us are typical for the three-dimensional case also.

§ 10. Plane Motions and their Composition; Classification of the Discontinuous Groups of Motions in the Plane

A mapping of the plane onto itself will be called a plane motion if the final position can be obtained from the initial position by a *continuous* motion in which the plane is considered rigid and in which each of its points describes a path which is *in the plane*. Henceforth, however, we shall characterize any motion of the plane by the initial and final positions only, without regard to the way in which the transition actually takes place in any particular case; of course, we can get from the initial to the final position in any number of entirely different ways, and some of these involve the leaving of the plane or distortions that ultimately cancel out. All that is required is the *possibility* of making the transition in the manner described at the beginning of the paragraph. It will be one of our first tasks to find the simplest possible way of effecting any given motion.

The simplest motions in the plane are the parallel motions or translations, in which every point of the plane moves through the same distance in the same direction and every straight line remains parallel to its initial position.

Another well-known type of motion are the rotations of the plane through a given angle about any given point. Here the direction of every straight line is changed by the given angle,[1] and the center of the rotation is the only point of the plane that remains fixed.

Also, for any motion other than the identity, there is at most one point that remains fixed. For if we keep two points of the plane fixed, then, apart from the identity, there is only one transformation of the plane onto itself that can be obtained by a rigid motion. This is the transformation that results when the plane is rotated through 180° about the line connecting the two fixed points, a motion that is not included in the class of motions described above. Moreover, we cannot obtain this transformation by motions of the above class, since it transforms a circle with a clockwise rotational sense into a circle with the reverse sense, whereas it follows from considerations of continuity that a proper motion never reverses a rotational sense. From this discussion we see that a plane motion is completely determined by the initial and final positions of two points. For if any two plane motions map two points in the same way, they can only differ by a plane motion that leaves two points fixed, i.e. they can not differ at all.

We shall prove that every motion of the plane can be carried out in one single translation or one single rotation, a fact that very considerably simplifies the study of plane motions. In order to prove this, let us consider any given motion b. Leaving aside the trivial case where b is the identity, we can choose a point A that is

---

[1] For straight lines through the center of the rotation, this is obvious. For all other straight lines it follows from the fact that there are lines parallel to them through the center of rotation and that any motion transforms parallels into parallels.

transformed into a different point A'. If B is the midpoint of the segment AA', then the motion either leaves B fixed or transforms it into another point B'. In the former case (Fig. 58) the truth of our assertion is obvious. For, in this case we need only consider the rotation b' through the angle π around B and note that it moves the points A and B into the same images A' and B into which they are moved by b, and since we have seen that a plane motion is completely determined by the initial and final positions of two points, it follows that b and b' are identical. If, on the other hand, B moves into a different point B', we have to distinguish between the special case where B' is on the straight line AA' and the general case where the straight lines AA' and BB' are distinct. In the first case B' is uniquely determined, because the

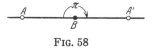

FIG. 58

distance between A and B must be left unchanged by the motion b. But since B was defined so that $AB = A'B$, we must have $A'B' = A'B$, and this, together with the condition $B' \neq B$, determines the position of B' uniquely (see Fig. 59). Now b is seen to be identical with the translation that moves A to A', for, this translation also moves B to the same image point B'. This leaves us with only the last case to consider, in which B' is not on AA'. In this case we erect the perpendicular to AB at B and the perpendicular to $A'B'$ at B' (Fig. 60). It follows from our assumptions and the construction that the two per-

FIG. 59

pendiculars are distinct and not parallel and consequently have a point of intersection M. We shall see that the motion b is identical with the rotation about M that moves A to A'. To prove this, we have to show that this rotation moves B to B', which amounts to the same as saying that the triangles AMB and $A'MB'$ are congruent. We know that $AMB \cong A'MB'$, since both triangles have right angles at B and have equal legs. But in addition $A'B'M \cong A'BM$, because these triangles have right angles at B and at B' and have

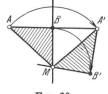

FIG. 60

the common hypotenuse $A'M$, and because, as we have seen before, $A'B' = AB = A'B$. This completes the proof.

We can make our result appear even simpler, at least from a formal point of view, if we agree to consider translations as rotations through the angle zero about an infinitely distant point. Heuristically, this convention can easily be justified as follows: If we consider a sequence of rotations about a point that moves out indefinitely in a fixed direction while the angle of rotation approaches zero, we can arrange, by a proper choice of such a sequence, that the rotations differ less and less—at least as regards their effect on any given finite region—from any pre-assigned translation.

If we adopt this point of view, we may regard any rigid motion of the plane as a rotation through some definite angle, which is zero in the case of translations. Thus it must always be possible to represent the resultant motion obtained when two rotations are carried out successively, by a single rotation through some definite angle. In this connection we have the following simple *theorem on additivity of angles of rotation*:

The resultant of a rotation through an angle α and a rotation through an angle β must be a rotation through the angle $\alpha + \beta$.

To prove this, let us recall the fact mentioned at the beginning, that the angle of rotation is given by the change in the direction of any straight line chosen arbitrarily. With our new convention, this theorem also applies to translations, since these leave directions unchanged. With this, the theorem is obvious. As an example of the theorem, we note that two rotations about different centers and through equal and opposite angles always produce a translation. For, the composite motion has the angle zero, but cannot be the identity since neither of the two centers of rotation remains fixed.

With this preparation we can return to the discontinuous groups of motions in the plane. We are now in a position to set up a simple classification of these motions. For, we need only indicate what translations are present and what the angles and centers of the rotations are. It will be found most convenient to consider the translations first, distinguishing between the following cases:

I. *The directions of all translations present in the group are parallel.*

II. *There are in the group two translations having different directions.*

Case I is understood to include the groups containing no translations at all.

Now we subdivide the two classes of groups by considering the rotations. Thus we shall distinguish between the following:

1. Groups that do not contain rotations, and 2. Groups that do contain rotations.

Instead of identifying a group by the rotations and translations it has, we can also characterize it by a simple geometrical figure known as the *unit cell*. By the unit cell of a group we mean any connected region that does not contain a pair of equivalent points in its interior but that cannot be enlarged without losing this property. Such unit cells are important not only in the theory of groups of rigid motions but indeed in the study of all discontinuous groups of transformations. In the general case, it is quite difficult to determine a unit cell for a given group or even just to prove the existence of unit cells for a class of groups. In the case of discontinuous groups of plane rigid motions, however, we can always construct unit cells quite easily.

For groups of type I it is found that every unit cell extends to infinity, while in case II, the unit cells are always finite.

Before we proceed to examine the unit cells of the plane groups, we shall mention some relations that always exist between the rotations and the translations of a group. Since we shall have occasion to refer repeatedly to these relations, they will be numbered as lemmas.

First Lemma. If a rotation through an angle α about a point P is an element of a group and if Q is equivalent to P, then the group also contains the rotation through the same angle α about Q.

Proof. By assumption, the group contains a motion b under which P goes into Q, and it also contains the rotation d through the angle α about P. From the defining properties of a group it follows, in terms of the symbolism explained in the last section, that the group must also contain the motion $b^{-1}db$. This last must be a rotation through α, for, if β denotes the angle of rotation of b, the additivity theorem for angles of rotation tells us that the angle of $b^{-1}db$ is $-\beta + \alpha + \beta = \alpha$. And the center of the rotation must be Q, because b^{-1} transforms Q into P, d leaves P fixed, and b transforms P back into Q.

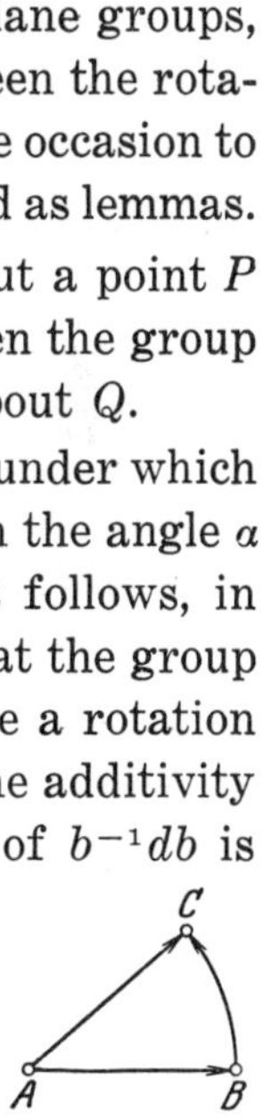

Fig. 61

Second Lemma. If a group contains a rotation through angle α and a translation t, it also contains the translation t' whose magnitude is the same as that of t and whose direction forms an angle α with the direction of t.

Proof. Let d, a rotation through angle α contained in the group, have the center A. Let t transform A into B and let d transform

B into C (Fig. 61). Then t' is simply given by $t' = d^{-1}td$. Indeed, this motion must be an element of the group, and it must be a translation, its angle, by the additivity theorem, being zero. All that remains to be proved is that it moves A into C, and this is true because d^{-1} leaves A fixed, t moves it to B, and d moves B to C.

One consequence of this lemma is that any group of type I that contains any translations at all can not contain rotations through any angle except π. For, if there were other rotations in the group, the presence of any translation would entail the presence of another translation in a direction not parallel to that of the first.

§ 11. The Discontinuous Groups of Plane Motions
with Infinite Unit Cells

To begin with, we shall deal with the case I, which gives rise to the simplest groups. First of all, let us take the subclass I, 1,

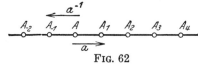

FIG. 62

comprising groups that do not contain any rotations. Starting from any point A, we note that there are only finitely many

points equivalent to it within a finite distance of A, so that among these points there is a point A_1 having the smallest possible distance from A (Fig. 62). Of course, there may be several equivalent points having this minimal distance from A, in which case we may choose one such point. The motion a of the group that brings A into coincidence with A_1 must be a translation, since we have assumed that there are no rotations in the group. If we extend the segment AA_1 by its own length to A_2, this point must also be equivalent to A, since it is obtained from A by the translation aa. By the same argument we see that there are further points $A_3, A_4, \ldots$ equally spaced on the straight line AA_1, all of which are equivalent to A

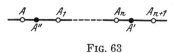

FIG. 63

and are obtained from A by repeated application of the motion a. And, by the same argument, the same straight line contains infinitely many equi-

distant points $A_{-1}, A_{-2}, \ldots$ on the other side of A that are also equivalent to A and are obtained by applying a^{-1} one or more times to A. Now it will be seen that the row of points we have constructed on AA_1 exhausts the totality of points equivalent to A. For, by assumption, all the translations of the group are parallel to AA_1, and therefore all points equivalent to A lie on AA_1. Suppose now that there were such a point A' which is not a point of division of our scale; then A' would have to be in the interior of an interval A_nA_{n+1} (Fig. 63). Then the distance A_nA' would be shorter than AA_1. But there is a translation in the group that moves A_n to A; this would move A' to a point A'' whose distance from A is less than that of A_1. This contradicts the initial choice of A_1 as an equivalent point having the smallest possible distance from A.

This completes the discussion of the groups of type I, 1; for, we have now found all the points equivalent to any given point, and we have thus described all the motions of the group—they are the translations a and a^{-1} applied once or several times. Thus all the groups of type I, 1 are essentially identical.

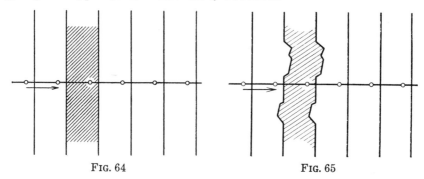

Fig. 64   Fig. 65

To construct a unit cell, we may simply start with a straight line that is not parallel to AA_1, say with a perpendicular to AA_1. a transforms this straight line into a parallel straight line. Now the strip of the plane cut off by the two parallel lines cannot contain two equivalent points in its interior. On the other hand, since the two bounding straight lines are equivalent, it is impossible to add to the strip without having the enlarged region contain a pair of equivalent points. Thus the strip is a unit cell (Fig. 64).[1] However, we can change it as much as we like without destroying its property of being a unit cell, by adding a patch on one side and omitting an equivalent piece on the other side (see Fig. 65). This type of alteration is also admissible in the case of unit cells for all the other

---

[1] The points of one of the bounding straight lines, say the left one, must be considered as belonging to the unit cell but not the points of the other line; otherwise the region would either contain equivalent points or be incomplete as a unit cell.

groups we shall consider and indeed for all transformation groups. Out of the variety of possible unit cells, we shall in each case choose one that has the simplest possible form.

If the translation a is applied to the whole unit cell, the result is a congruent adjacent strip of the plane. In this way the whole plane can be covered simply by unit cells of the group. The same property is shared by the unit cells of all the groups we shall consider; indeed, it can be proved that the unit cells of any discontinuous transformation group can be fitted together without overlapping or leaving gaps. There are cases, however, where they do not fill the whole plane; we shall encounter an example of this in a later chapter (p. 259).

The group I, 1 does not generate a regular system of points, since the points that are equivalent to any given point only form a row, so that the first defining condition for systems of points is not satisfied.

Nevertheless our discussion of these groups is not altogether without significance for the study of regular point systems. Consider any discontinuous group of motions whose structure may be of any degree of complexity and examine the totality of translations of this group that are parallel to a fixed one of them. This set of translations itself forms a group because it satisfies both group axioms. Any group that is contained in another group is called a subgroup of the group that contains it. Now it is clear that every subgroup of a discontinuous group must itself be discontinuous. Hence we conclude that the set of translations that we selected constitutes a group of type I, 1 and therefore has the structure described above, regard-

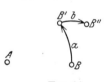

FIG. 66

less of the structure of the parent group. Reasoning of this and similar type will be applied repeatedly in what follows.

We now come to the groups I, 2 containing rotations but no two translations in non-parallel directions. Here we have to distinguish between groups of this type that contain translations and those which do not. Let us begin with the simpler case, which we shall classify as I, 2, a, where there are no translations in the group. We shall show that all the rotations of such a group have the same center. For if there were two rotations a, b with distinct centers A and B, the motion $a^{-1}b^{-1}ab$ of the group would, by the additivity theorem for angles of rotation, have to be either a translation or the identity. Now if B' were the image of B under a (Fig. 66), then B' could not coincide with B since B was assumed to be distinct from A and since a rotation leaves no point fixed except the center. Then the image B'' of B' under the rotation b would also have to be distinct from B'. But it is easy to see that $a^{-1}b^{-1}ab$ transforms B' into just the point B''. Hence $a^{-1}b^{-1}ab$ would be not the identity but a proper translation, contrary to the assumption that there are no translations in the group.

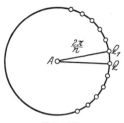

Fig. 67

Let A be the (one and only) center of rotation of the group and let Q be any other point. Then all the points equivalent to Q lie on the circle with center at A that passes through Q. Because of the discontinuity of the group, it follows that there is only a finite number of points equivalent to Q, and since every rotation about A that is in the group transforms the set of all equivalent points into itself, these points must be equally spaced on the circumference of the circle (see Fig. 67). Let Q_1 be one of the two neighbors of Q in this set of equivalent points, and let the total number of equivalent points (including Q itself) be n. Then $\angle QAQ_1$ is the smallest angle of rotation there is in the group, and it must be equal to $2\pi/n$. All the transformations are rotations about A through positive and negative multiples of the angle $2\pi/n$, and only a finite number of these are geometrically distinct. This concludes the discussion of case I, 2, a.

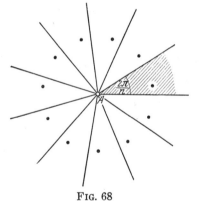

Fig. 68

A suitable unit cell in this case consists of a plane sector with the vertex at A and the angle of aperture $2\pi/n$ (Fig. 68). Once again, the unit cell is infinite. The group does not generate a regular system of points, since every point has only a finite number of equivalent points, so that the first condition of page 56 is violated.

This group has much the same significance for the study of the remaining discontinuous groups of motions as the group considered before. If any discontinuous group of motions contains a rotation about a point A, then the set of all rotations about A contained in the group is a subgroup that is discontinuous and that is, accordingly, of type I, 2, a. It follows that the angles of all these rotations are multiples of an angle of the form $2\pi/n$. We may thus consider the integer n as characteristic of the point A, and call A an n-fold center of rotation.

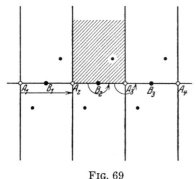

The only case among the groups of type I that remains to be studied is I, 2, β, where there is a rotation d and a translation t in the group and where all additional translations are parallel to t. By the second lemma of page 63, the angle of d must be π, i.e., in the notation introduced above, there can only be 2-fold centers of rotation. Let A_1

Fig. 69

be such a point (Fig. 69). The totality of translations of the group form a group of type I, 1. Let us consider the row $A_1, A_2, \ldots$ of points that are equivalent to A_1 under the motions of this subgroup. By the first lemma (p. 63) all these points are 2-fold centers of rotation. We shall prove that all the midpoints $B_1, B_2, \ldots$ of the

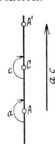

segments $A_n A_{n+1}$ are 2-fold centers of rotation as well. Let t be the translation that moves A_1 to A_2, and let a_2 be the rotation about A_2 with angle π. Then $t a_2$ transforms the pair of points $A_1 A_2$ into the pair $A_2 A_1$; for, t transforms $A_1 A_2$ into $A_2 A_3$, and a_2 transforms $A_2 A_3$ into $A_2 A_1$. The rotation about B_1 with angle π also transforms $A_1 A_2$ into $A_2 A_1$; therefore $t a_2$ is identical with this rotation, and B_1 is consequently a 2-fold center of rotation. Similarly all the points of the row generated by B_1, i.e. all the points B_n, must be 2-fold

Fig. 70

centers of rotation. On the other hand, there are no centers of rotation other than the points A_n and B_n. For, if A is any one of the points A_n and if C is any other center of rotation of the group (see Fig. 70), then C has to be 2-fold. Let c be the rotation through π about C and a the rotation through π about A, and consider the motion ac. If A' is the image of A under c, then C is the midpoint of AA', and therefore ac also transforms A into A'. But by the additivity theorem for angles of rotation, ac is a translation. Hence A' is one of the points that are the images of A under the translations of the group, i.e. A' is one of the points $A_1, A_2, \ldots$, and C, being half way between A and A', must be one of the points A_n or B_n.

Thus we have a complete description of the groups I, 2, β. Fig. 69 shows the two classes of centers of rotation, along with a suitable unit cell. Note that none of the points A_n can be equivalent to one of the points B_n, since every rotation and every translation of the group transforms each of the two rows into itself.

Fig. 69 also shows some mutually equivalent points other than the centers of rotation. They are arranged in zig-zag order. Since they are contained in a strip of finite width, the number of these points in the interior of a circle of radius r increases only as the first power of r; thus the points do not satisfy the first defining condition

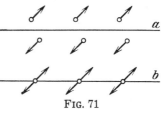

Fig. 71

for regular point systems. As in the first two cases we considered, the unit cells for the groups of type I, 2, β are infinite.

Any set of equivalent points that are not centers of rotation for the group can be visualized as two congruent parallel rows. Similarly, the more complicated groups will lead to systems of congruent parallel lattices. It is clear that the existence of several different rows or lattices of points all of which are equivalent to one point depends on the presence of rotations in the group. Thus, in particular, we see in our case that every rotation of the group changes one row into the other, the rows consisting of the centers of rotation themselves being the only exceptions.

Since a point is a configuration having no asymmetries, it does not lend itself to a satisfactory graphic representation of rotations. Thus it is better to illustrate rotations by drawing the set of all figures equivalent to some figure other than a point. The simplest figure that is not symmetrical in all directions consists of a "pointer," i.e. a point with an associated direction. Figs. 71 a and b exhibit sets of equivalent pointers for the group I, 2, β; two different types of figure are obtained depending on whether we begin with a pointer attached to a general point or one attached to a center of rotation. The first case, in particular, demonstrates the advantage of introducing pointers; the points of the two different rows are distinguished by the fact that their pointers have opposite directions, while all the pointers of the same row have like directions.

§ 12. The Crystallographic Groups of Motions in the Plane.
Regular Systems of Points and Pointers. Division of the
Plane into Congruent Cells

We now turn to the groups of type II, i.e. to groups containing two non-parallel translations. Unlike the groups of type I, all the groups of type II will be seen to generate regular systems of points; thus they may be called, in accordance with page 59, crystallographic groups. The fact that all these groups have finite unit cells is connected with this property. The study of these groups again leads to the plane lattices. As was already pointed out, the systems of equivalent points or pointers always form either a lattice or a figure composed of several congruent lattices in parallel positions.

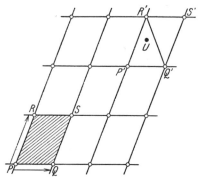

FIG. 72

On page 62 we subdivided the groups of type II into two classes. We shall treat first the simpler subclass II, 1, of groups containing two non-parallel translations but no rotations. We shall see that in this case the points equivalent to any given point always form a plane lattice.

To prove this, we start with any point P and choose a translation t of the group that moves P to an equivalent point Q having as small a distance as possible from P (Fig. 72). Then the translations whose directions are parallel to t generate a row of points equivalent to P on the straight line PQ. By assumption, there are other translations in the group that are not parallel to PQ. Hence there are additional points equivalent to P and not on PQ; let us pick such a point R as close to P as possible, and let t' be the translation in our group that moves p to R. Then we know that $PR \geq PQ$. If S is the image of Q under t', then $PQRS$ is a parallelogram. Clearly, all the points of the lattice generated by this parallelogram are equivalent, since each of them can be obtained from P by applying first the translation t (or t^{-1}) and then t' (or t'^{-1}) each a certain number of times. On the other hand, we shall see that this lattice exhausts all the points equivalent to P, i.e. that all the translations of the group can be obtained as combinations of t and t'. For otherwise, if this were not the case, the group would contain a translation u that transforms P into a point U not belonging to the lattice. Then there would be some parallelogram $P'Q'R'S'$ of the lattice congruent to $PQRS$ and containing U (see Fig. 72). Then one of the two congruent triangles $P'Q'R'$ and $S'Q'R'$, say the former, would have to contain U. Now the group would have to contain the translation $P' \to U$, because this is the resultant of the translation $P' \to P$, which is contained in the group, and u. But this leads to a contradiction, as follows: We have seen that $PR \geqq PQ$; consequently the vertex R' is the point of the triangle $P'Q'R'$ farthest from P'. Therefore the translation $P' \to U$ would be shorter than the translation t' that moves P to R and therefore P' to R'. Consequently the translation $P' \to U$ would have to have the same direction as t, and U would have to be on the segment $P'Q'$. But then the translation $P' \to U$ would also have to be shorter than t, contrary to the choice of t as a shortest translation of the group. The proof is analogous if U is supposed to lie in the triangle $S'Q'R'$, in which case we would have to consider the translation $S' \to U$ instead of $P' \to U$, reaching a contradiction as before.

We have shown that the points that are equivalent under the motions of a group of type II, 1 always form a point lattice. If the motions of such a group are applied to a pointer instead of a point, we obtain a lattice of parallel pointers (see Fig. 73).

Turning now to the last remaining category II, 2, where rotations are admitted along with translations, we shall find it necessary in every case to refer back to the result just obtained. For, like the groups of type II, 1, those of type II, 2 also contain two translations in different directions, and therefore the totality of translations in a group of type II, 2 necessarily forms a subgroup of type II, 1. Hence of the points equivalent to any point P under a group of type II, 2, all those that are obtained from P by translations of the group, form a lattice. The rotations of the group either transform the lattice into itself or move some lattice point into a point Q that does not belong to the lattice. But under the translations of the group, Q generates another lattice congruent and parallel to that generated by P, and all the points of the new lattice are equivalent to Q and to P. This process can be repeated as long as there are points equivalent to P that have not yet been used up; but only a finite number of distinct lattices can be obtained in this

way, since the group otherwise could not be discontinuous. Hence
we see that there can only be a relatively small number of groups
of type II, 2 and that the point systems corresponding to them
always consist of parallel congruent lattices.

We shall classify the groups II, 2 according to the angles of the
rotations in the group. All these angles must be of the form $2\pi/n$,

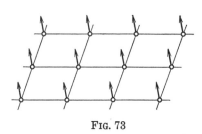

where n is an integer, because
the rotations about a single center
that are contained in the group
form a discontinuous subgroup of
type I, 2, a. Now we shall prove
that the only values different from
1 that can be assumed by n are 2, 3,
4, and 6. Choose a translation t of

FIG. 73

the smallest possible magnitude belonging to the group, let A be
an n-fold center of rotation of the group (Fig. 74), and let t move
A to B. The rotation through $2\pi/n$ about A brings B to some
point B'. By the second lemma on page 63, it follows that the group
also contains the translation t' that moves A to B'. The motion $t^{-1}t'$
evidently transforms B into B'. By the additivity theorem for angles
of rotation, $t^{-1}t'$ is a translation, and since the magnitude of the
translation t was chosen to be as small as possible, it follows that

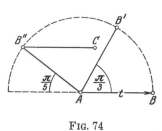

$BB' \geqq AB$. Hence $\angle BAB' = \dfrac{2\pi}{n} \geqq \dfrac{\pi}{3}$,
so that $n \leqq 6$. It only remains to show
that the case $n = 5$ is ruled out, which
we shall do by an indirect proof. Assume
that A is a 5-fold center of rotation
(Fig. 74). Let the rotation through

FIG. 74

$2 \cdot \dfrac{2\pi}{5}$ about A transform B into B''.

Then the group would have to contain the translation t'' that takes
A into B''. But then the translation $t''t$ would obviously move A
to the point marked C in the figure, and since the distance AC is
shorter than AB, the group would contain a translation shorter
than t, in contradiction to our definition of t.

Thus we see that the groups of type II, 2 can contain only 2-, 3-,
4-, and 6-fold centers of rotation. If φ denotes the smallest angle
of rotation for such a group, we have the following four possibilities
to consider:

$$\text{II, 2, } \alpha: \qquad \varphi = \pi,$$
$$\text{II, 2, } \beta: \qquad \varphi = 2\pi/3,$$
$$\text{II, 2, } \gamma: \qquad \varphi = \pi/2,$$
$$\text{II, 2, } \delta: \qquad \varphi = \pi/3.$$

We shall see that to each of these four possibilities there corresponds exactly one group.

II, 2, α. There is at least one 2-fold center of rotation in the group. The subgroup of translations contained in the group transforms A into the points of a latice; all these points, then, are equivalent to A and are 2-fold centers of rotation. Let $ABCD$ be one of the generating parallelograms of the lattice (see Fig. 75). Now we can refer back to the discussion of the groups I, 2, β (see p. 68), according to which the midpoint of every segment joining two of the lattice points is also a 2-fold center of rotation and every 2-fold center of rotation is the midpoint of such a segment. Let us consider the midpoint Q of AB, the midpoint P of AC, and the midpoint T of BC and AD. No two of these points are equivalent. Also, we have just seen that each of them is a 2-fold center of rotation and that their lattices and the original lattice together make up all the 2-fold centers of rotation of the group. Thus there are four distinct classes of 2-fold centers of rotation. The rotations about these points and the translations that leave the lattice $ABCD$ invariant exhaust all the transformations of the group, since we assumed that there were none other than 2-fold centers of rotation. Obviously the triangle ABC can be used as a unit cell.

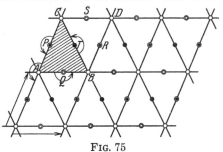

Fig. 75

Fig. 76 exhibits the set of equivalent pointers obtained by starting with a pointer attached to a general point. Fig. 77 exhibits the same in the case where the initial pointer is attached to a center of rotation. In the former case, we have two interlocking lattices distinguished by the fact that their pointers have opposite directions. In the latter case, the two lattices coincide, since there are two pointers attached to every center of rotation. If instead of the pointers we only consider the points, each of the figures represents a regular system of points. But then the system of Fig. 77 is no longer distinguishable from that corresponding to Fig. 72, which is the general plane lattice. Conversely, we may look for the group of symmetry operations of the general plane lattice and find that it is not II, 1 but, in every case, II, 2, a, for, the parallelogram $ABCD$ in Fig. 75 may be chosen at will, and the lattice generated by it will always be transformed into itself by the motions of the group. Here we can distinguish the various cases more clearly by considering pointers instead of points.

II, 2, β. Here we stipulate that $2\pi/3$ is the smallest angle of rotation occuring in the group. We assert that there are in this

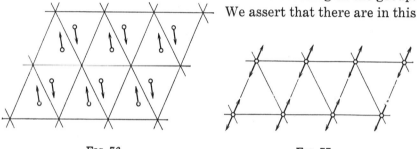

FIG. 76   FIG. 77

case no angles of rotation other than $\pm \frac{2\pi}{3}$. For, π would be the only other angle that might be admissible; but by the additivity theorem, a rotation through π together with a rotation through $-2\pi/3$ would result in a rotation through $\pi/3$, which is inadmissible in the group. Thus we see that there are in fact only 3-fold centers of rotation in these groups.

Let A be a 3-fold center of rotation (Fig. 78), and let $A \rightarrow B$ be a translation of the smallest possible magnitude belonging to the group. If the rotation through $2\pi/3$ about A moves B to C, it follows from the second lemma that the translation $A \rightarrow C$ also belongs to the group. The lattice corresponding to the subgroup of translations can be generated from the parallelogram $ABCD$, since, by construction, the parallelogram contains no other lattice points in its interior. The diagonal AD divides $ABCD$ into two equilateral triangles. Hence the translations of the group have to generate the lattice corresponding to the closest packing of circles, not just any lattice as in the case II, 2, a. (Similarly, we shall see in the two remaining cases as well that the lattices generated by

translations must be of a special form.) Now dt, the resultant of
the rotation d defined by $AB \to AC$ and the translation t defined
by $A \to B$, transforms AB into BD (Fig. 78). Thus dt must be
a rotation d' through the angle $2\pi/3$ and its center must be at the
center M of the triangle ABD, showing that M is also a 3-fold
center of rotation of the group. Furthermore $d'' = td'$ transforms
AC via BD into DA, so that d'' is the rotation
through $- 2\pi/3$ about the center N of triangle
ACD, showing that N is also a 3-fold center of
rotation. Like A, the points M and N also give
rise to lattices all of whose points are 3-fold
centers of rotation. We shall prove that this

FIG. 78

accounts for the entire set of rotations belonging to our group.
To this end, all that we need show is that the distance between two
3-fold centers of rotation E and F cannot be less than the distance
AM. Clearly, the resultant $d^{-1}d'$ of the rotations d^{-1} and d' is t.
By the same token the resultant of two equal and opposite rotations
about E and F respectively is a translation, and the ratio of the
magnitude of the translation to the distance EF equals the ratio
of the magnitude of t to the dis-
tance AM. Since it was assumed
that the group does not contain a
translation smaller than t, it follows that EF cannot be smaller
than AM. We have therefore
proved the assertion that there are
no centers of rotation other than
the points of the three lattices
generated by A, M, and N. Now,

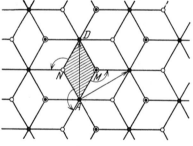

FIG. 79

since the rotations about A transform each of these lattices into
itself rather than one into the other, no two of the points A, M, N
are equivalent. Accordingly, a group of type II, 2, β has three distinct classes of centers of rotation (see Fig. 79). The points of
any one of these classes may be seen to be the centers of a system of
regular hexagons that covers the plane simply, where the vertices
of the hexagons coincide alternately with centers of rotation of the
other two classes. In this way we obtain three regular hexagonal
coverings for the plane which are superimposed in a definite way.
This figure, incidentally, can be interpreted as an orthogonal pro-

jection of three adjacent layers of the spatial structure representing graphite (see Fig. 56, p. 54).

In Fig. 79, the rhombus $AMND$ is chosen as a unit cell.[1] Also indicated in the figure are two translations that generate the lattice of translations.

A system of equivalent pointers which are not attached to centers

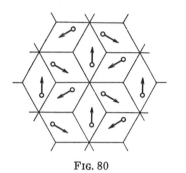

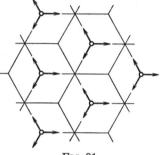

Fig. 80   Fig. 81

of rotation consists of three interlocking lattices, each characterized by a definite direction of its pointers (see Fig. 80). Generating parallelograms for these lattices are not indicated in the figure, as this would make it too confusing.

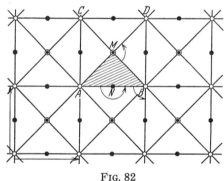

Fig. 82

If we start with a pointer attached to a center of rotation (see Fig. 81), the three lattices coincide, since each point must carry three pointers.

II, 2, γ. The smallest rotation of the group has the angle $\pi/2$. Thus there are 2-fold and 4-fold centers of rotation. There cannot be any other angles of rotation; for if there were, we could apply the additivity theorem to obtain a rotation through $\pi/3$ by combining a rotation through $2\pi/3$ with a rotation through π, and this would contradict our condition that no rotation through an angle smaller than $\pi/2$ be present.

Our procedure here will be similar to that followed in the preceding case. Let A be any 4-fold center of rotation, and let $A \to B$

---

[1] The same system of adjacent rhombuses occurs in the structure of honey-combs.

be a translation of the group having as small a magnitude as possible (Fig. 82). If the rotation about A through $\pi/2$ moves B to C, then the translation $A \to C$ is also contained in the group. Hence the lattice of translations of the group can be generated from the square $ABCD$, since the four vertices, but no other points of this square, are lattice points. As in the previous case, we note that the translation lattice can not be chosen freely but has to be of a special symmetrical form. If we take the translations and the rotations through π but not those through $\pi/2$, we obtain a subgroup, and this subgroup must be of type II, 2, a. The centers of the squares, such as M, together with the midpoints of the sides, e.g. N, and the vertices of the squares, together make up the complete set of centers of rotation of the subgroup. But the same points necessarily include as well the complete set of 2-fold and 4-fold centers of rotation of the full group, since all these points are the centers of rotation through π and as such have to be counted in with the 2-fold centers of rotation of the subgroup. If d is the rotation $AB \to AC$ and t is the translation $A \to B$, then $d' = dt$ must transform AB into BD and is therefore the rotation through $\pi/2$ about M. Accordingly, the centers of all the squares are not merely 2-fold but 4-fold centers of rotation. Now we can argue by the same reasoning as in the preceding case that there are no further 4-fold centers of rotation; $d^{-1}d'$ is the same as t, which is the shortest translation of the group; therefore the distance between two 4-fold centers of rotation cannot be less than AM, and there are therefore no 4-fold centers of rotation besides the points of the lattices generated by A and M. Since every motion we have considered so far transforms these two lattices into themselves and not into each other, A and M can not be equivalent. On the other hand, it is seen that all 2-fold centers of rotation are equivalent. Thus there is a single class of 2-fold centers of rotation consisting of two interlocking square lattices, and there are two classes of 4-fold centers of rotation consisting of one square lattice each. We may choose the triangle AMB as unit cell.

The system of pointers generated by a general point consists of four square lattices, each characterized by the common direction of all its pointers (see Fig. 83). A 2-fold center of rotation gives rise to two lattices whose pointers have different directions (Fig. 84). A 4-fold center of rotation gives rise to a single lattice (Fig. 85). If, as in Fig. 85, the arrows are directed towards each other in pairs, the figure can be interpreted as a regular arrangement of equivalent tetravalent atoms in the plane.

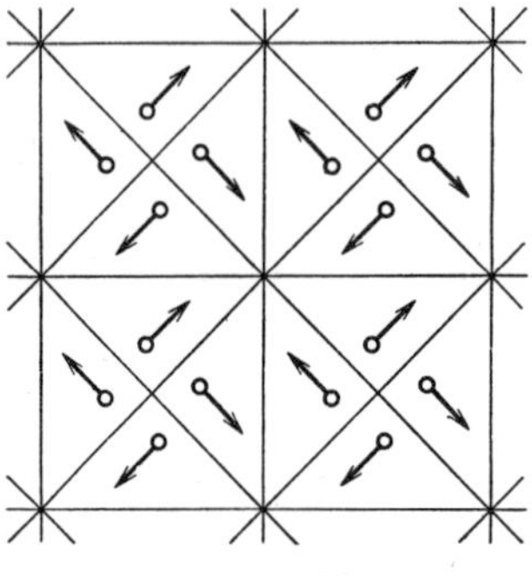

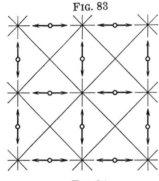

Fig. 83

II, 2, δ. In this case the variety of different rotations is the greatest. For, since 6-fold centers of rotation are admitted, 2-fold and 3-fold ones can also occur. On the other hand, 4-fold centers of rotation are ruled out; for, a group containing a rotation through $\pi/2$ and one through $\pi/3$ would also have to contain a rotation through $\pi/6$, and this cannot occur in any crystallographic group of motions in the plane.

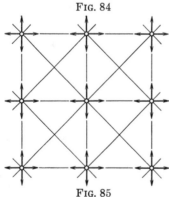

Fig. 84

Let A be a 6-fold center of rotation of the group (Fig. 86). First of all, we shall examine the subgroup consisting of translations and rotations through $2\pi/3$. The structure of this subgroup is known to us from II, 2, β; we know also that A is a 3-fold center of rotation for this subgroup. The lattice of the translations of this subgroup is the lattice of equilateral triangles, and not only do the vertices of the triangles, for example A, B, and C, appear as 3-fold centers of rotation, but the centers of the triangles, M for example, do so also. Since the subgroup takes into account all the translations of the parent group, the latter has the same translation lattice as the subgroup. But in the parent group, A is a 6-fold rather than a 3-fold center of rotation, and consequently all the points of the lattice generated by A must also be 6-fold centers of rotation. Should any further 6-fold centers of rotation occur

Fig. 85

in the group, they would have to be the centers of some of the triangles, since all 6-fold centers of rotation have been counted in as 3-fold centers of rotation for the subgroup. But the resultant of the rotation through $\pi/3$ about A and the rotation through $-\pi/3$ about B is the translation $A \to B$; and since there is no smaller translation in the group, the distance between two 6-fold centers of rotation cannot be less than AC, so that there are no 6-fold centers of rotation apart from the points of the lattice of A. Thus the centers of the triangles are only 3-fold centers of rotation. There are no further 3-fold centers of rotation in the group, for we have taken them all into account in the subgroup. Unlike the centers of rotation of the groups II, 2, β, all the 3-fold centers

of rotation of our group are equivalent; M, for example, can be transformed into N by a rotation about B.

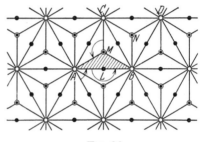

Fig. 86

To find any 2-fold centers of rotation that may be in the group, we use an analogous procedure: we examine the subgroup consisting of the translations and the rotations through π. From the discussion of the case II, 2, a we know that rotations through π about the following points are admissible: the vertices of the lattice parallelograms, their centers, and the midpoints of their sides, i.e. the midpoints of the sides of all the equilateral triangles. The vertices of the triangles have already been taken into account as 6-fold centers of rotation. This leaves us with the midpoints of the sides as the set of all 2-fold centers of rotation. We note that all of them are equivalent. Thus there is just one class each of 2-fold, 3-fold, and 6-fold centers of rotation, respectively. AMB is a unit cell for the group.

The system of pointers generated by a pointer in general position consists of six interlocking lattices, each characterized by the common direction of all its pointers. In Fig. 87, each of these lattices is represented by three parallel pointers attached to points that form an equilateral triangle. If we start with a pointer attached to a 2-fold center of rotation (as in Fig. 88), the lattices coincide in pairs, so that we are left with three lattices. This figure represents a possible regular arrangement in the plane for a complex of two types of atoms having the valences 6 and 2 respectively. By rotating all the pointers through $\pi/2$, we arrive at an arrangement linking atoms of valences 2 and 3. The system of pointers generated by a 3-fold center of rotation consists of two

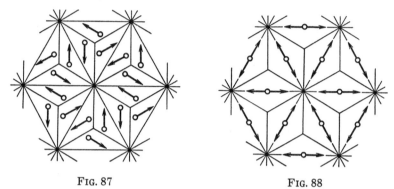

Fig. 87   Fig. 88

distinct lattices (see Fig. 89). When the directions of the pointers are as shown, the figure represents an arrangement of atoms with valences 3 and 6. A 6-fold center of rotation generates a system of pointers that forms a single lattice (see Fig. 90); when the pointers are directed as in the figure, the lattice may be interpreted as a regular plane arrangement of equivalent hexavalent atoms.

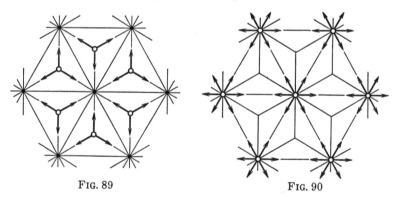

Fig. 89   Fig. 90

We have now completely solved the problem posed in § 9. We have constructed all the crystallographic groups of motions that can possibly exist in the plane, and in so doing we have found that there are only five such groups. The most general regular systems of points and pointers are obtained by applying each of these groups to a general point. For, the systems of points consisting of centers of rotation in the case of the more complicated groups also occur as systems consisting of general points when a simpler group is applied. On the other hand, the systems of pointers attached to centers of rotation yield new configurations.

Simultaneously with the above problem, we have solved another problem related to it, namely the problem of finding the different ways in which the plane can be divided into congruent finite pieces subject to the conditions that the whole structure can be brought into self-coincidence by a symmetry operation and that there is a symmetry operation that brings any given piece into coincidence with any other piece. The group of these symmetry operations must be discontinuous and must furthermore be a crystallographic group, because the number of pieces inside a circle goes to infinity as the square of the radius. Hence there are only two possibilities. Either there is no symmetry operation other than the identity that leaves one of the pieces invariant, in which case the piece must be a unit cell, or else there are pieces that are brought into self-coincidence by a symmetry operation; in this case, the set of all symmetry operations of this kind forms a discontinuous subgroup, and it is clear that the subgroup cannot contain any translations and therefore consists of rotations about a single point (so that the subgroup is of type I, 2, a). In this case, the pieces into which the plane is divided have rotational symmetry, and each of them is composed of unit cells. One example of this case is the division of the plane into congruent regular hexagons or squares, an arrangement often used in tiled floors.

Another problem, which is more difficult, is that of finding all possible "tilings"; this problem stipulates that the plane be covered by finite congruent tiles, but the construction need not be invariant under any symmetry operations.

§ 13. The Crystallographic Classes and Groups of Motions in Space. Groups and Systems of Points with Bilateral Symmetry

In space, as in the plane, there is only a finite number of crystallographic groups of motions. However, their number is much greater in space than in the plane. In order to determine what groups can be constructed in space, we start, as before, by characterizing the individual motions geometrically. In space it is also possible to replace any given rigid motion by a motion of a certain simple type. To begin with, it can be proved that every motion in space that leaves a point fixed also leaves fixed all the points of a straight line passing through the point and is identical with a rotation, through a definite angle, about this line as axis. An example of a motion in space that does not leave a point fixed is a translation.

Now it can be proved that any given rigid motion in space is the resultant of a uniquely defined rotation and a uniquely defined translation along the axis of the rotation; the rotations and translations themselves may be regarded as special cases in which one of the component motions reduces to the identity. If in the general case we think of the two component motions, the rotation and the translation, as being performed simultaneously and each at constant speed, the result is a screw-like motion of space. For this reason, the general rigid motion of space is called a screw, rotations and translations being regarded as limiting cases. It is also found expedient to consider the translations, in analogy with translations in the plane, as rotations through a vanishing angle about an infinitely distant axis.

The combining of two screws in space is not subject to a simple law analogous to the additivity theorem for the combining of two rotations in the plane. But there are two theorems of a more specialized nature that are sufficient for the study of crystallography in space; first, the resultant of any two translations is another translation, and second, two screws with parallel axes and equal angles of rotation differ only by a translation. Here "angle of rotation" of a screw refers to the angle of the rotation forming one of the components of the screw.

From the first of these theorems it follows that the translations of a group of motions in space always form a subgroup. As in the plane, the structure of this subgroup determines whether or not a discontinuous group of motions in space is crystallographic, i.e. whether or not it generates a three-dimensional system of points. For, if all the translations of the group are parallel to a fixed plane, the group is bound to have infinite unit cells and therefore can not give rise to a system of points. On the other hand, a group containing three translations whose directions are not all parallel to a fixed plane, is crystallographic. In this case, the points equivalent to a point P under the subgroup of translations always form a space lattice. If, in addition, the group contains a screw that moves P to a point Q that is not a lattice point, the subgroup of translations transforms Q into another lattice of points equivalent to P and Q. Since the group is discontinuous, the number of lattices obtained in this way is finite; as in the plane, this restriction enables us to obtain a classification of all the possible cases. At the same time, we see that every regular point system in space is composed of a finite number of interlocking congruent space lattices in parallel positions. We have already encountered an example of this, namely the system formed by the centers of spheres arranged in the tetrahedral packing.

The second of the above theorems, the one concerning screws with parallel axes, leads to an important geometrical procedure for classifying the motions of a group that are not translations. To this end, we single out any point M of space. For every axis a of a screw belonging to the group we draw a line a_0 through M parallel to a. With every screw s belonging to the group we then associate the rotation s_0 about a_0 having the same angle as s. Then s and s_0 can differ only by a translation. We have set up a correspondence in which every motion of the group G that is not a translation is associated with a motion that leaves M fixed. We shall make the correspondence complete by letting the identity correspond to every translation of G. In this way, the group G is associated with a set G_M of transformations all of which leave M fixed. G_M is a group. To prove this, let s_0 and t_0 be the rotations of G_M corresponding to the screws s and t of G, and note that $s_0 t_0$ is none other than the rotation in G_M that corresponds to st, as is easily deduced from the rule regarding screws with parallel axes. Thus the set G_M does in fact satisfy the following two group axioms: If it contains s_0 and t_0 then it also contains $s_0 t_0$ and s_0^{-1}.

The structure of the group G_M by no means uniquely defines G; it tells us nothing about the translations of G. For example, all the groups G consisting exclusively of translations are represented by one and the same group G_M consisting only of the identity. Thus G_M represents a whole family of groups which differ among themselves only in their translations. We shall refer to the set of all groups of motions in space that lead to the same group G_M, as a *class of groups of motions in space*. If a class contains a crystallographic group we call it a *crystallographic class*. This concept is of great importance both in practical crystallography and for the geometrical classification of space groups. Thus it is much easier to construct all the possible crystallographic classes first and then find out for each class separately what groups it contains.

Since all the motions of G_M leave the point M fixed, they also transform into itself the surface of a sphere with center at M, so that the "reduced" groups G_M may be regarded as groups of motions of the surface of the sphere. Now it is a theorem that the reduced group G_M must be a discontinuous group whenever G is a discontinuous group, a fact that will simplify our discussion considerably. Since the discontinuity of G means something entirely different from that of G_M, this theorem is by no means trivial. But in the case of crystallographic groups it is easily proved by considering their translation lattices. We shall omit the proof here.

According to the above result, we can find all the crystallographic classes of groups of space motions by examining only the discontinuous groups of motions on the sphere. There is yet another simplification: as in the plane, it may also be proved for the crystallographic groups of motions in space that there cannot be any rotations through angles other than multiples of π, $2\pi/3$, $\pi/2$, and $\pi/3$. Just as there were only 2-, 3-, 4-, and 6-fold centers of rotation in the plane groups, we may say (using analogous terminology) that the three-dimensional crystallographic groups of motion have only 2-, 3-, 4-, and 6-fold axes. Now the same must be true for the groups G_M of crystallographic classes, and this restriction leaves us with only eleven classes of crystal. We proceed to list the classes.

First of all, we take the cases in which there is only one axis in G_M, say an n-fold one. The corresponding classes are called C_n; there are five of them (Fig. 91):

1. C_1 (Identity, the class of translation groups.)
2. C_2,
3. C_3,
4. C_4,
5. C_6.

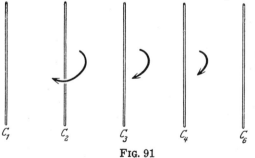

FIG. 91

Next, we assume that there are several axes, of which at most one is more than 2-fold. We refer to this n-fold axis ($n > 2$) as the "principal axis," and to the 2-fold axes as the "secondary axes." Then it is readily deduced from the group axioms that there are exactly n secondary axes, all perpendicular to the principal axis and forming equal angles with each other. The corresponding groups and classes are labelled D_n (dihedral groups or classes) ; there are four of them (Fig. 92) :

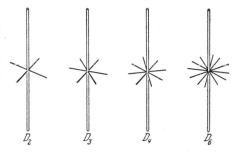

6. D_2, (3 equivalent axes.)
7. D_3,
8. D_4,
9. D_6.

FIG. 92

It is easy to see, moreover, that all the secondary axes are equivalent in the case $n = 3$, whereas they alternately belong to one or the other of two classes of equivalent axes in the remaining cases.

One possibility remains, viz. that there are several axes that are more than 2-fold. In this case, a closer scrutiny reveals that the equivalent points on the sphere must be at the vertices either of a regular tetrahedron (T) or of a regular octahedron (O). The arrangement of the axes follows automatically from the properties of symmetry of these polyhedra; we obtain all the axes by connecting the center of the sphere with the vertices, the mid-

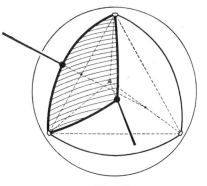

FIG. 93

points of the edges, and the centers of the faces. Thus the tetrahedron gives rise to the class

10. T (Fig. 93).

The line connecting the center of the sphere with a vertex of the tetrahedron also passes through the center of the opposite face. Since the opposite face is an equilateral triangle, while there are three faces meeting at each vertex, we obtain *four 3-fold axes*. In addition, we draw the lines connecting the midpoints of the six edges with the center of the sphere; this gives not six but three straight lines, since the midpoints of the edges are diametrically opposite in pairs. For it to be possible for the tetrahedron to be brought into self-coincidence by a rotation about these lines as axes, they must be 2-fold axes. Thus the class T has *three 2-fold axes*, and these axes, furthermore, are mutually perpendicular.

In order to construct a unit cell on the sphere, we may begin with a spherical triangle corresponding to one of the faces of the tetrahedron. Since such a triangle is brought into self-coincidence by a rotation about a 3-fold axis, it is not itself a unit cell. On the other hand, it is obvious that the triangle can be divided into three unit cells (see Fig. 93).

The last class,

11. O (Fig. 94),

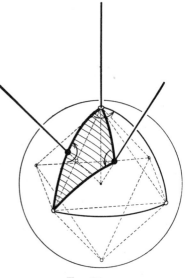

FIG. 94

can be treated analogously. The six vertices of the octahedron are diametrically opposite in pairs, and four faces meet at every vertex, so that we have *three 4-fold axes*. Similarly the eight faces of the octahedron are opposite in pairs, and are equilateral triangles, so that they give rise to *four 3-fold axes*. Finally, the octahedron has twelve edges, and they are opposite in pairs; thus the class O has *six 2-fold axes*. Once again, a third part of a spherical triangle corresponding to one of the faces of the octahedron will serve as unit cell (Fig. 94).

The eleven classes we have constructed lead to a total of sixty-five crystallographic groups in space. The study of this multiplicity of groups is thus very much simplified by the division into classes. As a matter of fact, the concept of classes could have been introduced in the same way for crystallographic motions in the plane. This leads to discontinuous groups of motions on the circumference of a circle, and these consist of the identity and the rotations through multiples of π, $2\pi/3$, $\pi/2$, and $\pi/3$. Thus there are only five classes, and each of them contains only one crystallographic group of motions; accordingly, there is nothing to be gained by dividing the plane crystallographic groups into classes.

As in the plane case, the crystallographic groups of motions in space generate systems of points, and they are also connected with the problem of dividing space into congruent finite pieces in such a way that there are symmetry operations by which any given piece can be brought into coincidence with any other piece. This problem has not yet been solved.

For the purposes of crystal chemistry it is expedient to consider not only systems of points but systems of pointers as well. But in space a single pointer associated with a point will not suffice, since this figure could be rotated about the direction of the pointer. A figure with fully defined orientation is obtained from a point by attaching to it two arrows of unequal length pointing in different directions.

A comparison of the various crystal structures observed in nature with all the systems of pointers that can be constructed geometrically leads to the following surprising observation. Not only does nature use up the supply of geometrically constructed systems of pointers, but there is even a large number of crystal structures that are not provided for in our concept of regular systems of points, although all their elements are equivalent. The reason for this is that the equivalence of all the points, as postulated in the third defining condition for regular systems of points, was defined to mean that every point can be transformed into every other point of the system by a *symmetry operation* of the system. We can obtain a generalization of the concept of point systems by admitting *reflections* as well—i.e. reflections of the plane in a straight line of the plane and reflections of space in a plane. These more general transformations leave all distances and angles invariant. But they interchange left and right, and the reflections in space cannot be effected by a continuous motion. If the term *symmetry transformations* is used to cover all transformations of space that leave distances and angles unchanged, then the discontinuous groups of symmetry transformations form a totality that not only includes the discontinuous groups but also contains numerous other groups. These more general groups have also been determined completely. Their study is simplified by the fact that the proper rigid motions contained in any one of them (i.e. those of its transformations that do not use reflections) form a subgroup, and this subgroup is of a type we can identify by the methods we used before. The division of the two-dimensional and three-dimensional crystallographic groups of motions into classes can also be extended to groups containing reflections. For, just like screws with parallel axes and equal angles, two reflections in parallel planes or parallel lines can only differ by a translation. A summary of all the classes and groups obtained in this way is given in the following table.

	Plane		Space	
	Crystallographic Groups	Crystallographic Classes	Crystallographic Groups	Crystallographic Classes
Proper Rigid Motions	5	5	65	11
Added by Inclusion of Reflections . .	12	5	165	21
Total	17	10	230	32

Only by supplementing the proper motions with reflections do we get all the various crystal structures found in nature. In the construction of systems of pointers either in the plane or in space it is necessary in each case to add one extra pointer; for, in the plane a single pointer is invariant under reflection in the straight line containing the pointer; and similarly in space, the figure consisting of two unequal pointers is unchanged by a reflection in the plane of the pointers. In space, then, we have to use a point carrying three pointers of unequal length that do not all lie in one plane.

Instead of using geometric methods, we may also find the discontinuous groups of symmetry transformations by using algebraic methods. In the plane case, this leads to remarkable relationships among complex numbers; in space, the method is based on hypercomplex number systems.

It would be an interesting problem to generalize the present discussion to spaces of higher dimensionality. Some results relating to the discontinuous groups of symmetry transformations of higher-dimensional spheres have been found, the analogues of the regular polyhedra being known for spaces of any number of dimensions. We shall have more to say about these higher-dimensional figures in the next chapter. Moreover, Bieberbach has proved that there is only a finite number of n-dimensional crystallographic groups for every n, and that each of these groups contains n linearly independent translations.

§ 14. The Regular Polyhedra

The construction of the crystallographic classes led us to the regular tetrahedron and the regular octahedron. We shall now define regular polyhedra in general and find out what regular polyhedra are possible besides the tetrahedron and the octahedron.

We shall require that all the vertices of a regular polyhedron be equivalent and that the same be true for all the edges and all the faces. Furthermore, we require that all the faces be regular polygons.

First of all, a polyhedron satisfying these conditions cannot have any re-entrant vertices or edges. For, it is clear that the vertices cannot all be re-entrant, and therefore the presence of any re-entrant vertices would imply that not all the vertices are equivalent; the same argument holds for edges. It follows that the sum of the face angles at a vertex is always less than 2π. For otherwise all the faces meeting at the vertex would have to lie in one plane, or some of the edges ending at the vertex would have to be re-entrant. Furthermore, since at least three faces must meet at every vertex and the regularity conditions imply the equality of all the face angles, the magnitude of all of these angles must be less than $2\pi/3$. But the angle of the regular hexagon is exactly $2\pi/3$, and the angle of a regular n-sided polygon increases with n. Therefore the only polygons that can occur as faces of a regular polyhedron are the regular polygons having three, four, and five sides. Now the angles of the regular 4-sided polygon, i.e. the square, are right angles, so that no more than three squares can meet at a vertex without the sum of the angles at the vertex being equal to at least 2π; by the same token, more than three pentagons can certainly not meet at a vertex of a regular polyhedron. Now the shape of a regular polyhedron is completely determined by the number of faces meeting at a vertex and the number of sides of each polygon forming a face. There can be, accordingly, at most one regular polyhedron bounded by squares and one bounded by regular pentagons. On the other hand, three, four, or five equilateral triangles can meet at a vertex D, since it takes six of them to make the sum of the angles at the vertex equal to 2π. Therefore equilateral triangles can form the faces of three different regular polyhedra, bringing the total number of possible regular polyhedra up to five. Now all five of these possible forms actually exist.

They were well known as early as Plato, and he gave them a very important place in his Theory of Ideas, which is why they are often known as the "Platonic Solids." The most important data on the regular polyhedra are tabulated below. Figs. 95-99 show parallel projections of the regular polyhedra.

Name of the Polyhedron	Polygons Forming the Faces	Number of			
		Vertices	Edges	Faces	Faces Meeting at a Vertex
Tetrahedron (Fig. 95) . . .	Triangles	4	6	4	3
Octahedron (Fig. 96) . . .	"	6	12	8	4
Icosahedron (Fig. 97) . . .	"	12	30	20	5
Cube (Hexahedron) (Fig. 98)	Squares	8	12	6	6
Dodecahedron (Fig. 99) . .	Pentagons	20	30	12	3

All the regular polyhedra have a relation to the sphere much the same as that we have already described for the tetrahedron and octahedron in the last section. All of them can be inscribed in a sphere, and each of them generates a discontinuous group of motions of the sphere under which the vertices form a system of equivalent points. Now the planes that are tangent to the sphere at the vertices of such a polyhedron must bound another polyhedron which is also brought into self-coincidence by the motions of the group. It is to be expected that the new polyhedron is regular too; and thus the construction sets up a pairwise correspondence between the five polyhedra. If the construction is applied to the octahedron it does indeed lead to a regular polyhedron, namely, the cube; Fig. 100 illustrates the two polyhedra in the positions indicated. Thus the reduced group O could have been defined just as well by means of the cube as the octahedron. In the table, the relation between the two polyhedra is expressed by the fact that each has as many vertices as the other has faces, that both have the same number of edges, and finally, that the number of faces meeting at every vertex of either of them equals the number of vertices on each face of the other. Hence the octahedron can also be circumscribed about the cube (see Fig. 101).

The table shows that the dodecahedron and the icosahedron are related in the same way. Therefore both figures give rise to the same group, which is usually called the icosahedral group. Our

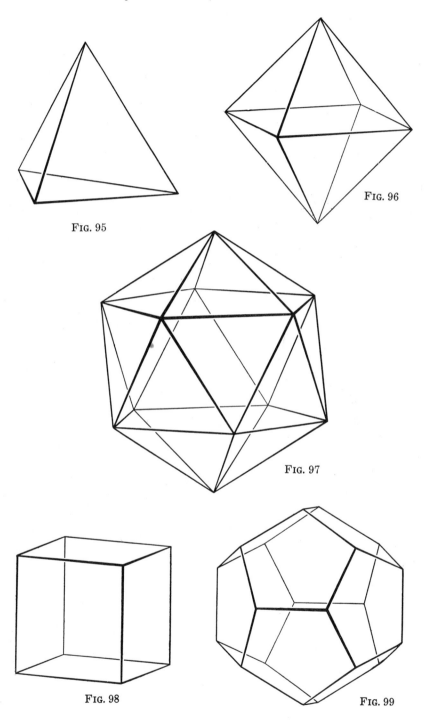

FIG. 96

FIG. 95

FIG. 97

FIG. 98

FIG. 99

crystallographic studies could not reveal this group, because the number five plays a part in it, whereas crystallographic classes cannot contain any 5-fold axes.

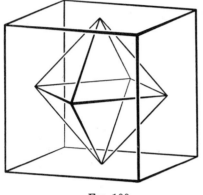

When the construction is applied to the tetrahedron, it generates not a different figure but another regular tetrahedron.

The principle of duality in space, which will be introduced in the next chapter, furnishes a more general method for setting up a correspondence between the points, straight lines, and planes of one figure and the planes, straight lines, and points, respectively, of another figure. According to this point of view, the cube corresponds "dually" to the octahedron, the icosahedron to

Fig. 100

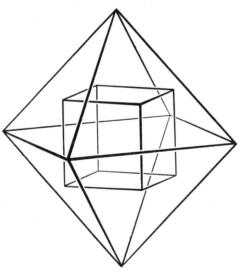

the dodecahedron, and the tetrahedron to itself.

We learn, on examining the matter further, that the tetrahedral group is a subgroup of the octahedral group; we had similarly recognized some of the discontinuous groups of motions of the plane as subgroups of others. The relation between the groups T and O has the consequence, manifest to the eye, that a regular tetrahedron can be inscribed in a cube in such a way that the vertices of

Fig. 101

the tetrahedron are at vertices of the cube and its edges are diagonals of the faces of the cube. Two distinct tetrahedra can be inscribed in the cube in this way (see Fig. 102).

Similarly, it turns out that the octahedral group is a subgroup of the icosahedral group. This is the reason why a cube can be

inscribed in a dodecahedron in the same way as the tetrahedron
was inscribed in a cube (Fig. 103). A closer inspection reveals
that five cubes of this kind can be found in every dodecahedron.

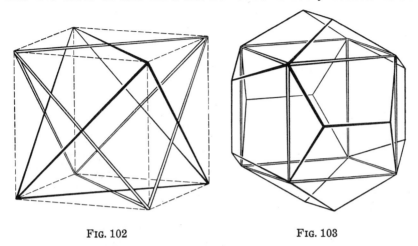

FIG. 102   FIG. 103

On every face of the dodecahedron there is one edge of each of the
cubes, and two cubes meet at each vertex of the dodecahedron.

CHAPTER III

PROJECTIVE CONFIGURATIONS

In this chapter we shall learn about geometrical facts that can be formulated and proved without any measurement or comparison of distances or of angles. It might be imagined that no significant properties of a figure could be found if we do without measurement of distances and angles and that only vague statements could be made. And indeed research was confined to the metrical side of geometry for a long time, and questions of the kind we shall discuss in this chapter arose only later, when the phenomena underlying perspective painting were being studied scientifically. Thus, if a plane figure is projected from a point onto another plane, distances and angles are changed, and in addition, parallel lines may be changed into lines that are not parallel; but certain essential properties must nevertheless remain intact, since we could not otherwise recognize the projection as being a true picture of the original figure.

In this way, the process of projecting led to a new theory, which was called projective geometry because of its origin. Since the 19th century, projective geometry has occupied a central position in geometric research. With the introduction of homogeneous coordinates, it became possible to reduce the theorems of projective geometry to algebraic equations in much the same way that Cartesian coordinates allow this to be done for the theorems of metric geometry. But projective analytic geometry is distinguished by the fact that it is far more symmetrical and general than metric analytic geometry, and when one wishes, conversely, to interpret higher algebraic relations geometrically, one often transforms the relations into homogeneous form and interprets the variables as homogeneous coordinates, because the metric interpretation in Cartesian coordinates would be too unwieldy.

The elementary figures of projective geometry are points, straight lines, and planes. The elementary results of projective geometry deal with the simplest possible relations between these entities, namely their *incidence*. The word incidence covers all the following relations: A point lying on a straight line, a point lying in a plane, a straight line lying in a plane. Clearly, the three statements that a straight line passes through a point, that a plane passes through a point, that a plane passes through a straight line, are respectively equivalent to the first three. The term incidence was introduced to give these three pairs of statements symmetrical form: a straight line is incident with a point, a plane is incident with a point, a plane is incident with a straight line.

The theorems relating to incidence are by far the most important theorems of projective geometry. However, we use two other fundamental concepts, which can not be derived from the concept of incidence. First, we have to distinguish between two different ways in which four collinear points may be arranged; second, we need the concept of continuity, which relates the set of all points on a straight line to the set of all numbers. This completes the list of the basic concepts of projective geometry.

We shall study a particularly instructive part of projective geometry—the configurations. This will also reveal certain aspects of various other geometrical problems. It might be mentioned here that there was a time when the study of configurations was considered the most important branch of all geometry.[1]

§ 15. Preliminary Remarks About Plane Configurations

We define a plane configuration as a system of p points and l straight lines arranged in a plane in such a way that every point of the system is incident with a fixed number λ of straight lines of the system and every straight line of the system is incident with a fixed number π of points of the system. We characterize such a configuration by the symbol $(p_\lambda \, l_\pi)$. The four numbers p, l, π, and λ may not be chosen quite arbitrarily. For, by the conditions we have stipulated, λp straight lines of the system, in all, pass through the p points; however, every straight line is counted π times because it passes through π points; thus the number of straight lines l is equal to $\lambda p / \pi$. It is seen, then, that the following

---

[1] A comprehensive treatment of the subject is given in the book *Geometrische Konfigurationen* by F. Levi (Leipzig, 1929).

relation must be true for every configuration:

$$p\lambda = l\pi.$$

The simplest configuration consists of a point and a straight line passing through it; it has the symbol $(1_1 1_1)$. The triangle forms the configuration next in order of simplicity, $(3_2 3_2)$. Four straight lines in the plane, no two of which are parallel and no three of which have a common point, give us six points of intersection A, B, C, D, E, and F (see Fig. 104). The figure thus obtained, which is the well-known figure of the complete quadrilateral, is a configuration with the symbol $(6_2 4_3)$. (Note that the equation $6 \cdot 2 = 3 \cdot 4$ confirms our general formula.) In this case, as opposed to the first two trivial cases, not all the straight lines joining points of the configuration are lines of the configuration; similarly, in the general case the points at which the straight lines of a configuration intersect need not all belong to the configuration.

In order to obtain all the straight lines connecting points of the configuration of Fig. 104, we need to adjoin the diagonals AD, BE, CF. This also gives us the vertices P, Q, R of the triangle

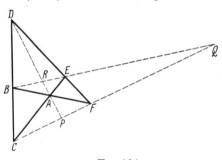

FIG. 104

formed by the diagonals as additional points of intersection. One might think that the continued process of connecting points and adjoining new points of intersection of straight lines might ultimately lead to a configuration that shares the property of the triangle that the straight line connecting any two points of the configuration is itself a line belonging to the configuration and the point of intersection of any two straight lines of the configuration is itself a point belonging to the configuration. However, it may be proved that, except for the triangle, no configuration with this property exists. If, starting with a quadrilateral, we keep connecting points by straight lines and adjoining new points of intersection, it can even be shown that there will ultimately be such points of intersection lying as close as we please to every point of the plane. The figure obtained in this way is called a Moebius net; it may be used for defining projective coordinates.

For the sake of subsequent application, we remind the reader of the significance of the quadrilateral for the construction of harmonic sets of points. Four points C, P, F, Q on a straight line are called a harmonic set—or Q is called the fourth harmonic of P with respect to C and F—if a quadrilateral can be constructed in which these points are determined by the same incidence relations as in Fig. 104. A theorem that is fundamental for projective geometry says that any three points on a straight line have exactly one fourth harmonic. According to this theorem,[2] we may use the points C, P, F as starting points for the construction of two different quadrilaterals but we will come out both times with the same point Q (see Fig. 105).

In the following pages we shall discuss principally those configurations in which the number of points is equal to the number

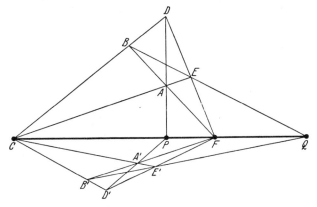

Fig. 105

of lines, i.e. for which $p = l$. Then it follows from the relation $p\lambda = nl$ that $\lambda = n$, so that the symbol for such a configuration is always of the form $(p_\gamma\, p_\gamma)$. We shall introduce the more concise notation (p_γ) for such a configuration. Furthermore, we shall make the reasonable stipulation that the configuration be connected and be not decomposable into separate figures.

The cases $\lambda = 1$ and $\lambda = 2$ are unimportant. $\lambda = 1$ yields only the trivial configuration consisting of a point and a straight line passing through it. For, if a configuration with $\lambda = 1$ had several

---

[2] This theorem is an immediate consequence of the theorem of Desargues discussed in § 19.

points, it would necessarily consist of separate parts, since no straight line of the configuration may contain more than one point. The case $\lambda = 2$ is realized by the closed polygons in the plane; and conversely, the conditions that each point of a configuration (p_2) be incident with two straight lines and each straight line with two points may be seen to imply that every configuration of the form (p_2) consists of the vertices and sides of a p-sided polygon.

On the other hand, the case $\lambda = 3$ gives rise to many interesting configurations. In this case the number of points (and straight lines), p, must be at least seven. For through any given point of the configuration there pass three lines, on each of which there must be two further points of the configuration. We shall go into detail only for the cases where $7 \leqq p \leqq 10$.

§ 16. The Configurations (7_3) and (8_3)

In constructing a configuration with the symbol (p_γ), the following method will be found the simplest: We label the p points with the numbers 1 through p and label the p straight lines, similarly, with the numbers (1) through (p). Then we set up a rectangular scheme of $p\lambda$ points in which the λ points incident with any given straight line are arranged in a column; there will be p columns corresponding to the p straight lines.

In this way, the scheme corresponding to the configuration (7_3) is as follows:

$$p$$

	(1)	(2)	(3)	(4)	(5)	(6)	(7)
λ	·	·	·	·	·	·	·
	·	·	·	·	·	·	·
	·	·	·	·	·	·	·

In filling in the spaces, the following three conditions must be satisfied. First, the numbers written in any one column must all be different to ensure that no less than three points are on any given straight line. Second, two different columns cannot have two numbers in common, as this would make the straight lines corresponding to the columns coincide. And third, every number must occur three times in all, since three straight lines are supposed to pass through every point. These three conditions are certainly necessary if a geometrical counterpart for the schematic table is to exist. On the other hand, they are not sufficient, as we shall soon see by some examples. The reason for this is that the geometrical realization of a table also depends on some geometric or algebraic considerations which cannot be directly expressed in terms of the arithmetic scheme. But if a table does represent a configuration, then it admits several alterations that do not affect the configuration in any way. Thus the vertical order of the numbers in any column may be changed. Also, the order of the columns themselves may be changed, as this only corresponds to a renumbering of the straight lines. And finally, the numbering of the points may also be changed at will. Since all these alterations in the schematic representation leave the configuration unchanged, we shall consider all tables differing only by such transformations as identical.

With this understanding, we may construct one, but only one, table having the symbol (7_3). To begin with, we denote the points on the first straight line by 1, 2, and 3. Then two more straight lines pass through the point 1, and they cannot contain the points 2 and 3. Let us denote the points of the second straight line by 4 and 5, and those of the third straight line by 6 and 7. Now all the points are numbered and the table is partly filled in, as follows:

$$
\begin{array}{ccccccc}
1 & 1 & 1 & . & . & . & . \\
2 & 4 & 6 & . & . & . & . \\
3 & 5 & 7 & . & . & . & . \\
\end{array}
$$

In the remaining columns, each of the numbers 2 and 3 has to appear two more times, subject to the condition that they be not both in one column. Hence we complete the first row as follows:

$$
\begin{array}{ccccccc}
1 & 1 & 1 & 2 & 2 & 3 & 3 \\
2 & 4 & 6 & . & . & . & . \\
3 & 5 & 7 & . & . & . & . \\
\end{array}
$$

The numbers 1, 2, and 3 are used up, and only 4, 5, 6, and 7 are available for filling in the remaining eight places. The number 4 has to appear two more times and may not be written under the same number both times. Thus we may place the 4's as follows:

$$
\begin{array}{cccc}
2 & 2 & 3 & 3 \\
4 & . & 4 & . \\
. & . & . & . \\
\end{array}
$$

All the other possible arrangements are not essentially different from this one. Again, 5 has to occur twice, but may no longer occur under a 4. Thus we may write

$$
\begin{array}{cccc}
2 & 2 & 3 & 3 \\
4 & 5 & 4 & 5 \\
\cdot & \cdot & \cdot & \cdot
\end{array}
$$

The first two of the four remaining places have to be occupied by 6 and 7 because they are the only numbers left and because we can not use the same one of them in both columns containing a 2. Interchanging the numbers 6 and 7 would not constitute an essential modification, and so we may write

$$
\begin{array}{cccc}
4 & 5 & 4 & 5 \\
6 & 7 & \cdot & \cdot
\end{array}
$$

The remaining places are necessarily filled in the order 7, 6. Thus we have indeed obtained just one possibility for the configuration (7_3), namely

(1)	(2)	(3)	(4)	(5)	(6)	(7)
1	1	1	2	2	3	3
2	4	6	4	5	4	5
3	5	7	6	7	7	6

We have already mentioned earlier that the existence of this table does not imply the existence of an actual configuration (7_3). Now it will turn out that such a configuration is indeed impossible. This may be seen by trying to find the equations of the straight lines of the table by the methods of analytic geometry, which leads to an incompatible sys-

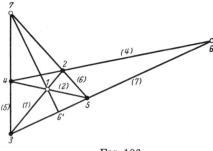

Fig. 106

tem of equations. We can also demonstrate the non-existence of the configuration by means of a diagram. To begin with, we draw the straight lines (1) and (2) of Fig. 106, denote their point of intersection by 1 as indicated in the table, and let 2, 3 and 4, 5 be arbitrary pairs of points on the lines (1) and (2) respectively. Then we draw the straight lines (4) and (7) whose positions are fixed by the pairs of points 2, 4 and 3, 5 and whose point of intersection, according to the table, has to be labeled 6. Similarly, the pairs of points 2, 5 and 3, 4 determine the lines (5) and (6) and their point of intersection 7. All the points of the configuration are now determined. But the three points 1, 6, and 7, which are supposed to be on the remaining straight line (3), are not collinear, so that the intersection of the lines (17) and (7) gives us an additional point 6'. It might be imagined that this is due to an unfortunate choice of the points 2, 3, 4, and 5. But such is not the case. For, our figure is a reproduction of the harmonic construction of Fig. 104; consequently, 6' is the fourth harmonic of the point 6 with respect to 3 and 5, and it follows by an elementary theorem of projective geometry that 6' cannot coincide with any of these three points.

We turn to the configuration (8_3). By the same method as before, it can be shown that there is essentially only one possible table, namely

(1)	(2)	(3)	(4)	(5)	(6)	(7)	(8)
1	1	1	2	2	3	3	4
2	4	6	3	7	4	5	5
5	8	7	6	8	7	8	6

The configuration may be interpreted as consisting of two quadrilaterals 1234 and 5678 each of which is inscribed in and at the same time circumscribed about the other (see Fig. 107; see also the footnote on p. 110). For, the line 12 passes through the point 5, the line 23 through the point 6, the line 34 through the point 7, and the line 41 through the point 8, and at the same time the sides 56, 67, 78, and 85 are incident with the points 4, 1, 2, and 3, respectively. Obviously, it is not possible to draw a configuration of this kind. Applying analytic

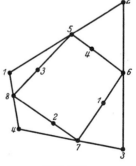

Fig. 107

methods, we find that the table gives rise to a system of equations which—while it does not contain a contradiction, as in the case of (7_3)—has, however, complex solutions only, and never any real solutions.

The configuration is nevertheless not without geometric interest and has an important role in the theory of third-order plane curves without double points. These curves have nine points of inflection, but at most three of them can be real. Furthermore, it can be demonstrated algebraically that every straight line connecting any two of these points of inflection must pass through a third point of inflection. No four points of inflection, on the other hand, can ever be collinear, because a third-order curve cannot meet a straight line in more than three points. Now, the straight lines connecting points of inflection form a configuration, and we have for this configuration $p = 9$, $\pi = 3$. Also, $\lambda = 4$, which can be seen as follows: If any point of inflection is selected, the remaining eight of them are collinear with it in pairs, so that each point is in fact incident with four straight lines. The formula $l = p\lambda/\pi$ gives the value 12 for l. Thus the configuration is of the type $(9_4 12_3)$. For the table of such a configuration there is essentially only one possibility, namely

(1)	(2)	(3)	(4)	(5)	(6)	(7)	(8)	(9)	(10)	(11)	(12)
1	1	1	2	2	3	3	4	1	2	5	6
2	4	6	3	7	4	5	5	3	4	7	8
5	8	7	6	8	7	8	6	9	9	9	9

If the point 9 and the lines passing through it, viz. (9), (10), (11), and (12), are omitted from this table, what remains is precisely the same as our table (8_3). The configuration (8_3) is also obtained on the omission of any other one of the nine points together with the four straight lines passing through it. For it is found that all the points of the configuration $(9_4 12_3)$ are equivalent.

§ 17. The Configurations (9_3)

While the cases $p = 7$ and $p = 8$ gave rise to only one table each, neither of which could be realized geometrically, the case $p = 9$ gives rise to three essentially different tables, and all of them represent configurations of real points and lines.

By far the most important of these configurations, and indeed the most important configuration of all geometry, is the one known

as the Brianchon-Pascal configuration.   For the sake of brevity
we shall give it the symbol $(9_3)_1$ and use the symbols $(9_3)_2$ and
$(9_3)_3$ for the other two configurations of type (9_3).

The table for the configuration $(9_3)_1$ may be written as follows:

(1)	(2)	(3)	(4)	(5)	(6)	(7)	(8)	(9)
1	1	1	2	2	3	3	4	5
2	4	6	4	7	6	5	6	7
3	5	7	8	9	8	9	9	8

In drawing such a configuration, we begin with the points 8 and
9, which may be chosen arbitrarily (see Fig. 108), and draw the
arbitrary straight lines (4), (6), and (9) through 8, and (5), (7),
and (8) through 9.   Six of

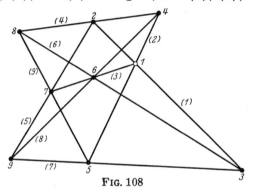

FIG. 108

the nine resulting points of
intersection belong to the
configuration; in accord-
ance with the table, we
shall designate them by 2,
3, 4, 5, 6, and 7. These six
points fix the positions of
the remaining straight lines
(1), (2), and (3).   First of
all, we draw the line (1)
through 2 and 3, and the line (2) through 4 and 5.   Their point of
intersection has to be labeled 1.   The straight line (3) is determined
by the points 6 and 7.   According to the table, this line must pass
through 1.   Now it is found that this condition is automatically
satisfied despite the arbitrary choice of the points 8 and 9 and of
the three straight lines through each of these points.

The geometric reason for this surprising phenomenon lies in the
theorems of Brianchon, which we shall now study.

Our point of departure is the hyperboloid of one sheet.   As we
have seen in Chapter I, the surface contains two families of
straight lines such that every straight line of one family intersects every straight line of the other, while two lines of the same
family never meet.   Let us pick three straight lines of one family
(drawn as double lines in Fig. 109) and three of the other (drawn
as heavy single lines in the figure), from which we obtain the

hexagon $ABCDEFA$ in space, as follows: On a straight line of the first family we move from A to B; a definite line of the second family passes through B, and along this we move to a point C; from C we follow the straight line of the first family passing through that point to another point D; thence we move to E along a line of the second family, and finally follow a line of the first family to that point F where it intersects the line of the second family that goes through A. Thus the sides of the hexagon belong alternately to the first family and the second.

We shall now prove that all three diagonals AD, BE, and CF of the hexagon have a point in common. We begin with AD and BE. The sides AB and DE of the hexagon have a common point because AB belongs to one and DE to the other family of straight lines on

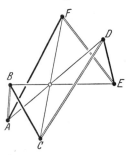

FIG. 109

the hyperboloid. Therefore the four points A, B, D, E lie in one plane, and so AD and BE also have a point in common. In exactly the same way it can be shown that each of the other two pairs of diagonals also intersects at a point. But three straight lines that intersect each other in pairs are coplanar, or, if not, must all pass through a common point. Now if the three diagonals of the hexagon $ABCDEF$ were all in one plane, the hexagon itself would also have to lie in this plane, and any two of its sides would have a point in common; this is ruled out, since AB and CD (to give one example) are straight lines of the same family and therefore cannot intersect each other. All three diagonals do, accordingly, pass through one point.

This theorem of the geometry of space leads to the Brianchon theorems of plane geometry. To obtain them, we look at the hyperboloid of one sheet from a point P, which for the time being we shall assume not to lie on the surface. The contour of the hyperboloid as seen from this point is a conic section which may be either a hyperbola (Fig. 110) or an ellipse (Fig. 111). The area on one side of the contour appears empty, while the region on the other side appears doubly covered, what appear to be two layers in the picture being connected along the conic forming the contour. The straight lines of the surface are partly visible in the picture, and partly covered. Thus, they extend from one layer into the other and must therefore meet the contour. On the other hand, they can not intersect that curve, since one side of it is empty. Hence our hexagon in space has become a plane hexagon whose sides are tangent to a conic; this gives us the following theorem of plane geometry:

The diagonals of a hexagon that is circumscribed about a conic intersect at one point.

So far we have not proved the theorem except for those conics that can be obtained as the outline of a hyperboloid of one sheet, that is, only for certain ellipses and hyperbolas. But we shall immediately see that the outline can also be a parabola. For, the lines of sight which give rise to the outline—or, more technically,

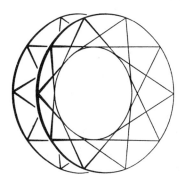

FIG. 110   FIG. 111

a central projection—form the tangent cone of the surface with the vertex P, i.e. a second-order cone (see p. 12); but the outline, or central projection, is the curve in which this cone intersects the image plane, and this is a parabola if we choose as the image plane a plane parallel to one of the generators of the cone (see pp. 12, 13, 8).

We shall now go over to the case where the surface is observed from a point P (the center of projection) that is on the surface itself. Here, the two straight lines of the surface that pass through P are seen as two points, while the other straight lines are still seen as straight lines. And since every line of one family intersects the line of the other family that passes through the center of projection, the first family is seen as a pencil of lines whose vertex is the image of the straight line g of the other family that passes through P. Similarly, the other family is also seen as a pencil of lines. The vertices of the two pencils are distinct, being the images of two different straight lines passing through P. The following theorem is accordingly a consequence of the theorem about the space hexagon:

The diagonals of a plane hexagon whose sides pass alternately through two fixed points, meet at a point.

These theorems about the tangent hexagons of one of the three

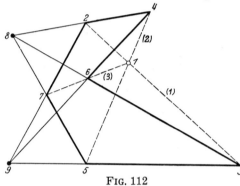

Fig. 112

types of conics or of a degenerate conic consist-ing of a pair of points are called Brianchon's theorems, after their discoverer. The point at which the three diagonals meet is called the Brian-chon point.

Our space construction does not, to be sure, com-plete the proof of Brianchon's theorems, as it might be possible that not every Brianchon hexagon can be obtained as a projection of a space hexagon of the type we have considered. It can be proved, however, that it is indeed possible to start with any hexagon that satisfies the Brianchon assumptions and construct from it a spatial

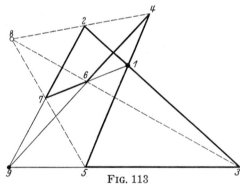

Fig. 113

figure of the sort we have been considering.

Now the last of the Brianchon theorems is closely connected with the configuration $(9_3)_1$ and explains the fact that the last incidence condition is automatically satisfied in the construction of this configuration. Indeed we

see that, in the notation of Figs. 112 and 108, the points 2, 4, 6, 3, 5, 7 form a hexagon whose sides pass alternately through the points 8 and 9, and the straight lines (1), (2), and (3) are the diagonals 23, 45, and 67 of this hexagon. So (3) must pass through the point of intersection 1 of the straight lines (1) and (2), and 1 is the Brianchon point of the hexagon:

In our construction, the points of the configuration $(9_3)_1$ do not all play the same roles: the points 2, 4, 6, 3, 5, 7 form the hexagon; 8 and 9 are the points through which the sides pass; and 1 is the Brianchon point. But this lack of symmetry is not inherent in the configuration but is due to an arbitrary choice on our part. For we may also assign the role of the Brianchon point to 8 or 9. It is sufficient to make this clear as regards the point 8 (see Fig. 113), since we see from Fig. 112 that 8 and 9 are alike. Similarly, we may choose any one of the

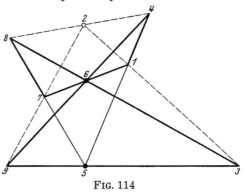

Fig. 114

points 2, 4, 6, 3, 5, 7 for the role of Brianchon point. Again, it is sufficient to show this for the point 2 (see Fig. 114), since all the points 2, 4, 6, 3, 5, 7 are alike in their relation to the rest of the figure.

Owing to this inherent symmetry, $(9_3)_1$ is called a *regular* configuration. In much the same way as in the study of point systems and polyhedra, we arrive at the concept of regularity by the study

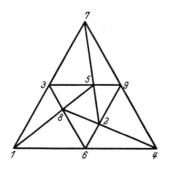

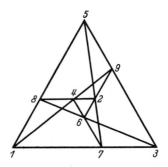

Fig. 115   Fig. 116

of certain mappings of a configuration into itself which are called "automorphisms" and are analogous to the symmetry transformations in the case of point systems and polyhedra. We obtain an automorphism of a configuration if we can permute its points and its lines in such a way that no incidence is lost and no new incidence added. It is easy to see that the automorphisms form a group. Now a configuration is called regular if the group of its automorphisms is "transitive," i.e. if it contains enough transformations so that every point of the configuration can be transformed into every other point of the configuration by one of them.

For the study of the automorphisms of a configuration it suffices to consider its abstract scheme. In this way it may be shown that the tables for (7_3) and (8_3) are regular. The same is true for $(9_4 12_3)$ (see p. 102).

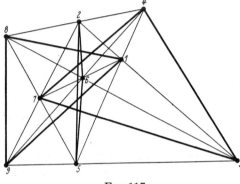

Fig. 117

Let us now turn to the other two configurations (9_3). They are shown in Figs. 115 and 116. In order to see what it is that differentiates the three configurations of the type (9_3), we may proceed as follows. Since every point in a configuration (p_3) is connected with exactly six others by lines of the configuration, it follows in the case $p = 9$ that for every point of the configuration there are exactly two others not connected with it. For example, in $(9_3)_1$ the points 8 and 9 are not connected with 1. Also there is no line connecting 8 with 9. Hence 1, 8, and 9 form a triangle of unconnected points. Similarly 2, 5, 6 and 3, 4, 7 form such triangles

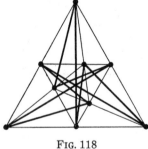

Fig. 118

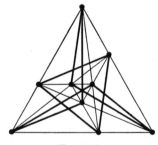

Fig. 119

(Fig. 117). Let us use the same procedure for $(9_3)_2$ and $(9_3)_3$, combining the paths between unconnected points to form polygons. In the case $(9_3)_2$ we get a nonagon (Fig. 118), and in $(9_3)_3$ a hexagon and a triangle (Fig. 119). This tells us, first, that the three figures 108, 115, and 116 do not merely differ in the positions of their points but are essentially different configurations. Furthermore, we may conclude that the configuration $(9_3)_3$ cannot possibly be regular. For, an automorphism can transform points of the hexagon only into points of the hexagon, and never into points of the triangle. In the case $(9_3)_3$, on the other hand, the regular arrangement of the unconnected points leads us to conjecture that the configuration is regular. This is confirmed by further inspection of the table.

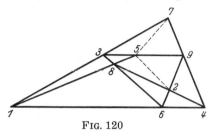

FIG. 120

We may try to construct the other two configurations step by step in much the same way as we constructed $(9_3)_1$. But we then find that the last incidence condition is no longer satisfied automatically but is satisfied only if special provisions have been made in the preceding steps. This is the reason why $(9_3)_2$ and $(9_3)_3$ are not of such fundamental importance as $(9_3)_1$; they do not express a general theorem of projective geometry. Fig. 120 illustrates a case in which the last straight line of $(9_3)_2$ cannot be drawn.

The auxiliary constructions that are necessary to make possible the construction of $(9_3)_2$ and $(9_3)_3$ are, however, distinguished by a special property: they can be carried out by means of a ruler alone, so that all three of the configurations (9_3) can be constructed without any instruments except a ruler This is expressed analytically by the fact that all the ele-

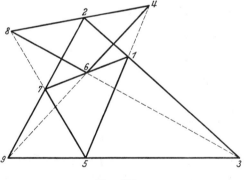

FIG. 121

ments of the configuration can be determined by the successive solution of linear equations in which the coefficients of each equation are rational functions of the characteristic quantities of the configuration that have already been determined from the preceding equations. It is quite true, of course, that the equations of straight lines are always linear. But in obtaining the system of equations of a configuration, the coefficients of some of the equations have to be computed from other equations by elimination, since some of the straight lines are fixed by the straight lines that have been constructed before. In the general case, this elimination

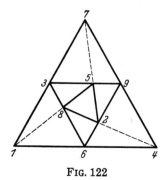

Fig. 122

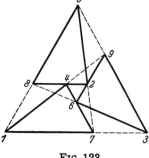

Fig. 123

gives rise to equations of higher degree; this must be the case in (8_3) since we could not otherwise get any complex elements. Now the special property of the configurations (9_3) is that all the auxiliary equations are linear, with the result that all three con-

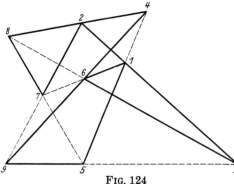

Fig. 124

figurations can be constructed in the real plane and with the sole use of a ruler.

The arrangement of the elements in the configurations (9_3) may be interpreted in a variety of different ways. For example, each of the configurations can be considered as forming three triangles of which the first is inscribed in the second, the second in the third, and the third in the first.[1]

---

[1] The word "inscribed" is used here in a generalized sense; thus in Fig. 121, the triangle 468 is said to be inscribed in triangle 157 because 4 is on the straight line 15, 6 on the straight line 17, and 8 on the straight line 75, although 4 and 8 are not on the segments 15 and 75 but on their continuations. "Circumscribed" is used in the corresponding general sense, triangle A being "circumscribed" about triangle B if triangle B is "inscribed" in triangle A. The same remarks apply to the use below of "inscribed" and "circumscribed" in reference to general polygons. [*Trans.*]

The triangles 157, 239, 468 of Fig. 121, the triangles 258, 369, 147 of Fig. 122, and the triangles 147, 258, and 369 of Fig. 123 are examples of such systems of triangles. Similarly we interpreted (8_3) as a pair of mutually inscribed and circumscribed quadrilaterals (see Fig. 107, p. 101). The three configurations (9_3) can also be interpreted as nonagons inscribed in and circumscribed about themselves; examples of such nonagons are 2361594872 of Fig. 124, 1627384951 of Fig. 125, and 1473695281 of Fig. 126. In the configuration $(9_3)_1$ we can find several additional nonagons with the same properties, by applying suitable automorphisms.

The construction of p-sided polygons that are inscribed in and circumscribed about themselves necessarily leads to configurations

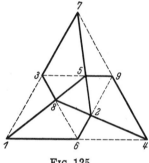

FIG. 125

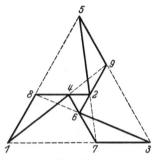

FIG. 126

of the type (p_3). For, every side of the polygon contains one vertex of the polygon in addition to the vertices it connects, and every vertex, likewise, must be incident with three sides of the polygon. The only assumption needed in this argument was that all the sides and all the vertices of the polygon play the same role. If this assumption were not made, one side could contain two or more extra vertices; but then some other side of the polygon would have to be empty.

(7_3) and (8_3) may also be interpreted as being p-sided polygons of this type. In the notation of the configuration tables, the heptagon 12457361 and the octagon 126534871 are inscribed in and circumscribed about themselves.

In order to understand another important property of configurations, we must study the principle of duality. It is this principle that confers upon projective geometry its special clarity and symmetry. It may be derived in visual terms from the method of projecting, which we have already used in arriving at Brianchon's theorems.

§ 18. Perspective, Ideal Elements, and the Principle of Duality in the Plane

If we draw the picture of a flat landscape on the blackboard, the landscape being a horizontal plane and the blackboard a vertical plane, then the image of the horizontal plane appears to be bounded

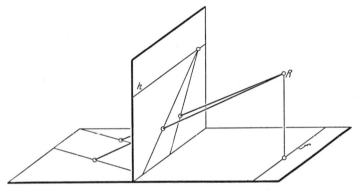

FIG. 127

by a straight line h, the horizon (see Fig. 127). Two parallel straight lines in the horizontal plane which are not parallel to the plane of the blackboard appear in the picture as straight lines that meet on the horizon. In painting, the point of intersection of the two lines in the image is called the vanishing point of the parallel lines.

We see, then, that the images of parallel lines under central perspective are not usually parallel. We see furthermore that the mapping effected is not one-to-one. The points of the horizon on the image plane do not represent any points of the original plane. Conversely, there are points of the plane which do not have an image. These are the points of the straight line f that is vertically below the observer R and parallel to the image plane (Fig. 127).

The description of this phenomenon can be simplified by replacing each point of the plane by the line of sight passing through the point. Thus we replace every point P of the plane e (Fig. 128) by the straight line $AP = p$ connecting P with A, the point where the observer's eye is located. Then the image of P on an arbitrarily placed board t is the point P' at which the straight line p meets the board; thus the mapping is determined once P is given. If P describes a curve in e, then p sweeps out a cone with A as vertex. The image of the curve on t is the intersection of t and the cone. In particular, if P moves along a straight line g in e, the cone becomes the plane γ that contains A and g. Thus, while the points of e become straight lines through A, the straight lines of e give rise to planes through A. The image on t of the straight line g is the intersection of t and γ, i.e. another straight line g'. This property of transforming straight lines into straight lines is the most important property of a central perspective.

We have expressed the perspective mapping as the resultant of

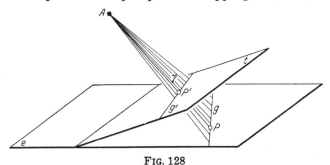

Fig. 128

two transformations that are of types that may be considered as the inverses of each other. First the points (P) and straight lines (g) of a plane are replaced by the straight lines (p) and the planes (γ) passing through A, and then the straight lines and planes through A are transformed into the points (P') and straight lines (g') of another plane. For reasons of symmetry, it therefore suffices to study only the first step.

This transformation $e \to A$ is fully defined only in the given direction, not in the reverse direction $A \to e$. The transformation assigns a special role to those straight lines through A that are parallel to e; they do not correspond to any point of e, while each of the remaining straight lines through A belongs to a definite point of e, namely the point at which it intersects e. The straight lines p_u through A parallel to the plane e fill out a plane γ_u, the plane through A that is parallel to e (see Fig. 129). Of all the planes containing A, γ_u is also the one that plays an anomalous role in the transformation $A \to e$. For, each of the other planes through A is associated with a definite straight line g of e, the line in which it cuts e, but no such straight line corresponds to the plane γ_u, since it does not meet e.

Now it is expedient to eliminate these exceptions conceptually by assigning additional points P_u to the plane e, as "infinitely distant" or "ideal" points. These "points" are defined by the stipulation that they shall be the images of the rays p_u in the transformation $A \to e$. They are regarded as constituting, in their totality, the image of the plane γ_u. In order to divest this plane of its anomalous position in relation to the other planes passing through A, we have to call its image a straight line. We therefore say that the infinitely distant points of e form a straight line g_u, the so-called infinitely distant[1] or "ideal" line of e. Clearly the mapping of the points and straight lines of e into the straight lines and planes through A is fully defined and one-to-one once we have supplemented the plane e in the manner described.

The suitability of the definitions we have introduced becomes apparent on examining the central perspective of e onto any other plane t. The plane t must also be supplemented by ideal points constituting the ideal line of this plane. But unless e and t happen to be parallel, the plane that goes into the ideal line l_u of t under the transformation $A \to t$ is not γ_u but some other plane λ through A. λ meets e in a straight line l. Hence the perspective mapping $e \to t$ associates the points of the infinitely distant line of the second plane with the points of an ordinary straight line in the first plane. It is only the introduction of the ideal points that makes the central perspective a one-to-one mapping of the points and straight lines of one plane into the points and straight lines of another plane. In this mapping, the infinitely distant points are on a par with the finite points.

We shall now look into the question of how the concept of incidence between points and straight lines must be extended to accommodate the ideal elements we have added. As before, we begin with the transformation $e \to A$. An *ordinary* point P and an *ordinary* straight line g of e are incident if and only if the corresponding p and γ are incident. Let us generalize this to cover

---

[1] The term "infinitely distant" stems from the fact that the ray from a point of e to the eye approaches one of the straight lines p_u if the point of e recedes indefinitely in a fixed direction.

arbitrary points and straight lines of e. An infinitely distant point P_u and a straight line g shall be called incident if the ray p_u is incident with γ. If γ coincides with γ_u, i.e. if g is the ideal line of e, this does not tell us anything new. But if g is an ordinary straight line, then γ and γ_u intersect in a definite straight line p_u. Hence every ordinary straight line has exactly one infinitely distant point, its point of intersection with g_u. If g' and g are parallel, this means that the plane γ' belonging to g' passes through p_u (see Fig. 129). Accordingly, two straight lines are parallel if and only if they have the same infinitely distant point; this is the

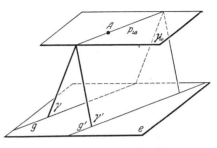

FIG. 129

meaning of the occasionally used mode of expression "parallels meet at infinity," which in itself, and when stated without further explanation, would be meaningless. At the same time we recognize the reason for the fact mentioned at the beginning of this section, that two parallel straight lines appear to meet at their vanishing point on the horizon.

As an example of the way geometrical notions are simplified by the introduction of the ideal elements, we may cite the conics. Since, as we have proved in Chapter I, they can be obtained as the plane sections of a circular cone, they may all be regarded as perspective images of a circle. According to whether no projecting

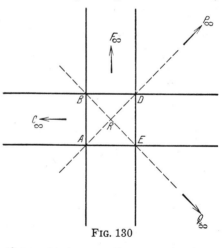

FIG. 130

ray, one ray, or two rays are parallel to the image plane, we obtained an ellipse, a parabola, or a hyperbola, respectively. We may now formulate this as follows: A conic section is an ellipse, a parabola, or a hyperbola according to whether it meets the ideal line in no point, in one point, or in two points, respectively. A central projection onto another plane transforms the conic under consideration into another conic that either does not meet the horizon, or touches it, or intersects it in two points, as the case may be. What type of conic the image will be depends on the position of the image plane.

In other cases too, central projection is an important tool for getting much more general figures from special figures. For example, the complete quadrilateral (p. 96) can always be derived from the simple construction of the adjoining figure (Fig. 130).

The importance of the ideal elements, however, lies mainly in the fact that they enable us to modify and considerably simplify the axiomatic foundation of plane geometry. If we confine ourselves to the finite points of the plane, the incidence of points and straight lines is subject to the following axioms:

1. Two distinct points define a straight line with which they are incident.

2. Two distinct points define only one straight line with which they are incident.

From the second axiom it follows that two straight lines in a plane either have one point or no point in common. For if they had two or more common points, they would necessarily be one and the same straight line.

The case where two straight lines have no point in common is elucidated by and subject to the Euclidean axiom of parallels:

If there is given in a plane any straight line a and any point A, where a and A are not incident, there is in the plane one and only one straight line b that passes through A and does not intersect a; the straight line b is called the *parallel* to a through A.

Now if we no longer consider only finite points but enlarge the plane into the "projective plane" by adding the ideal line, then we are in a position to use the two following axioms as a basis instead of the three axioms above.

1. Two distinct points determine one and only one straight line.

2. Two distinct straight lines determine one and only one point.

These two axioms determine the incidence of points and straight lines in the projective plane. Ideal points and the ideal straight line are in no way distinguished here from other points and straight lines. If it is desired to represent the projective plane by a real structure where the equivalence of all points and of all straight lines can be recognized visually, we may refer back to the bundle of straight lines and planes through a fixed point, regarding the straight lines as "points" and the planes as "straight lines." In this model the validity of the two axioms last mentioned is easily verified.

Now this pair of axioms has the purely formal property of remaining unchanged if the word "straight line" is replaced by "point" and the word "point" by "straight line." On closer inspection we see that the remaining axioms of plane projective geometry are also left unchanged when these two words are interchanged. But the two words must then also be interchangeable in all the theorems deduced from these axioms. The interchangeability of points and lines is called the principle of *duality* in the projective plane. According to this principle, there belongs to every theorem a second theorem that corresponds to it dually, and to every figure a second figure that corresponds to it dually. Under this dual correspondence, the points of a curve correspond to a collection of straight lines that in general envelop a second curve as tangents. A more detailed study reveals that the family of straight lines corresponding dually to the points of a conic always envelops another conic.

By the principle of duality we can deduce a number of other theorems from Brianchon's theorems. They are called Pascal's theorems, after their discoverer. In order to bring out the duality of the two groups of theorems more clearly, we shall write them side by side in exactly corresponding forms.

Brianchon Theorems

1, 2, 3. Let there be given a hexagon formed by six straight lines that are tangent to a conic (hexagon circumscribed about a conic). Then the three lines joining opposite vertices intersect at one point.

4. Let there be given six straight lines of which three are incident with a point A and three are incident with a point B. Choose six points of intersection, which together with the appropriate connecting lines form a hexagon whose sides pass alter-

Pascal Theorems

1, 2, 3. Let there be given a hexagon formed by six points that lie on a conic (hexagon inscribed in a conic). Then the three points of intersection of opposite sides lie on one straight line.

4. Let there be given six points of which three are incident with a straight line a and three are incident with a straight line b. Choose six connecting lines, which together with the appropriate points of intersection form a hexagon whose ver-

nately through A and B. Then the straight lines connecting opposite vertices intersect at one point (the Brianchon point of the hexagon).

tices lie alternately on a and b. Then the points of intersection of opposite sides lie on one straight line (the Pascal line of the hexagon).

Evidently the figure corresponding to the last theorem of Pascal must be the dual of the configuration $(9_3)_1$. Now the dual figure of a configuration $(p_\gamma l_\pi)$ is always another configuration, and its symbol is $(l_\pi p_\gamma)$. The special configurations we have denoted by the symbol (p_γ), and they only, have as duals configurations with the same symbol. It is conceivable that the configuration of Pascal's theorem, i.e. the dual of $(9_3)_1$, might be one of the other two con-

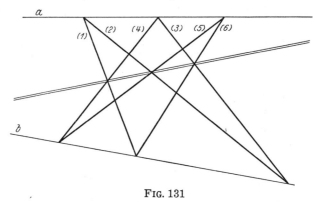

Fig. 131

figurations (9_3). It is found, however, that Pascal's theorem is also represented by the symbol $(9_3)_1$ (see Fig. 131). This is the reason why we have called the configuration the Brianchon-Pascal configuration from the very beginning. Thus $(9_3)_1$ is "dually invariant" or "self-dual." Just as the Brianchon point could be chosen arbitrarily, so we can also choose an arbitrary straight line of the configuration to serve as the Pascal line.

By using the ideal elements we can arrive at a special case of the last Pascal theorem which would not otherwise seem to have any connection with the original theorem. For, by moving the Pascal line to infinity we get the following theorem (Fig. 132): If the vertices of a hexagon lie alternately on two straight lines, and if two pairs of opposite sides are respectively parallel, then the third pair of opposite sides is also parallel.

This special case of Pascal's theorem is called Pappus' theorem.[2]

Having seen that $(9_3)_1$ is self-dual, it is easy for us to conclude that $(9_3)_2$ and $(9_3)_3$ must also be self-dual. For, the only other possibility would be that the figure obtained from $(9_3)_2$ by applying the duality principle is $(9_3)_3$. But since $(9_3)_2$ is a regular con-

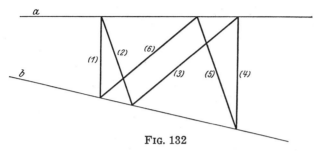

Fig. 132

figuration and $(9_3)_3$ is not, neither of these figures can be the dual of the other.

We shall now take up the configurations (10_3). In order to understand the most important one of these, Desargues' configuration, it is necessary to extend the method of introducing ideal elements, and the principle of duality, from the plane to three-dimensional space.

§ 19. Ideal Elements and the Principle of Duality in Space. Desargues' Theorem and the Desargues Configuration (10_3)

We have arrived at the concept of the projective plane by studying projection in space. Now projective geometry also changes the space as a whole, by the addition of ideal elements, into "projective space," an entity that is in many ways simpler. Only, it is not possible in this case to justify the procedure in visual terms; it is purely abstract. To begin with, we introduce the ideal elements in all the planes of ordinary space according to the principle discussed earlier. Then it appears reasonable to interpret the entity formed by all the ideal points and straight lines as a plane, the "infinitely distant" or "ideal" plane of the space. For, this entity shares with the ordinary planes in space the property that any given plane intersects it in a straight line, the ideal straight line

---

[2] Frequently the more general theorem, which is called here the fourth Pascal theorem, is also referred to as Pappus' theorem. [*Trans.*]

of the given plane. Every ordinary straight line has only one point, its ideal point, in common with the ideal plane, just as it has only one point in common with any other plane that does not contain the line. Moreover two planes are parallel if and only if they have the same ideal line.[1]

A great many phenomena of the geometry of space are simplified by this point of view. Thus parallel projection can be regarded as a special case of central projection in which the center of projection is an infinitely distant point. Furthermore, to give another example, the difference between the hyperboloid of one sheet and the hyperbolic paraboloid may be characterized by the property that the hyperboloid intersects the ideal plane in a non-degenerate conic whereas the paraboloid intersects it in a pair of generating straight lines of the surface; this distinction amounts to the same thing as the fact explained on page 15, that three skew straight lines lie on a paraboloid rather than on a hyperboloid if and only if they are parallel to a fixed plane; for, this is equivalent to the condition that the three straight lines meet one ideal line, which consequently lies on the surface since it has three points in common with it.

It is clear that all planes of projective space must be regarded as projective planes, so that the principle of duality in the plane is true for them. But the space as a whole is also governed by a different principle of duality as well.

To arrive at this, we proceed as in the plane, compiling the list of axioms by which the incidence of points, straight lines, and planes in space must be regulated if finite and infinitely distant elements are treated alike. The axioms may be formulated as follows:

1. Two planes determine one and only one straight line; three planes that do not pass through a common straight line determine one and only one point.

2. Two intersecting straight lines determine one and only one point and one and only one plane.

3. Two points determine one and only one straight line; three points not on one straight line determine one and only one plane.

This system of axioms remains unaltered if the words "point" and "plane" are interchanged. (The first axiom is interchanged

---

[1] For, the property of two planes being parallel, and also the property of their having the same ideal line, are each equivalent to the property that parallels to every straight line of one plane can be drawn in the other.

with the third, and the second is unchanged.) The set of remaining
axioms of the projective geometry of space is also left unaltered
by this interchange. Thus the point and the plane correspond to each
other dually, and the straight line corresponds to itself. The set
of all points of a surface corresponds dually to the set of all tangent
planes to another surface. As was the case with the conics in the
plane, the second-order surfaces in space are self-dual.

The simplest and at the same time most important theorem of
three-dimensional projective geometry is named after Desargues.
Desargues' theorem may be stated as follows (see Fig. 133) :

Two triangles ABC and $A'B'C'$ in space being given, let them
be so placed that the lines connecting corresponding vertices pass

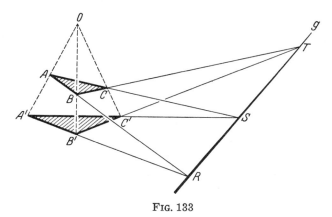

FIG. 133

through a single point O. Then the three pairs of corresponding
sides have points of intersection, R, S, and T, and these points of
intersection are, moreover, collinear.

The first part of the theorem is easy to prove. By the second
axiom for space, the two intersecting straight lines AA' and BB'
define a common plane. The straight lines AB and $A'B'$ also lie
in this plane, whence it follows, by the second axiom for incidence
in the plane, that these two straight lines have a point of intersection R. (R may be a finite or an ideal point.) The existence of
the two other points of intersection, S and T, is proved analogously.

The truth of the second part of the theorem is easy to see in the
case where the triangles are in different planes. In this case the
planes of the triangles determine a common—ordinary or ideal—
straight line of intersection (by Axiom 1 for space). Of every

pair of corresponding sides of the triangles one lies in one of these planes and the other lies in the other plane. Since we have seen that the sides of such a pair intersect, their point of intersection must be on the straight line that the two planes have in common. This proves Desargues' theorem for the general case.

But it is precisely the special case where the triangles are coplanar that is of particular importance. Here we may apply a method of proof similar to the proof for Brianchon's theorem, in which we project a spatial figure onto the plane. We only need show that every plane Desargues figure is a projection of a three-dimensional Desargues figure. To this end, we connect all the points and straight lines of the plane Desargues figure with a point S out-

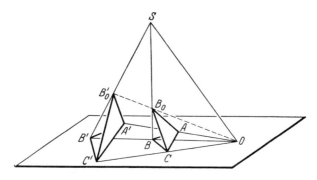

Fig. 134

side the plane of the figure (see Fig. 134). We then pass a plane through the straight line AC intersecting BS at a point B_0 distinct from S, and draw OB_0. The straight lines OB_0 and $B'S$ are coplanar and therefore have a point of intersection B_0'. But now the triangles AB_0C and $A'B_0'C'$ form a three-dimensional Desargues figure, since all the straight lines connecting corresponding vertices pass through O. Projecting the line in which the planes of these triangles intersect from S onto the original plane, we get a straight line on which the pairs of corresponding sides of the original triangles ABC and $A'B'C'$ must intersect. This completes the proof of Desargues' theorem.

The principle of duality for the plane and the one for space both lead to interesting consequences of Desargues' theorem. To begin with, it is readily seen that the converse of the theorem is also true; i.e. the existence of a Desargues line containing the points of intersection of pairs of corresponding sides of the two triangles implies the existence of the Desargues point through which the lines connecting corresponding vertices pass. In the case where the triangles are coplanar, the converse of Desargues' theorem proves to be the same as the theorem we obtain from Desargues' theorem by applying the principle of duality in the plane. We can elucidate this by writing the two theorems side by side, as follows:

Let three pairs of points AA', BB', CC' be given, such that the three lines determined by the pairs pass through a common point. Then the three points of intersection of the pairs of straight lines AB and $A'B'$, BC and $B'C'$, CA and $C'A'$, lie on one straight line.

Let three pairs of straight lines aa', bb', cc' be given, such that the points of intersection of the pairs lie on one straight line. Then the lines joining the pairs of points (ab) and $(a'b')$, (bc) and $(b'c')$, (ca) and $(c'a')$, pass through a common point.

Let us examine the figure (Fig. 135) consisting of the vertices and sides of two coplanar Desargues triangles together with the lines joining pairs of corresponding vertices, the points where pairs of corresponding sides meet, the Desargues point O, and the

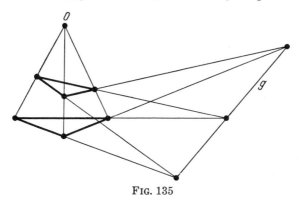

FIG. 135

Desargues line g. It is a simple matter of counting to see that the figure is a configuration of type (10_3). It is called the Desargues configuration. This configuration shares with Pascal's configuration the property that the last incidence condition is automatically satisfied when the figure is constructed step by step from its table. Furthermore, the Desargues configuration, like Pascal's, is self-dual. This is seen to be true because the configuration represents both Desargues' theorem and its converse, and the latter is the dual of the former.

We next consider the result obtained from the three-dimensional case of Desargues' theorem on applying the principle of duality *in space*. We get the following juxtaposition:

Let three pairs of points AA', BB', CC', be given such that the three lines determined by the pairs pass through a common point. Then the three points of intersection of the pairs of straight lines AB and $A'B'$, BC and $B'C'$, CA and $C'A'$, lie on one straight line.	Let three pairs of planes $\alpha\alpha'$, $\beta\beta'$, $\gamma\gamma'$, be given such that the three lines of intersection determined by the pairs lie in one plane. Then the three planes containing the pairs of straight lines $(\alpha\beta)$ and $(\alpha'\beta')$, $(\beta\gamma)$ and $(\beta'\gamma')$, $(\gamma\alpha)$ and $(\gamma'\alpha')$, pass through one straight line.

Fig. 136 illustrates the theorem that appears in the right-hand column. In this theorem the two triangles are replaced by two

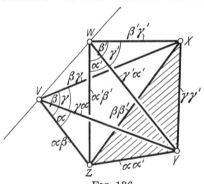

FIG. 136

trihedral angles formed by the planes α, β, γ and α', β', γ', respectively. Paralleling what we have done in the case of the plane Desargues figure, we shall now examine the three-dimensional figure consisting of the two Desargues trihedra together with the planes determined by pairs of corresponding edges, the lines of intersection of corresponding pairs of faces, the "Desargues plane" ($\alpha\alpha'$, $\beta\beta'$, $\gamma\gamma'$ in Fig. 136), and the "Desargues line" (VW in the figure). The intersection of this three-dimensional figure with any plane that does not contain any of the points V, W, X, Y, Z is a plane Desargues configuration, since the Desargues trihedra intersect the plane in Desargues triangles. To the planes and straight lines of the space figure there correspond the straight lines and points of the plane configuration. However, the three-dimensional figure has an intrinsic symmetry that is not reflected in the plane figure. The space figure consists of all the connecting straight lines and plane of the five points V, W, X, Y, Z, and the roles of the five points are completely equivalent. Conversely, every complete five-point in space becomes a three-dimensional Desargues figure if two of the vertices are arbitrarily chosen as vertices of the Desargues trihedra.[2] From the fact that all the straight lines and all the planes of the spatial figure play the same role, it follows that the same is true for the points and the straight lines of the plane Desargues configuration. This proves that the Desargues configuration is regular, so that the choice of the Desargues point or the Desargues line in the configuration can be made quite arbitrarily.[3]

We shall now represent the Desargues configuration as a pair of mutually inscribed and circumscribed pentagons. To this end, we first look for any pentagons at all in the configuration, where it is required that all the vertices and sides of the polygon be elements of the configuration and no three consecutive vertices be collinear. The problem is considerably simplified by going back to the five-point in space. The vertices of the plane polygon are associated with the corresponding edges of the five-point in space. Since it is required that any two consecutive vertices of the plane polygon lie on a straight line of the configuration, the corresponding edges must be in one plane and must therefore intersect. To ensure that no three consecutive vertices are collinear, we need only see to it that the corresponding edges are not coplanar; this would happen if and only if three consecutive edges formed a triangle. By passing through the vertices V, W, X, Y, Z of the three-dimensional five-point in any order, say in the order in which they are written, we obtain a closed polygonal path of the kind we need; in the plane

---

[2] The only condition the five points must satisfy is that they be in general position, i.e. that no four of them be coplanar and hence no three of them collinear.

[3] By a complete n-point in space we mean the set of all the straight lines and planes connecting n points in general position in space. As in the case $n = 5$, the section of the complete n-point, for any value of n, by a plane that does not pass through any of the vertices is a configuration. These configurations are regular and of type $p = \dfrac{n(n-1)}{2}$, $\gamma = n - 2$, $g = \dfrac{n(n-1)(n-2)}{6}$, $\pi = 3$.

It follows that a configuration of the special type where $p = l$ is only obtained in the case $n = 5$. Other regular configurations can be obtained by using n-points in general position in higher-dimensional spaces. All these configurations are called "polyhedral."

configuration it furnishes a pentagon of the required type. But the
edges of the three-dimensional five-point that were not used in this
path constitute a second three-dimensional polygon of the same
kind. For, two unused edges pass through every vertex of the five-
point in space, since every vertex is incident with four edges in all,

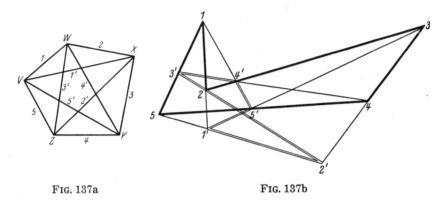

Fig. 137a   Fig. 137b

two of which were used up for the first path. This second polygonal path corresponds to a second pentagon in the configuration,
and a simple enumeration reveals that this must be inscribed in the
first pentagon. Because of symmetry, the first pentagon is also
inscribed in the second pentagon. Figs. 137a and 137b illustrate

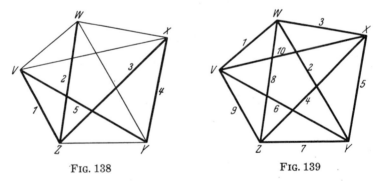

Fig. 138   Fig. 139

the way in which the three-dimensional arrangement and the plane
pair of pentagons are related.

We can also find other types of systems of five edges of the five-
point in space corresponding to pentagons contained in the plane
configuration. An example is given in Fig. 138. But it can be verified
that it is then impossible to arrange the five remaining edges

cyclically in such a way that any two consecutive edges have a common point and no three consecutive edges form a triangle. Hence the construction given in the beginning exhausts all the possibilities. Since an automorphism of the configuration corresponds to every permutation of the vertices and since the decomposition of the five-point in space into two polygonal paths is completely determined by the order of the vertices in the first path, we see that, leaving aside automorphisms, there is only one possible decomposition of the Desargues configuration into two mutually inscribed pentagons.

The question of whether, and in how many ways, the Desargues configuration can be considered as a self-inscribed and self-circumscribed decagon, can be settled by the same method. It is

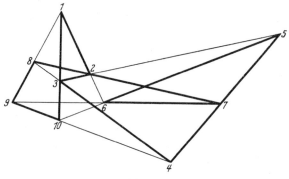

FIG. 140

found that the arrangement of edges in space corresponding to such a decagon can always be chosen as indicated in Fig. 139. Accordingly there is one way, and except for automorphisms only one way, of interpreting the Desargues configuration as a ten-sided polygon inscribed in and circumscribed about itself (Fig. 140). The figure exhibits a certain regularity; if we move along the sides of the decagon from the point 1 to the point 2, from 2 to 3, etc., in order, then one vertex is omitted on each side, and the numbers of the omitted vertices form a sequence in which pairs of successive numbers differ alternately by 1 and 3 (the vertex 5 is omitted on side 23, 8 on 34, 7 on 45, 10 on 56, etc.). Another feature of the decagon revealed by the three-dimensional arrangement is that the sides belong alternately to two mutually inscribed pentagons.

Desargues' configuration is not the only configuration with the symbol (10_3). In fact, there are nine other possibilities for the

schematic table of such a configuration. One of these tables has
the same property as the table for (7_3), namely that its configuration cannot be realized either in the real plane or in terms
of complex coordinates, because its equations are incompatible. On
the other hand, the remaining eight configurations of the form
(10_3), like the configurations (9_3), can all be constructed with a
ruler alone. But they are differentiated from the Desargues configuration by the fact that the last incidence condition is not automatically satisfied in their construction. Thus they do not express
a geometrical theorem and are therefore not as important as the
configuration of Desargues. One of these configurations is drawn
in Fig. 141. It also represents a self-inscribed and self-circumscribed

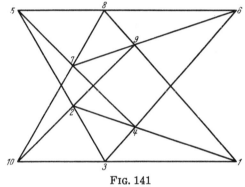

decagon if the points are
taken in the numerical
order given in the figure,
but here the numbers of
the vertices successively
omitted on the sides of
the polygon always differ
by 1. In this arrangement
all the vertices play the
same role, and the sides are
interchangeable with the

Fig. 141

vertices. It follows that the configuration is regular and self-
dual.

§ 20. Comparison of Pascal's and Desargues' Theorems

We have found Desargues' theorem and the last of Pascal's
theorems to be analogous in many ways. Both theorems were
proved by the projection of three-dimensional figures. Both theorems gave rise to configurations, and quite similar configurations
at that, both configurations were regular and self-dual, both could
be constructed with a ruler alone, the last incidence in both
occurred automatically, and both could be regarded as self-
inscribed and self-circumscribed polygons.

Nevertheless there is a fundamental difference between the two
theorems. The space figure used in the proof of Desargues' theorem
can be constructed on the basis of the given axioms for incidence

in space, without the assumption of any additional axioms. The Pascal-Brianchon configuration, on the other hand, was obtained by studying a second-order surface. To be sure, the core of the proof appears to be purely a consideration of the incidence relations between the points, straight lines, and planes of a hexagon in space, but on closer examination it is found that the construction of such hexagons in space is essentially equivalent to the construction of a ruled surface of the second order and that the possibility of such a construction cannot be proved from the axioms of incidence alone.

In the first chapter we introduced the conic sections and quadric surfaces on the basis of metric considerations. It might therefore be thought that Pascal's theorem could not be proved without comparisons of lengths and angles. But the curves and ruled surfaces of the second order can also be generated without the help of metric methods, by using the method of projection. By this method, the points of a given straight line can be mapped into the points of any other straight line in such a way that any three pre-assigned points on the first line go into three pre-assigned points on the second line and all harmonic sets of points on the first line become harmonic sets on the second. The first straight line is then said to be mapped projectively onto the second straight line. The construction of such a mapping (or "projectivity") requires only the axioms of incidence in the plane and in space. But the proof that the mapping is uniquely determined for all the points of the straight lines by the two given conditions—that harmonic sets become harmonic sets and that the mapping of three points is given—requires more than just these axioms. We need for this purpose an axiom of continuity which we shall formulate presently. But once the uniqueness of the projectivity in the given sense is proved, we can define the most general ruled surface of the second order as the surface swept out by a variable straight line that always connects corresponding points in a projectivity of two fixed skew straight lines. It then follows from the uniqueness property of the projectivity that a second family of straight lines also lies on the surface defined in this way. If the straight lines related by the projectivity are not skew but intersecting, then the straight line connecting pairs of corresponding points moves in a plane and envelops a curve of the second order. All the properties of the second-order curves that matter in projective geometry can be derived from this definition.

For the complete comprehension of the concept of continuity, two different axioms are needed. But only one of these, the *Archimedean* axiom, is used in the proof of the uniqueness of the projective mapping. In arithmetical terms, this axiom is formulated as follows: Let a and A be any two positive numbers; then— no matter how small a may be and no matter how large A may be—if we add a to itself a sufficient number of times we can always reach a point after a finite number of steps where the sum exceeds A;

$$a + a + a + \ldots + a > A.$$

This axiom is necessary if it is required to measure one length in terms of another length; the axiom in this form thus constitutes an essential part of the foundation of metric geometry. Independently of metric concepts, we can formulate the axiom as follows:

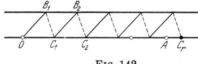

FIG. 142

Let two parallel straight lines be given (as in Fig. 142) and let O and A be two different points on one of them. Draw the line connecting O with an arbitrary point B_1 on the other straight line, and the line connecting B_1 with a point C_1 lying between O and A on the first straight line. Now draw the line parallel to OB_1 through C_1, cutting the other line at a point B_2; then draw the line parallel to B_1C_1 through B_2, cutting the first line at a point C_2, and in this way continue drawing lines parallel to OB_1 and B_1C_1. The Archimedean axiom then states that after a finite number of steps a point C_r on the straight line OA will be reached that does not lie between O and A. In this formulation of the Archimedean axiom we have made use of the notion of a point on a straight line lying between two other points of the straight line. For statements of this sort to be made more precise we need another set of axioms, the axioms of order, which we shall not discuss in detail here. The notion of parallels, on the other hand, was only used to make possible a more concise and readily understood formulation of the axiom. For the purposes of projective geometry it is sufficient that a construction of the kind indicated by Fig. 143 be possible. The figure is obtained from Fig. 142 by a central projection onto another plane.

The axioms of incidence in the plane and in space, together with the axioms of order and the Archimedean axiom, are sufficient to prove the uniqueness of the projectivity that maps three specified points into specified images, albeit the proof is exceedingly lengthy and tedious. From the uniqueness of the projective mapping in the plane we can then prove the last of the theorems of Pascal and Brianchon listed earlier (and the proof proceeds without the aid of any constructions in space).

Desargues' theorem can be proved in space by using only the axioms of incidence. But in order to prove the two-dimensional

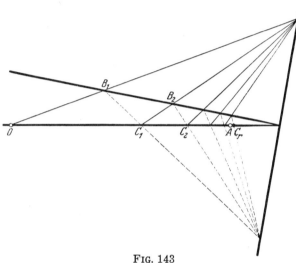

Fig. 143

form of the theorem without three-dimensional constructions, even the axioms of incidence combined with the Archimedean axiom and the axioms of order will not suffice. On the other hand, the axioms of incidence in the plane together with the axioms of order and the axioms of congruence will do, and we can dispense with the Archimedean axiom.

Omitting the axioms of incidence in space affects Pascal's theorem in the same way as it does Desargues', making the plane axioms of incidence, order, and congruence necessary for the proof. Nevertheless a significant difference between the two theorems can also be observed in the plane without the aid of spatial constructions. Pascal's theorem can not be proved from the axioms of incidence together with the validity of Desargues' theorem in the plane.

But Desargues' theorem can be proved from the axioms of incidence in the plane together with Pascal's theorem. We shall prove this for the special case where the Desargues line is the ideal line of the plane. As in the statement of the Archimedean axiom, this additional assumption only serves to make the formulation of the proof shorter and more readily comprehended. Thus we assume the following (see Fig. 144):

The three straight lines AA', BB', CC' pass through a single point O. Furthermore $AB||A'B'$ and $AC||A'C'$. It is to be proved by means of Pascal's last theorem that $BC||B'C'$ follows.

In proof, let us draw the parallel to OB through A, intersecting $A'C'$ at a point L and OC at a point M. Let the straight lines LB' and AB intersect at N. We shall apply Pascal's theorem three times

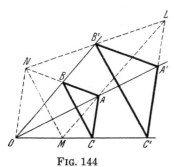

FIG. 144

(From *Grundlagen der Geometrie* by D. Hilbert, 7th ed., p. 111. English translation in prep. (Chelsea Publishing Company).)

to this figure, always using the special form referred to as Pappus' theorem on page 119. First of all, $ONALA'B'$ is a Pascal hexagon since the six points lie alternately on two straight lines. Also $NA||A'B'$ by assumption, and $AL||B'O$ by construction. Hence it follows from Pappus' theorem that the third pair of opposite sides of the hexagon is also parallel, i.e. that $ON||AC$. Next we consider the Pascal hexagon $ONMACB$. Here $ON||AC$ as we have just proved, and $MA||OB$ by assumption. It follows by Pappus' theorem that $NM||CB$. Finally, we consider the Pascal hexagon $ONMLC'B'$. In this hexagon, $ON||LC'$ and $ML||B'O$, and it follows as before that $NM||C'B'$. And since we have just proved in the previous step that $NM||CB$, the proof of our assertion that $BC||B'C'$ is complete.

Any theorems concerned solely with incidence relations in the plane can be derived from the theorems of Desargues and Pascal. And we have now seen that Desargues' theorem is a consequence of Pascal's. Therefore we may say that Pascal's theorem is the only significant theorem on incidence in the plane and that the configuration $(9_3)_1$ thus represents the most important figure in plane geometry.

§ 21. Preliminary Remarks on Configurations in Space

The concept of a configuration can be generalized from the plane to three-dimensional space. A set of points and planes is called a configuration in space if every point is incident with the same number of planes, and every plane with the same number of points. A simple example of such a configuration is furnished by the three-dimensional Desargues theorem. Here we use the same ten points as we did in the corresponding plane configuration. As planes of the configuration we use the two planes of the triangles and the three planes containing the Desargues point and pairs of corresponding sides of the triangles. Then three planes pass through each point, and six points lie on each plane. For the same reason as for plane configurations, the four characteristic numbers for this configuration satisfy the equation $5 \times 6 = 10 \times 3$.

Apart from configurations of points and planes, we can also consider configurations in space which, like plane configurations, consist of points and straight lines, each point being incident with the same number of lines and each line with the same number of points. These two different points of view are often applicable to the same figure. Thus the three-dimensional Desargues figure we have just been considering gives rise to a combination of points and straight lines in space that is essentially identical with the plane Desargues configuration. Analogously, many of the more complicated configurations of points and planes give rise to configurations of points and straight lines consisting of some of the lines in which the planes intersect, together with the points of the original configuration; conversely, a configuration of points and straight lines can often be converted into a configuration of points and planes by adding to it some of the planes common to the intersecting straight lines of the configuration.

In analogy to what we did in the plane, we shall at first confine our attention to configurations in which the number of points equals the number of planes, so that we are dealing with a configuration of p points and p planes. If every point is incident with n planes it follows for the same reason as before that every plane of the configuration must also be incident with n points. We shall denote such a configuration by the symbol (p_n).

In order to exclude the trivial cases, we must take n to be at least 4. For $p \leq 7$, a configuration (p_4) cannot exist. But for

$p = 8$, five different tables can be set up, and all of them can be realized geometrically. One of these configurations (8_4), the so-called Moebius configuration, is geometrically important because it satisfies the last incidence condition automatically and thus expresses a geometric theorem. This configuration consists of two mutually inscribed and circumscribed tetrahedra.

Going on to higher configurations, the number of possibilities keeps growing, and it soon becomes impossible to get an over-all view of them. Thus there are no less than 26 configurations of the type (9_4) that can be realized geometrically. Accordingly, we shall examine in greater detail only two three-dimensional configurations that are particularly important and play a role in other parts of mathematics as well. These are Reye's configuration and Schaefli's double six.

§ 22. Reye's Configuration

Reye's configuration consists of twelve points and twelve planes. It embodies a theorem of projective geometry, so that the last incidence always follows automatically, regardless of the positions of the points and planes. For the time being, however, we shall arrange the points in a special symmetrical order, so as to facilitate the visualization of the configuration.

We shall use as points of the configuration the eight vertices of a cube together with the center of the cube and each of the three ideal points where four parallel edges of the cube meet (Fig. 145). As planes of the configuration we shall use the planes of the six faces and each of the six diagonal planes passing through a pair of opposite edges. In the figure defined in this way, there are six points lying on each plane: four vertices and two ideal points on each of the planes containing a face of the cube, and four vertices, the center of the cube, and an ideal point on each of the diagonal planes. There are six planes through each point: the six diagonal planes pass through the center of the cube, three face planes and three diagonal planes through each vertex, and four face planes and two diagonal planes through each of the ideal points. Thus we have indeed constructed a configuration of points and planes, and its symbol is (12_6).

But the construction may also be interpreted as being a configuration of points and straight lines. To this end, we select some of the straight lines of intersection of the planes, namely the twelve edges and the four diagonals of the cube. There are three points of the configuration on each of these straight lines: two vertices and one ideal point on each edge, two vertices and the center on each diagonal. Furthermore, there are four straight lines through each point: three edges and one diagonal through each vertex, four diagonals through the center of the cube, and four edges through

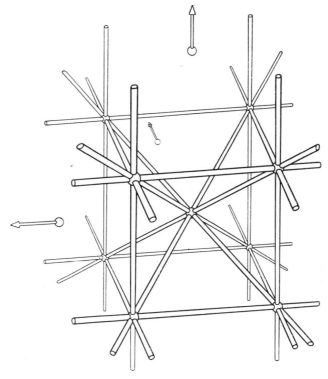

FIG. 145

each ideal point. Hence the points and straight lines of Reye's configuration form a configuration of the type $(12_4 16_3)$.

We can also see, if we count them, that three planes pass through each of the lines and that four lines lie on each plane. The straight lines on any one of the planes together with the six points of the configuration lying in the plane constitute a complete quadrilateral.

Reye's configuration appears in various geometrical contexts. An example is the system of centers of similitude of four spheres, which we shall now study.

The term *centers of similitude* of two circles or spheres denotes the two points that divide the line joining the centers of the circles or spheres in the ratio of their radii. The point on the segment that lies between the centers is called the *internal* center, the one on the extension of the segment the *external* center of similitude. If we are dealing with circles, and each of them lies outside the other, the internal center of similitude is the point of

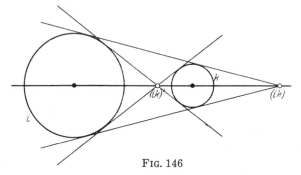

FIG. 146

intersection of the two straight lines tangent to the circles on opposite sides, and the external center of similitude is the point of intersection of the straight lines tangent to the circles on the same side

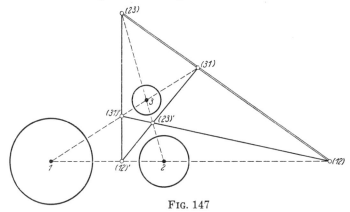

FIG. 147

(see Fig. 146). By rotating this figure about the straight line containing the centers we get an analogous property relating the centers of similitude of two spheres with common tangents to the spheres. (But in addition the spheres have many common tangents that do not pass through a center of similitude.) We shall use the symbols (ik) and (ik') respectively for the external and internal centers of similitude of two circles or spheres i and k.

Let us now consider three circles or spheres, 1, 2, and 3. They have three internal centers of similitude and three external centers of similitude, making six in all. We shall assume that the centers of the circles or spheres are not collinear but form a triangle; no two of the centers of similitude can then coincide, and the six can not all be collinear. By a theorem of Monge, the three external centers of similitude, (12), (23), and (31), are collinear, and each external center of similitude is collinear with the two internal centers of similitude that belong to different pairs of circles or spheres, e.g. (31) with (12)′ and (23)′ (see Fig. 147).[1] Accordingly, all the centers of similitude lie on four straight lines, which are called the axes of similitude of 1, 2, and 3. Monge's theorem may be summarized by saying that the centers of similitude and axes of similitude constitute the six points and four lines of a complete quadrilateral in which the centers of 1, 2, and 3 form the diagonal triangle. We shall denote the axes of similitude by the following symbols: (123) for the straight line containing the external centers of similitude, (1′23) for the straight line on which (23), (12)′, and (13)′ lie, etc.

With this preparation we turn to the consideration of four spheres 1, 2, 3, 4 whose centers are not all in one plane, so that, moreover, no three of the centers can be on one straight line (cf. Fig. 148, p. 140). We shall see that all the centers of similitude and axes of similitude of these spheres collectively constitute the points and straight lines of a Reye configuration. Since six different pairs can be selected from the spheres 1, 2, 3, 4, and since each pair gives rise to an external and an internal center of similitude, there are twelve centers of similitude in all. Also we have the right number, 16, of axes of similitude, for there are four different ways we can select three out of the four spheres, and each set of three spheres gives rise to four different axes of similitude, e.g. (123), (1′23), (12′3), and (123′). Each axis is incident with three points, e.g. (123) is incident with (12), (23), and (13). Similarly, every point is incident with four different axes, e.g. (12)

---

[1] *Proof:* Let the radii of 1, 2, and 3 be equal to r_1, r_2, and r_3, respectively. Then the external centers of similitude divide the sides of the triangle formed by the centers in the ratios $-\dfrac{r_1}{r_2}, \; -\dfrac{r_2}{r_3}, \; -\dfrac{r_3}{r_1}$. The product of these ratios is -1, and it follows by a theorem of Menelaus that the external centers of similitude are collinear. If two of the external centers of similitude are replaced by the corresponding internal centers of similitude, two of the ratios change their sign. The product is therefore still -1, so that we once more have three collinear points.

is incident with (123), (123′), (124), and (124′), and (12)′ with
(1′23), (12′3), (1′24), and (12′4).

We thus see that the centers and axes of similitude do indeed
form a configuration and that its type is $(12_4, 16_3)$. To see that
it is identical with Reye's configuration, we need to find twelve suitable planes. First we take the four planes containing the centers
of three spheres each. The points and axes lying on any one of
these planes form a complete quadrilateral, as in Reye's configuration. To get eight more planes with this property, we simply take
all the remaining planes spanned by any two axes that intersect at
a point of the configuration. Two axes of this kind must certainly
belong to different number triples, for, any two axes associated with
the same set of three numbers, e.g. (123) and (1′23), define the
plane containing the centers of three spheres (1, 2, and 3 in our
case), so that nothing new is obtained. Let us begin with two axes
containing only external centers of similitude, e.g. (123) and
(124). They span a plane that contains (12). In addition, this
plane contains the other four points of those axes, i.e. (13), (23),
(14), and (24). But (23) and (24) also lie on the axis (234)
which contains as well the remaining external center of similitude
(34). Hence all six external centers of similitude lie on the single
plane we have been considering. This plane also contains the
remaining "external" axes (134) and (234); thus it is incident
with six points and four straight lines, as it should be. We proceed
to the case of two intersecting axes one of which is "external" and
one "internal" and which are associated with two different number
triples. Since their point of intersection must be an external center
and since all the numbers play the same role, we may pick the axes
(123) and (124′) as a representative pair. Apart from their point
intersection, (12), these axes contain the points (13), (23),
(14)′, and (24)′. By the same reasoning as before, we see that
the axes (134′) and (234′) and the point (34)′ are also in the
plane of (123) and (124′). Thus the three internal centers of
similitude defined by the sphere 4 together with the three other
spheres are in a single plane with the three external centers of similitude of the spheres 1, 2, and 3. There must be altogether four
planes of this kind. Only the case based on two intersecting internal
axes of similitude remains to be considered. Of course the last plane
considered above contains three internal axes which intersect in

pairs; but the points of intersection are always internal centers of similitude, so that the case of two axes intersecting at an external center of similitude is still open. Let us begin, then, with two internal axes, say (123′) and (124′), which intersect at an external center of similitude—(12) in this case. Apart from the point of intersection, the plane of these axes contains the points (13)′, (23)′, (14)′, and (24)′. Hence this plane also contains the axes (1′34) and (2′34) and the point (34). Thus there are four internal axes of similitude in this plane, and it meets the opposite edges 1, 2 and 3, 4 of the tetrahedron 1, 2, 3, 4 at the external centers of similitude and the remaining edges at the internal centers of similitude. There are three planes of this type, since a tetrahedron has three pairs of opposite edges. Thus we have obtained altogether 1 + 4 + 3 = 8 planes.

For the sake of clarity, we shall set up the two tables that give the incidence relations between the points and the planes and between the points and the lines, respectively. The faces of the tetrahedron are labelled I, II, III, and IV, where I is the face opposite the point 1. The plane of the external centers of similitude is called e_a, the four planes containing three external and three internal centers are called e_1, e_2, e_3, e_4 respectively, according to the number of the exceptional sphere, and the three remaining planes are denoted by (12, 34), (13, 24), and (14, 23) respectively, according to the exceptional pair of opposite edges of the tetrahedron. For the sake of brevity, parentheses are omitted in the notation for points and straight lines.

					Planes							
	I	*II*	*III*	*IV*	e_a	e_1	e_2	e_3	e_4	(12,34)	(13,24)	(14,23)
Points	23	13	12	12	12	23	13	12	12	12	13	14
	24	14	14	13	13	24	14	14	13	34	24	23
	34	34	24	23	14	34	34	24	23	13′	12′	12′
	23′	13′	12′	12′	23	12′	12′	13′	14′	14′	14′	13′
	24′	14′	14′	13′	24	13′	23′	23′	24′	23′	23′	24′
	34′	34′	24′	23′	34	14′	24′	34′	34′	24′	34′	34′

					Planes							
	I	*II*	*III*	*IV*	e_a	e_1	e_2	e_3	e_4	(12,34)	(13,24)	(14,23)
Lines	234	134	124	123	123	234	134	124	123	123′	12′3	1′23
	2′34	1′34	1′24	1′23	124	1′23	12′3	123′	124′	124′	1′24	12′4
	23′4	13′4	12′4	12′3	134	1′24	12′4	13′4	134′	1′34	134′	13′4
	234′	134′	124′	123′	234	1′34	2′34	23′4	234′	2′34	23′4	234′

The configuration is depicted in Fig. 148.[2] That this configuration is identical with that of Fig. 145 becomes manifest on moving
the three points (12), (12)′, and (34) to infinity in mutually perpendicular directions; the three points then assume the positions of the

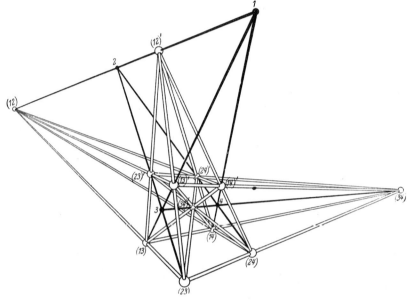

FIG. 148

ideal points of the configuration given in Fig. 145. The eight points
(13), (14), (23), (24), (13)′, (14)′, (23)′, and (24)′ become
the vertices of the cube, and (34)′ becomes the center of the cube.
But the points 1 and 2 also move to infinity. In order to find the
four spheres belonging to
Fig. 145 it is consequently
necessary to extend the
definition of center of similitude by the addition of
limiting cases. First, the

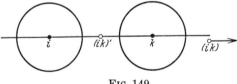

FIG. 149

external center of similitude of two equal circles or spheres must
be defined as the ideal point on the line connecting the centers (see
Fig. 149). Furthermore, the centers of similitude of a sphere k

---

[2] Viewed as a *plane* figure, Fig. 148 represents a plane configuration of type
$(12_4 16_3)$ consisting of the centers and axes of similitude of four coplanar circles.
The centers of the circles are also at 1, 2, 3, and 4, and the radii may be chosen
to be the same as in the three-dimensional case.

and a plane e (Fig. 150) must be defined as the extremities (ke) and $(ke)'$ of the diameter of k that is perpendicular to e. For, if e is replaced by a family of spheres K tangent to e at the point P where the extension of the diameter meets e, it is seen that the centers of similitude of k and K approach (ke) and $(ke)'$ as the diameter of K increases to infinity. Finally we consider the case

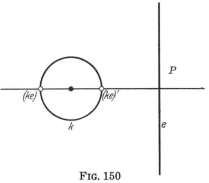

of two planes e and f intersecting in a straight line g (Fig. 151). The centers of similitude must be defined in this case as the ideal points having directions that are perpendicular to g and bisect the two angles formed by e and f. This definition too may be justified by a limiting process, as follows: Replace g by the circle of inter-

FIG. 150

section of two congruent spheres tangent at a fixed point of g to e and f respectively, and then let the radius of the spheres increase to infinity.

With these definitions, we are in a position to interpret Reye's configuration in its original version also, as a system of centers of similitude. Let the spheres 3 and 4 have their centers at the midpoints of the front and back faces of the cube in Fig. 145. Let the radii·be equal and of such length that each sphere goes through the four corners of the face on which its center lies. Let 1 and 2 be any two planes that are respectively perpendicular to the two diagonals of the faces under consideration.

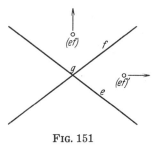

FIG. 151

Then the points of the configuration are the centers of similitude of 1, 2, 3, and 4, arranged in the same order as in Fig. 148.

Instead of this limiting case, we may consider the configuration based on four equal spheres with their centers at the vertices of a regular tetrahedron. Here the external centers of similitude must be at the ideal points of the six edges of the tetrahedron, so that the ideal plane belongs to the configuration and constitutes, in our notation, the plane e_a. The internal centers of similitude are the mid-

points of the edges; they form the six vertices of a regular octahedron (see Fig. 152). All the face-planes of the octahedron belong
to the configuration, being the face-planes I, II, III, and IV, of the
tetrahedron and the planes called e_1, e_2, e_3, and e_4 in our notation.
The three remaining planes of the configuration are the three planes
of symmetry of the octahedron. The straight lines of the configuration are the four ideal lines of the face-planes of the tetrahedron

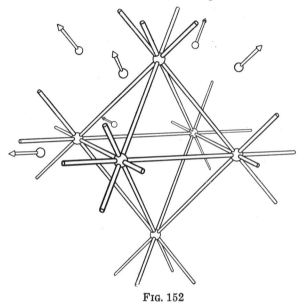

FIG. 152

(external axes of similitude) and the twelve edges of the octahedron
(internal axes of similitude).

In the second chapter we have already pointed out how the cube
and the octahedron are related. In accordance with § 19, we may
say that the cube and the octahedron correspond dually to each
other. Similarly, it can be shown more generally that the points
and planes of Fig. 152 correspond dually to the planes and points
of Fig. 145; the vertices and faces of the cube correspond to the
faces and vertices respectively of the octahedron, the center of the
cube and the six planes through it correspond to the ideal plane
and the six points on it in Fig. 152, and the three ideal points
associated with the cube correspond to the three planes of symmetry
of the octahedron.[3]   It follows that Reye's configuration of points

---

[3] This correspondence is produced by a polarity with respect to the inscribed
sphere of the cube.

and planes is self-dual. Of course the two dual Reye configurations obtained from the cube and octahedron look quite different, but for the purposes of projective geometry, all Reye configurations must be considered as identical.[4]

We shall now show that Reye's configuration also has the other important property of symmetry that we observed in some plane configurations, viz., that it is regular. This is by no means evident from the foregoing discussion. Indeed, the planes belong to four different classes relative to the system of centers of similitude, and in the realization of the configuration either by a cube or an octahedron, both the points and the planes play different sorts of roles. In the following section, we shall obtain Reye's configuration by a method that reveals the equivalence of all the elements. To this end, we need to learn more about the regular polyhdra of three-dimensional and four-dimensional space. For, the figures of four-dimensional space can be projected into three-dimensional space in the same way that the figures of three-dimensional space can be projected into a plane, and a suitable projection of one of the four-dimensional figures gives us Reye's configuration.

§ 23. Regular Polyhedra in Three and Four Dimensions, and their Projections

In Chap. II we listed the five regular polyhedra of three-dimensional space. Among these, the tetrahedron plays an anomalous role in that it is self-dual, whereas the four remaining polyhedra are mutually dual in pairs—the octahedron with the cube, and the dodecahedron with the icosahedron. Possibly this singularity of the tetrahedron is connected with a second phenomenon that distinguishes it from the other polyhedra; the others are symmetrical with respect to a point, which means that the vertices come in pairs that are symmetrical about the center, and the same is true for the edges and the faces (e.g. the straight line connecting any vertex of a cube with the center meets the cube at a second vertex). The tetrahedron, however, is not symmetrical with respect to a point, (does not have "central symmetry") ; the straight line connecting

---

[4] We obtain a projective generalization of the octahedron by starting with any system of projective coordinates in space; in every case the unit points on the six coordinate axes and the six points of intersection of these axes with the unit plane are the points of a Reye configuration.

a vertex with the center cuts the tetrahedron at the midpoint of one of its faces.

A study similar to the one made at the end of the second chapter proves that the number of regular polytopes[1] that are possible in four-dimensional space is also finite and is equal to six.[2] Of course the boundary of such a polytope comprises three-dimensional regions (called *cells*) in addition to points, edges, and plane faces. Just as we stipulated for regular polyhedra that the faces be regular polygons, so we must stipulate for the regular polytopes in four dimensions that the boundary cells be regular polyhedra. The polytope is called an *n-cell* if it is bounded by n polyhedra. The essential data for the regular polytopes of four-space are given in the following table:

4-Dimensional Space

		Number and Type of Boundary Polyhedra	Number of Vertices	Duality
1.	5-cell	5 Tetrahedra	5	self-dual
2.	8-cell	8 Cubes	16	} mutually dual
3.	16-cell	16 Tetrahedra	8	
4.	24-cell	24 Octahedra	24	self-dual
5.	120-cell	120 Dodecahedra	600	} mutually dual
6.	600-cell	600 Tetrahedra	120	

The duality relations listed in the last column can be readily deduced from the table. For in four-space, points correspond dually to three-dimensional spaces and straight lines to planes.

We see from the table that the 5-cell is analogous to the tetrahedron, while the 8-cell, 16-cell, 120-cell, and 600-cell take the place of the cube, octahedron, dodecahedron, and icosahedron, respectively. The 24-cell has a singular role; it is not only self-dual but also centrally symmetric, while the other self-dual polytope, the regular 5-cell, shares the property of its analogue, the regular tetrahedron, of having no symmetry about a point.

---

[1] The polyhedra of n-dimensional space for $n \geq 4$ are called *polytopes* (or, in the earlier literature, *polyhedroids*). [*Trans.*]

[2] Cf. the book *Die Vierte Dimension* by H. de Vries (Leipzig and Berlin, 1926).

Cf., also, *Regular Polytopes* by H. S. M. Coxeter (Methuen & Co. Ltd., London, 1947) and the last chapter of *Geometry of Four Dimensions* by H. P. Manning (MacMillan, New York, 1914). [*Trans.*]

Analogous studies have also been made for spaces of higher dimensionalities. Here we find a greater simplicity and regularity, as only three regular polytopes can be found in any such space. We again give the most important data in the form of a table.

n-Dimensional Space, $n \geqq 5$

	Number and Type of Boundary $(n-1)$-Dimensional Cells		Number of Vertices	Duality
1. $(n+1)$-cell	$n+1$	n-cells	$n+1$	self-dual
2. $2n$-cell	$2n$	$(2n-2)$-cells	2^n	⎱ mutually dual
3. 2^n-cell	2^n	n-cells	$2n$	⎰

The three-dimensional polyhedra corresponding to these three types of polytopes are the tetrahedron, the cube, and the octahedron ($n+1 = 4$, $2n = 6$, $2^n = 8$). The four-dimensional analogues are the 5-cell, the 8-cell, and the 16-cell. Thus the dodecahedron and the icosahedron of three-space as well as the 24-cell, 120-cell, and 600-cell of four-space have no analogues in spaces of higher dimensionality.

We shall now study the projections of the regular polyhedra and polytopes into spaces whose dimensionality is smaller by one than that of the spaces in which the polyhedra and polytopes lie. We begin with the projections of the regular polyhedra into a plane. Of course, the appearance of these projections will vary greatly with the choice of the center of projection and of the image plane. In Figs. 95 through 99 of page 91 we used parallel projections, i.e. projections with the center at an ideal point. This has the advantage of representing parallel lines by parallel lines. But it has the disadvantage of making pieces of faces overlap. The disadvantage can be eliminated by moving the center of projection to a point very close to one of the faces. For the sake of symmetry we move it to a point at a small distance from the center of one of the faces and project into the plane of that face. In this way the five regular polyhedra give us the projections drawn in Figs. 153 through 157. This is the way we see the polyhedra when we remove one of the faces and look at the interior through the hole.

If the center of projection is located on the surface of the polyhedron, the faces passing through it appear as straight lines, so that the image becomes quite unsymmetrical.

If the center of projection is located inside the polyhedron, the image is significantly altered; then it must extend to infinity irrespective of the choice of the image plane. This is so because every plane through the center of projection intersects the polyhedron. This applies, in particular, to the plane going through the center

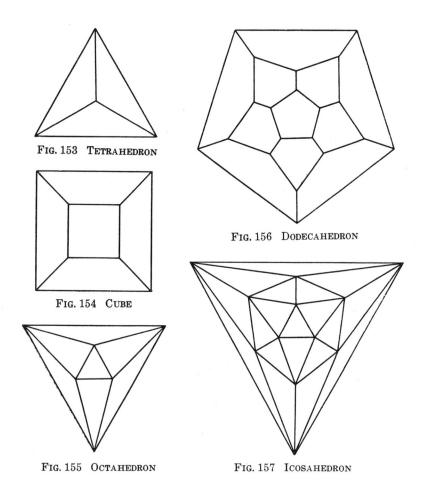

Fig. 153 Tetrahedron

Fig. 154 Cube

Fig. 155 Octahedron

Fig. 156 Dodecahedron

Fig. 157 Icosahedron

which is parallel to the image plane and which therefore gives rise to the ideal points of the projection (cf. p. 114). Nevertheless, this type of projection leads to a phenomenon of geometric interest in the special case where the center of projection is at the center of the polyhedron. For, in this case—and in this case only—the bundle of rays through the center is arranged symmetrically. As was already noted on page 116, the bundle of rays can be looked on as a model of the projective plane by interpreting the straight lines of the bundle as "points" and the planes of the bundle as "straight lines." Thus the regular polyhedra induce regular partitions of the projective plane. But only in the case of centrally symmetric polyhedra can this partition cover the projective plane simply; in the case of the tetrahedron, every straight line through the center yields two different image points corresponding to the two points where it meets the surface of the polyhedron, so that the projective plane is covered twice. But on all other regular polyhedra every pair of diametrically opposite elements produces one single piece of the projective plane. If we consider the intersection of the bundle of rays with a plane, i.e. if a projection in the

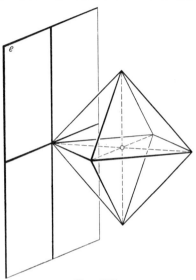

FIG. 158

proper sense is under consideration, we cannot preserve all the symmetry. The image is particularly simple, however, if its plane is chosen so as to contain a vertex of the polyhedron and to be perpendicular at that vertex to the line connecting the vertex with the center (see Fig. 158 for the octahedron). Figs. 159 through 163 show the five projections obtained in this way. One of the regions extending to infinity is shaded in each diagram. In the projection of the tetrahedron, the image plane is covered twice. In the remaining figures, every polygon in

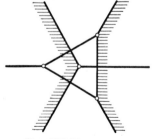

FIG. 159 TETRAHEDRON

the image plane represents exactly two diametrically opposite faces of the polyhedron.

Another series of simple figures is obtained from the symmetrical polyhedra by using a face plane as image plane, as shown in Fig. 164 for the cube. (For the tetrahedron this does not give us a new figure.)   The projections are shown in Figs. 165 through 168.[3]

Using analogous methods of projection, we can depict the regular polytopes of four-space by figures in three-space. Parallel projec-

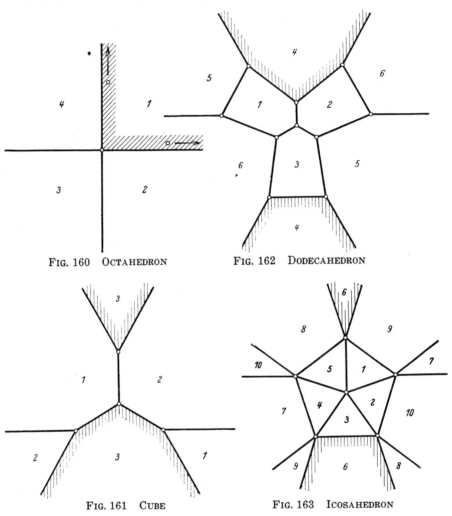

FIG. 160   OCTAHEDRON   FIG. 162   DODECAHEDRON

FIG. 161   CUBE   FIG. 163   ICOSAHEDRON

tion is not found to be suitable, as it represents the boundary poly-hedra of the polytopes by polyhedra in space which partly overlap and intersect each other. On the other hand, the procedure followed in obtaining Figs. 153 through 157 can be used to give us clear

---

[3] In this case, the projection of the octahedron is equivalent to the division of the plane into four triangles by a projective coordinate system.

pictures of the four-dimensional polytopes.   The boundary polyhedra of the polytope are represented by a set of polyhedra in space

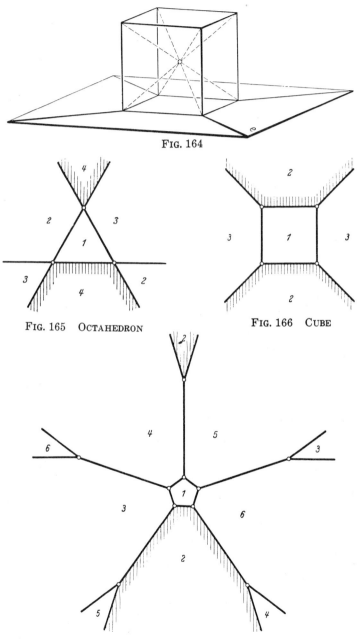

Fig. 164

Fig. 165   Octahedron

Fig. 166   Cube

Fig. 167   Dodecahedron

of which one plays a special role and is filled up simply by the others. If these models are in turn projected into the plane, we get

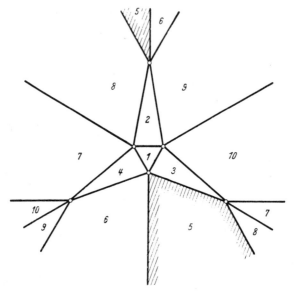

FIG. 168   Icosahedron

four pictures as shown in Figs. 169 through 172. In Fig. 172 it may be ascertained, though somewhat laboriously, that the large octahedron is filled by 23 smaller octahedra (which are of four different forms) making 24 poly-hedra in all. The figures for the 120-cell and the 600-cell would get too confusing.

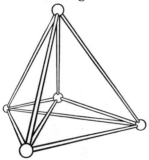

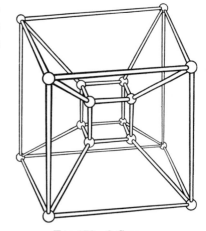

FIG. 169   5-Cell   FIG. 170   8-Cell

If the center of projection is moved to the center of the polytope, the result has to be a regular partition of the projective space.

We cannot produce a model for the projective space that is as symmetrical as the bundle of lines representing the projective plane; for, this would involve consideration of a four-dimensional figure. It is necessary, therefore, to single out a particular three-space as image space, and some of the symmetry is lost in the process. But in order to preserve part, at any rate, of the symmetry, we let the image space assume positions analogous to those of the image plane in the case where the dimensionality is one less: either we use one of the boundary spaces, in analogy to the arrangement of Fig. 164,

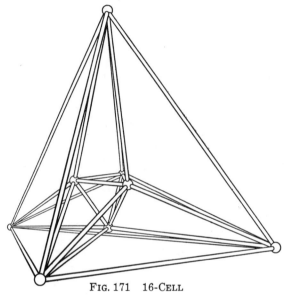

FIG. 171   16-CELL

or we choose a space passing through one of the vertices of the polytope and having the position corresponding to that of the image plane in Fig. 158. In the first case, the boundary polyhedron we select will be reproduced without any distortion, because it is in the image space to begin with; in the second case, the projection is symmetrical with respect to the chosen vertex, which is its own image. First we shall consider the pictures of the 16-cell and the 8-cell obtained by these two methods of projection (Figs. 173 and 174).[4] Here the space is partitioned into eight and four parts respectively, and each part corresponds to two diametrically opposite boundary cells of the polytope. In Fig. 173a, the three-dimensional seg-

---

[4] This method of projection is not suitable for the 5-cell, as this polytope does not have central symmetry.

ments that extend to infinity are of two different forms. Four of
them have one boundary face (e.g. 1, 3, 4) that is wholly confined
to the finite part of space and from which they extend across the
ideal plane to the opposite vertex (e.g. 2). On the other hand, three

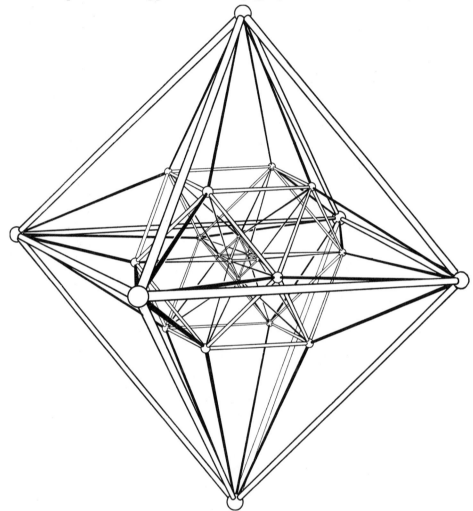

Fig. 172   24-Cell

of the regions have a pair of opposite edges that are finite (e.g. 1, 2,
and 3, 4), but no faces that do not extend across infinitely distant
elements. In Fig. 173b, the ideal plane itself is a boundary plane.
We note that the 16-cell leads to familiar partitions of space—the
division into octants by a projective or a Cartesian coordinate

system. In the representation of the 8-cell shown in Fig. 174a, all
the regions that extend to infinity are of the same form. In Fig.

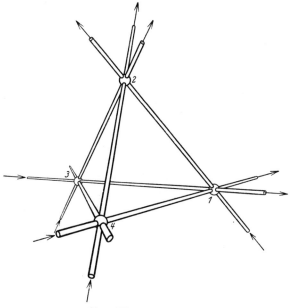

Fig. 173a   16-Cell

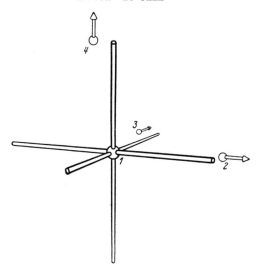

Fig. 173b   16-Cell

174b, arrows marks off the edges of the region that corresponds to
the finite cube of Fig. 174a; the edges of this region include the

finite edges containing the point 1 with the exception of the edge 1, 6.

We next apply the same two methods of projection to the 24-cell. The results are shown in Figs. 175 and 176. We thus get a partition of the space into twelve octahedra, all of which, with the exception

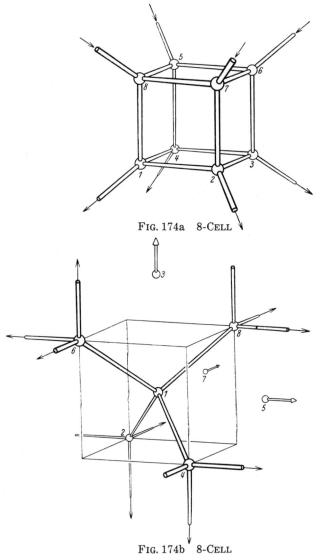

Fig. 174a   8-Cell

Fig. 174b   8-Cell

of the octahedron in the center of Fig. 175, extend to infinity. It is seen that Figs. 175 and 176 reproduce the two symmetrical forms of Reye's configuration that we studied in the preceding sec-

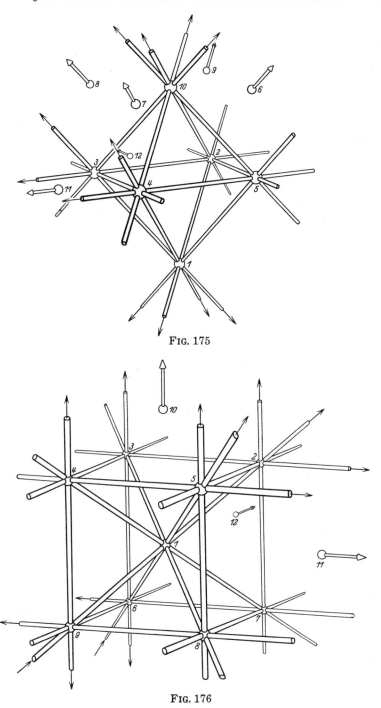

FIG. 175

FIG. 176

tion.[5] We see from the finite octahedron in Fig. 175 that the planes of the configuration serve both as the boundary planes and as the planes of symmetry of the twelve octahedra. A closer study reveals the underlying reason for this; a complete quadrilateral divides the

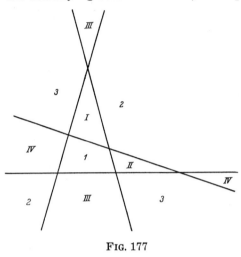

FIG. 177

projective plane into three quadrangles and four triangles (in Fig. 177, the quadrangles 1, 2, 3 and the triangles I, II, III, IV). In Reye's configuration the straight lines partition each of the planes in this way; and since the faces of the octahedra are triangles, while the planes of symmetry intersect the octahedra in quadrangles, it is seen that each plane of the configuration serves as symmetry plane in three octahedra and as common boundary in 2·4 octahedra, while one of the twelve octahedra is not incident with it; thus the ideal plane is a configuration plane in Fig. 175, and one of the octahedra is located in the finite part of the space.[6]

---

[5] We had seen there that the two figures are related by a polarity with respect to a sphere. Now we see them as projections of one and the same four-dimensional figure each of which can be changed into the other by moving the three-dimensional image space.

[6] In analogy to the three planes of symmetry of the octahedron which pass through the center and intersect the boundary in a square, the 24-cell has twelve three-dimensional spaces of symmetry that pass through its center and intersect it in a cubo-octahedron. (The cubo-octahedron is illustrated in Fig. 178; a cubo-octahedron is also marked out in Fig. 172.) In the projection we are studying, the spaces of symmetry,

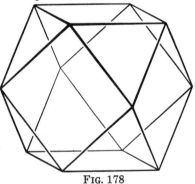

FIG. 178

like all spaces containing the center of the polytope, become planes. And these planes are precisely the planes of the Reye configuration. The three diametrically opposite pairs of squares and the four diametrically opposite pairs of equilateral triangles of the cubo-octahedron correspond to the three quadrilaterals and four triangles in each plane of Reye's configuration.

Fig. 176 is simpler than Fig. 175 in that only two different kinds of octahedra occur in Fig. 176 (where six octahedra are congruent with the octahedron 1, 2, 3, 4, 5, 10 and the other six with 2, 5, 6, 9, 10, 11) while three different kinds of octahedra are present in Fig. 175—here one of the octahedra is regular, in three of them the ideal plane is a plane of symmetry (e.g., 1, 6, 7, 8, 9, 10), and in eight of them the ideal plane belongs to the boundary (e.g., 3, 4, 7, 8, 10, 11).

From this approach to the configuration the assertion made at the end of the last section follows immediately: *Reye's configuration is regular.*

The foregoing discussion suggests the idea of projecting the n-dimensional regular polytopes onto a space of the lowest possible dimensionality, i.e. onto a straight line. Let us study the projection of the n-dimensional cube onto one of its principal diagonals by the method of orthogonal parallel projection. The extremities A and B of such a diagonal are projected into themselves. Let us call the images of the other vertices of the cube $V_1, V_2, \ldots$ in the order of their positions on AB beginning with the point nearest to A. From A there emanate n edges, all forming the same angle with AB; hence all their endpoints must be projected into the point V_1 on AB. Furthermore, every edge of the cube is parallel to one of the edges through A, and it follows that the distance $V_k V_{k+1}$ between consecutive points is always equal to the distance $A V_1$ and is thus constant. Accordingly, the principal diagonal is divided into equal segments. It can be shown that there are exactly n of these segments and that the point V_k is the image of $_nC_k$ vertices for all k between 1 and $n-1$, where $_nC_k$ is the well-known symbol denoting the binomial coefficients. For, V_k is the image of all those vertices, and only those, that can be connected with A by k, but not by less than k, edges of the cube, and we see, by counting, that there are exactly $_nC_k$ such vertices. In the case of the square and of the ordinary (three-dimensional) cube, these facts can be readily verified.

§ 24. Enumerative Methods of Geometry

The last three-dimensional configuration that we shall consider is Schläfli's double-six. The study of this configuration leads us to

a special geometrical method called enumerative geometry. We
shall discuss the method first, because we wish to avoid interrupting
the study of the double-six and also because the enumerative
methods are of great intrinsic interest.

The plane contains infinitely many straight lines and infinitely
many circles. In order to characterize the multiplicity of all straight
lines in the plane, we begin by fixing a Cartesian coordinate system
in the plane. Then a straight line is in general completely determined by the sign and magnitude of its two intercepts with the
coordinate axes. Hence any straight line—with exceptions we shall
mention presently—can be analytically defined by two numbers.
The straight lines that are parallel to one of the axes can also be
included in this scheme by assigning the value infinity to the
appropriate intercept. On the other hand, all the straight lines
through the origin, and they only, are not defined by the intercepts;
all of them give us the same data, namely zero, for both intercepts.

The straight lines that do not pass through the origin are said
to form a two-parameter family; this means that every member
of the family is determined by two numbers (the "parameters" of
the family) and that a continuous change in the parameters is
accompanied by a continuous change in the entity defined by them.
According to this definition, the straight lines through the origin
form a one-parameter family, as they can be determined by the
angle that they form with one of the axes. Now it is usual to think
of a two-parameter family as being, roughly speaking, not significantly enlarged by the addition of a one-parameter family which
can be continuously imbedded into the first family. In this sense
the set of *all* straight lines in the plane is also called a two-parameter
family. We shall soon recognize the usefulness of this point of view.

The straight lines in the plane can also be determined in a variety
of other ways, e.g., by a point through which they pass and the
angle they make with an arbitrary fixed straight line. Since it
takes two coordinates to define a point in the plane, we need altogether three parameters to characterize a straight line in this
manner. However, the defining point may be picked arbitrarily on
the straight line, and the points of a straight line obviously form
a one-parameter family. We find much the same phenomenon when
we define a straight line by two of its points. We need four parameters in this case, but a two-parameter family of pairs of points

defines one and the same straight line. To get the correct number of parameters it will therefore be necessary to subtract two parameters in the latter example, or one parameter in the former; then we find, as we did by the first method, that the straight lines of the plane form a two-parameter family. This procedure, which is only sketched here, can be given a precise analytic formulation, and it can then be proved that the number of parameters associated with a family of geometrical figures is independent of the way in which the parameters are chosen. By using the symbol ∞ we can write this kind of argument more concisely. We shall say that there are ∞^2 straight lines in the plane, ∞^1 points on a straight line, and ∞^2 pairs of points on a straight line. In this way, enumeration becomes analogous to dividing one power of a number by another; to get the correct "number" ∞^2 of straight lines in the plane, we must "divide" the "number" ∞^4 of pairs of points in the plane by the "number" ∞^2 of pairs of points on a straight line.

Let us apply the procedure to the characterization of the size of the family of all circles in the plane. A circle is defined by its center and radius, i.e. by three numbers, and at the same time only one such number-triple is associated with every circle. The plane thus contain ∞^3 circles. Since the family of all straight lines in the plane has only two parameters and every straight line may be considered as a limiting case of a circle, the family of all circles *and* straight lines also has three parameters. This is in accord with the fact that through any three points of the plane one circle or one straight line can be drawn, as there are ∞^6 triples of points, and any one curve contains ∞^3 of them. Similarly, it can be shown that in any n-parameter family there is always a curve that passes through an arbitrarily chosen n-tuple of points of the plane but, in general, none that passes through $n + 1$ arbitrary points of the plane. This is only true, however, if all the limiting cases are included in the family, just as a unique correspondence between circles and number-triples becomes possible only on including straight lines as limiting cases in the family of circles. To make a rigorous formulation of these statements possible, analytic and algebraic methods are necessary, and in particular it is necessary to consider the imaginary elements along with the real ones.

Let us find the "number," in the above sense, of all the conics. An ellipse is defined by its two foci (four parameters) along with the constant sum of the distances from these points, i.e. by five parameters, and every ellipse is associated with only one such set of five numbers. Hence there are ∞^5 ellipses in the plane. Similarly it is shown that there are ∞^5 hyperbolas in the plane. The ellipses can also be fixed by the lengths of the two axes along with the position of their center and the direction of the major axis; this makes five parameters again, consonant with the general theory. It follows that the family of all parabolas in a plane has four parameters, for, by the construction given on page 4, we get the parabolas from the ellipses by a limiting process in which a one-parameter family of ellipses always determines a single parabola and each ellipse belongs to finitely many—two, to be specific—of the families.

If the values given for the lengths of the two axes of an ellipse are equal, we get a circle. At this point it would be easy to come to the erroneous conclusion that there are ∞^4 circles, rather than ∞^3, for if the axes are to be equal, we are still left with the choice of four numbers. The contradiction is resolved on noting that the equality of the axes makes it unnecessary to know the directions of the axes, since any given pair of perpendicular diameters of a circle can be regarded as constituting the limiting case of the axes of ellipses.

The above discussion does not entitle us to expect that we can always draw an ellipse through an arbitrary set of five points in the plane. At best, this might be the case if the ellipses are supplemented by inclusion of their limiting cases, the parabolas and the circles. It is found, however, that the hyperbolas must be included as well. The totality of all the conics in the plane, i.e. the set of all hyperbolas, parabolas, ellipses, circles, pairs of straight lines, and doubly-counted straight lines, constitutes a single family in the sense of enumerative geometry. In accordance with the above, this must be a five-parameter family; for, each of the different types of conics belongs to a family with five parameters or less. For the totality of conics it is indeed true that a member of this family passes through any set we may choose of five points of the plane. A closer study by methods outside the realm of enumerative geometry reveals that the conic is uniquely determined by the five given points except when four of them are on a straight line. In this exceptional case it is clear that the conic is not uniquely defined; through four points lying on one straight line l and a fifth point P

we can draw ∞^1 special conics consisting of the pair of straight lines l and m where m is an arbitrary straight line passing through P. If, in addition, P is also on l we can even draw ∞^2 pairs of straight lines, since the choice of the straight line m is then completely arbitrary.

We proceed to the application of enumerative methods to three-dimensional figures. By characterizing a plane by its three intercepts in a fixed coordinate system in space, we see that the space contains ∞^3 planes; for, the only planes that can not be defined by their intercepts are the planes that pass through the origin, and these latter are only a two-parameter family. By the method of enumeration we verify the elementary theorem that a plane can be found which passes through any three given points in space; indeed, there are ∞^9 triples of points in space and ∞^6 such triples on every plane, so that the triples of points in space define "∞^9/∞^6," i.e. ∞^3, planes.

In determining a straight line by means of two points, we find that in space there are ∞^4 straight lines; for, there are ∞^6 pairs of points in space and ∞^2 on a straight line.

The spheres can be characterized by their center and radius. It follows that there are ∞^4 spheres in space. Adding the planes as limiting cases to the family of spheres, we can use enumeration to verify the well-known fact that a sphere or plane can be drawn through any four points in space. Just as in the case of the conics, the determination of the sphere is not always unique although it is unique if—and only if—the four points are not on a common straight line or circle. Analogous conditions govern the general case. If an n-parameter family of surfaces is defined so as to be sufficiently inclusive (like the family of all conics as opposed to the family of ellipses, in the plane), then there is a surface of the family through every set of n points in space. The surface is not always uniquely defined by the n points. It is, however, uniquely defined if the points are "in general position," i.e. if they do not satisfy certain geometrical relations whose nature depends on the given family of surfaces.

A ruled surface of the second order is defined by three skew straight lines. Space contains $\infty^{4\cdot3} = \infty^{12}$ triples of straight lines. But since every straight line on a ruled quadric is a member of a one-parameter family, ∞^3 triples of straight lines define the same surface. Hence there are ∞^4 ruled quadrics.

Likewise there are ∞^9 general ellipsoids. This follows from the fact that we get every ellipsoid once, and only once, by varying the choice of the center (three parameters), the lengths of the axes (three parameters), the direction of the major axis (two parameters), and—the minor axis lying in the plane through the center perpendicular to the major axis—the direction of the minor axis within that plane (one parameter).

From analytic considerations we learn that there are ∞^9 quadrics altogether. We have, for this family, the theorem that every set of nine arbitrary points in space lies on a surface belonging to the family. In order that the definition of a quadric by nine points be unique, i.e. that the position of the points be sufficiently general for the family of quadrics, it is necessary to stipulate that the points shall not lie on certain space curves of the fourth order; for, these can be obtained as the curves of intersection of pairs of quadrics, so that naturally it would be impossible that any number of points on such a curve could define a quadric uniquely.

We shall now establish the plausibility of the fact that there are infinitely many straight lines on every second-order surface. To this end we begin with the fact, immediately deducible from the analytic definition of second-order surfaces, that every straight line having three points in common with such a surface is wholly embedded in it. Evidently there are ∞^6 triples of points on a quadric (and, for that matter, on any surface). Let us select only those triples of points that are collinear. Enumerative geometry yields the result that there are ∞^4 of them, i.e. that two parameters are lost. For, it takes two analytic relations to express the incidence of one of the points with the straight line defined by the other two; and there is a general theorem that the number of parameters associated with a family is diminished by n if we select only the members satisfying a certain set of n independent relations (where n relations are called independent if they cannot be replaced by less than n equivalent relations). Hence it is true that ∞^4 triples of collinear points lie on any given quadric. And it was pointed out before that every straight line that is incident with such a triple of points must lie on the surface. But there are ∞^3 triples of points on a straight line. Hence the triples of collinear points on a second-order surface lie on ∞^1 straight lines belonging to the surface.

On the ellipsoid, the elliptic paraboloid, and the hyperboloid of two sheets, these straight lines are imaginary.

In conclusion, we add a few remarks on the third-order surfaces, since these surfaces are intimately connected with the properties of Schläfli's double-six to be studied in the next section. Analytically, the third-order surfaces are characterized by the property of having an equation of the third degree in Cartesian coordinates. Now, the general third degree equation in three unknowns has twenty coefficients, and they are determined up to a common factor by the surface associated with the equation. It follows that there are ∞^{19} third-order surfaces and that through any set of 19 points arbitrarily chosen in space there passes a surface of the family. It is necessary here, however, to include certain degenerate cases in the family of third-order surfaces, e.g. a second-order surface and a plane, taken together.

In general, a straight line has three points in common with a third-order surface, and a straight line having four points in common with such a surface must lie on the surface. This is easily deduced from the fact that the surface has an equation of third degree. We shall show by enumeration that the most general third-order surface can only contain a finite number of straight lines. On every surface there are ∞^8 quadruples of points. It takes four conditions to insure that such a quadruple of points be collinear— two conditions for the third point and two for the fourth point to lie on the straight line common to the first two points. Hence there are ∞^4 collinear quadruples of points on a general third-order surface. Every straight line containing such a quadruple lies on the surface and contains ∞^4 other such quadruples. The existence of an infinity of straight lines on the surface would imply that more than ∞^4 quadruples of collinear points could be found on it.

But the third-order surfaces also include a great many ruled surfaces. These surfaces, then, contain ∞^5 or even more quadruples of collinear points. Accordingly, the equation of a ruled surface of the third order must have the special property that this equation together with the four conditions for the collinearity of four points can be replaced by an equivalent system of fewer equations. It may be shown that such a reduction is possible only if the twenty coefficients of the third-degree equation satisfy certain special relations. This also shows the truth of the statement that the general third-order surface contains at most a finite number of straight lines.[1]

An enumeration similar to the above shows that the general surfaces of order higher than the third do not in general contain any straight lines.

§ 25. Schläfli's Double-Six

We begin with some simple considerations concerning the possible positions of straight lines in space. Three skew straight lines a, b, and c define a hyperboloid H. In general, an arbitrary fourth straight line d intersects H at two points, although it may also be tangent to H or lie on H. In the general case, each of the points at which d and H intersect is incident with a straight line lying on H that does not belong to the same family as a, b, c and therefore intersects a, b, and c. Conversely, every straight line that intersects a, b, c, and d, is on H and is incident with one of the points at which d intersects H. Hence there are in general two, and not more than two, straight lines that intersect four given straight lines. In the case where d is tangent to H there is only one (double) straight line that intersects a, b, c, and d. If, on the other hand, there are more than two straight lines that intersect a, b, c, and d, then d must lie on H, and then there are infinitely many straight lines intersecting a, b, c, and d. In this case we say that the four straight lines are in a hyperboloidal position.

In the construction of Schläfli's double-six we start with any

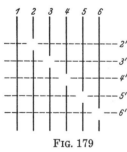

FIG. 179

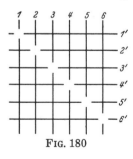

FIG. 180

straight line 1 and draw three mutually skew straight lines intersecting 1, which we shall call 2', 3', and 4', for reasons that will become apparent later (see Fig. 179). Then we draw another straight line 5' through 1, which is to have the most general possible position relative to 2', 3', and 4': 5' will not intersect any of the straight

---

[1] E.g., there is no straight line on the surface $xyz = 1$ which passes through a finite point of the surface.

lines 2′, 3′, and 4′, and there will be besides 1 just one straight line—
we shall call it 6—that intersects 2′, 3′, 4′, and 5′. Finally we draw
a straight line 6′ through 1 which must not intersect 6, 2′, 3′, 4′,
or 5′, and which must furthermore be such as to make the positions
of the quadruples 2′3′4′6′, 2′3′5′6′, 2′4′5′6′, and 3′4′5′6′ as general
as possible. Then there is exactly one straight line 5 in addition

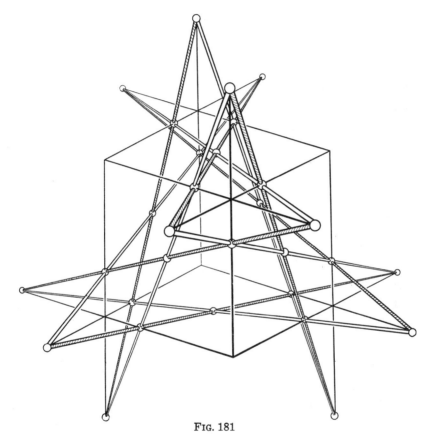

Fig. 181

to 1 which intersects 2′, 3′, 4′, and 6′, and the straight lines 4, 3,
and 2 are defined analogously (e.g. 4 is distinct from 1 and intersects 2′, 3′, 5′, and 6′, etc.). In this way we obtain the system of
intersections represented schematically in Fig. 179. It is easily
seen that our choice of the straight lines 2′, 3′, 4′, 5′, 6′ precludes
the possibility of additional intersections. Turning now to the four
straight lines 2, 3, 4, and 5, we shall show that they cannot be in a
hyperboloidal position. For if they were, every straight line that

intersects three of them would also intersect the fourth, and in particular, this would apply to each of the straight lines 2', 3', 4', and 5', according to our scheme. Then these four straight lines would also be in a hyperboloidal position, contradicting the conditions of our construction. Thus there are at most two straight lines that meet 2, 3, 4, and 5. But according to our construction, 2, 3, 4, and 5 all intersect 6'. Let us denote the second straight line that intersects 2, 3, 4, and 5, by 1'; we assert that 1' does not coincide with 6' and that it cuts 6. Pending the proof of this assertion (to be given below), we may supplement the arrangement represented by Fig. 179, changing it into that of Fig. 180. The latter scheme represents the double-six. It is immediately seen that we are dealing with a regular configuration of points and straight lines whose symbol is $(30_2 12_5)$. A particularly clear and symmetrical form of the double-six can be constructed by suitably choosing one of the straight lines of each set of six on each face of a cube. The arrangement should be apparent from Fig. 181 (cf. also Fig. 102, p. 93).

We must now prove the assertion made above that there is a straight line 1' distinct from 6' which meets 2, 3, 4, and 5, and that this 1' must meet 6. Let us tentatively assume that the first part is already proved and prove on the basis of this assumption that 1' intersects 6. To this end, we select four points on the straight line 1 and three points on each of the straight lines 2' to 6', making sure that none of the points of intersection of the lines under consideration are included among the nineteen points thus chosen. According to the argument of the last section, a third-order surface F_3 can be drawn through these nineteen points. Now F_3, having four points in common with the straight line 1, must contain the entire straight line. Furthermore, F_3 has four points in common with each of the straight lines 2' to 6'—the three points chosen in the beginning and the point (distinct from these) where the line meets 1; thus F_3 contains 2' to 6' as well. From this it follows in turn that F_3 also contains the straight lines 2 to 6, as each of them intersects four straight lines lying on the surface. And finally, F_3 contains 1' for the same reason. Supposing now that 1' did not intersect 6, let us consider the straight line l which, like 5', intersects 2, 3, 4, and 6. As in the construction of 1', we shall rule out for the time being the case where l coincides with 5'. l cannot coincide with 1', since it was assumed that 1' does not meet 6. Since l

meets four straight lines lying on F_3, namely 2, 3, 4, and 6, l itself lies on F_3. By our construction, each of the four straight lines l, 1', 5', 6' meets 2, 3, and 4. Hence the four straight lines are in a hyperboloidal position. Then the entire associated hyperboloid must be a part of F_3; this follows directly from the fact that every straight line that intersects l, 1', 5', and 6', lies on F_3, while the set of all such straight lines covers the hyperboloid.

Now, it is easy to prove algebraically that a third-order surface that contains all the points of a second-order surface must consist of the second-order surface and a plane: If $G = 0$ and $H = 0$ are the equations of the third-order and second-order surface respectively, the polynomial G of the third degree must be divisible by the polynomial H of the second degree, and this can only be the case if G is the product of H and a linear expression. From the conclusion that the surface F_3 defined by our nineteen points must be a degenerate case of this sort, we can easily deduce a contradiction. For, no four of the straight lines 2', 3', 4', 5', 6' have a hyperboloidal position; hence at most three of them could be on the hyperboloid that forms a part of F_3. Hence at least two would have to be on the plane that constitutes the other component of F_3 and these two would therefore have a point of intersection, in contradiction to our construction.

If we admit the possibility, previously excluded, that 1'(2345) may coincide with 6' or l(2346) with 5', the proof is not essentially changed. In this case, too, we can conclude that the hyperboloid defined by 2, 3, and 4 would have to be a part of F_3. But the limiting process by which this case is derived from the general case can not be justified without the use of algebraic methods.

In the proof of the last incidence relation (1'6) of the double-six we used the fact, interesting in itself, that there is always a third-order surface F_3 that contains this configuration. It is easy to supplement the configuration with several additional straight lines which also lie on F_3. Consider, for instance, the plane spanned by the intersecting straight lines 1 and 2' and the plane spanned by 1' and 2 and let (12) denote the line in which the two planes intersect. Then (12) meets the four straight lines 1, 1', 2, and 2', all of which lie on F_3; hence (12) also lies on F_3. In all there are fifteen straight lines that bear the same relation to the double-six as (12) and therefore lie on F_3 as well. For, fifteen different pairs can be chosen from the numbers from 1 to 6. We have thus found $2 \times 6 + 15 = 27$ straight lines all lying on F_3.

Among the straight lines of the enlarged configuration that we have obtained in this way there are further incidence relations. In fact, it may be shown that all those pairs of the straight lines denoted by two numbers whose symbols have no number in common, and those only, will have a point of intersection. The proof can be based on the same idea as our proof that 1′ and 6 intersect, and we shall only give an indication of it. For reasons of symmetry it suffices to show that (12) meets (34). To this end, we consider the three straight lines 1, 2, (34), and note that 3′ and 4′ intersect them. If (12) did not intersect (34), there would be a straight line a that would meet the four lines 1, 2, 1′, and (34), and a straight line b that would meet 1, 2, 2′, and (34). b would necessarily be distinct from a, for if they were one and the same straight line, this would meet the four lines 1, 2, 1′, 2′, and would therefore be identical with (12) and yet meet (34), whereas we are assuming for the time being that (34) does not meet (12). Similarly a and b would have to be distinct from 3′ and 4′; for if, say, a coincided with 3′, then 3′ would intersect 1′, in contradiction to our construction. Now a and b, like 3′ and 4′, would have to lie on F_3, and because all of them meet the triple 1, 2, (34), the four straight lines would be hyperboloidal. But we have already seen that it is impossible for F_3 to contain a set of four straight lines in the hyperboloidal position. It follows that (12) does meet (34). For the same reasons it must meet (35), (36), (45), (46), and (56). Since (12) also meets 1, 2, 1′, and 2′, it follows that (12) intersects ten straight lines of the enlarged configuration, and does every one of the straight lines we denoted by two numbers. The same is true for the straight lines of the double-six itself; 1, for example, intersects the five lines 2′ to 6′ and the five lines (12), (13), (14), (15), (16). Accordingly, the configuration consisting of the 27 straight lines on F_3 together with their points of intersection has the symbol $(135_2 27_{10})$. The fact that there are exactly 135 points follows from the equation $135 \times 2 = 27 \times 10$. It can be shown, moreover, that the configuration is regular, and that many different double-sixes can therefore be found in it. Considering in addition the planes spanned by intersecting pairs of lines of the configuration, we can verify by referring to the incidence table that every such

plane contains a third line of the configuration. This can also be
seen by the following simple algebraic argument. Every plane
necessarily intersects F_3 in a third-order curve. If the plane contains two straight lines of the configuration, this curve is bound
to contain them, and it can be deduced algebraically that the curve
must then consist of these two straight lines and a third straight
line. It is easy to check by counting that five of our planes pass
through each of the twenty-seven straight lines and that the planes
number forty-five in all. Thus we see that the configuration is not
self-dual, although the double-six, being built up on the self-dual
relation of the incidence of two straight lines, is self-dual. The
double-six can easily be extended to a configuration that is the dual
of the configuration we have just constructed. To this end, we
need to add a different set of straight lines $[ik]$ instead of the
straight lines (ik), where, for example, [12] passes through the
points at which 1 intersects 2' and 1' intersects 2. The configuration obtained in this way has the symbol $(45_3 27_5)$.

Let us return to the original configuration of twenty-seven
straight lines. We shall show by enumerative methods that there
is such a configuration K on every third-order surface F_3. Here,
as in all enumerative considerations, the cases where K is partly
imaginary or degenerate must also be taken into account. The proof
begins with the enumeration of the family of all double-sixes.
According to our construction, the choice of the straight line 1 is
completely free, and thus involves four parameters; the points
where 1 intersects the straight lines 2' to 6' depend on another five
parameters, and each of the lines 2' to 6' can assume ∞^2 positions
once its point of intersection with 1 is fixed (thus accounting for
ten more parameters). Since the straight lines 1, 2', 3', 4', 5', and 6',
uniquely define the double-six, we see that there are ∞^{19} double-sixes
$(19 = 4 + 5 + 10)$. The family of configurations K has the same
number of parameters; for, each configuration of this type is defined
by one of the double-sixes in it, and obviously there is only a finite
number of double-sixes in any one configuration K. Now we have
given a construction for passing an F_3 through any given K; it
follows either that the family of the surfaces F_3 constructed in this
way comprises ∞^{19} surfaces or, should there be fewer surfaces, that
at least ∞^1 configurations K lie on the same F_3, i.e. that F_3 would
have to be a ruled surface of the third order. It can be shown, how-

ever, that there are less than ∞^{18} ruled surfaces of the third order; hence the F_3 we constructed would have to contain at least ∞^2 double-sixes. But since it was already demonstrated that the F_3 do not contain a hyperboloid and since any ruled surface of order higher than the second contains only one family of straight lines, such an F_3 cannot possibly carry ∞^2 double-sixes. Therefore our surfaces cannot in general be ruled surfaces, and it follows that our construction accounts for not less than ∞^{19} surfaces. On the other hand, as we have mentioned in the last section, there are only ∞^{19} third-order surfaces. From this, the algebraic nature of the figures under consideration being borne in mind, the truth of our assertion that every third-order surface contains a configuration of the type K can be rigorously deduced.

CHAPTER IV

DIFFERENTIAL GEOMETRY

So far we have examined geometrical figures with regard to their overall structure. Differential geometry represents a fundamentally different method of approach. Specifically we will, to start with, investigate curves and surfaces only in the immediate vicinity of any one of their points. For that purpose we compare the vicinity, or "neighborhood," of such a point with a figure which is as simple as possible, such as a straight line, a plane, a circle, or a sphere, and which approximates the curve as closely as possible in the neighborhood under consideration; in this way one obtains, for example, the familiar concept of the tangent to a curve at one of its points.

This approach, known as local differential geometry, or differential geometry in the small, is supplemented by another important point of view, differential geometry in the large: if a continuous geometrical figure is known to have a certain property in the neighborhood of *every one* of its points, then it is possible, as a rule, to deduce certain essential facts relating to the total structure of the figure. If, for example, we are given a plane curve of which it is known that at no point of the curve does a neighboring portion lie entirely on one side of the tangent at the point, then it may be proved that the curve must of necessity be a straight line.

Besides dealing with continuous sets of points, differential geometry also deals with manifolds composed of other elements, e.g. manifolds of straight lines. Problems of this kind arise, for example, in the field of geometrical optics, which is concerned with the study of continuous systems of light rays.

And finally, differential geometry leads to the problem, first posed by Gauss and Riemann, of building up a complete geometrical system on the basis of concepts and axioms that only affect the immediate neighborhood of each point. This gave rise to an abundance of possibilities, not exhausted to this day, of building more

171

general geometries, of which "non-Euclidean" geometry is an important, but very special, example. From the general theory of relativity we have learned than an effective description of physical reality must be based not on ordinary Euclidean Geometry, but on a more general Riemannian Geometry.

§ 26. Plane Curves

We shall begin with the simplest topic, that of plane curves. Our attention will be confined to a small piece of the curve on which it does not intersect itself.

A straight line that intersects the curve in two points is called a *secant* of the curve. If a secant *s* is rotated about one of its points of intersection in such a way that the other point of intersection

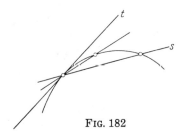

FIG. 182

approaches the first one (see Fig. 182), then the secant approaches a definite position *t*. The straight line that has this position is called a *tangent* to the curve, the fixed point is called its point of contact (or point of tangency). Of all the straight lines passing through the point of contact, the tangent evidently provides the closest approximation to the course of the curve at that point; for this reason, the direction of the tangent at that point is also called the direction of the curve at the point. Two curves are said to intersect at an angle *α* at a common point if their tangents at the point intersect at angle *α*; if the tangents coincide, the curves are said to be tangential to each other at the common point. A straight line perpendicular to a tangent at its point of contact is called a *normal* to the curve.

At any point of a curve, the tangent and the normal constitute the axes of a system of rectangular coordinates. This particular coordinate system is especially well suited to the study of the behavior of the curve at the point under consideration. Let us fix one of the directions along the curve as the direction of traversal. Then let us number the four quadrants into which the plane is divided by the coordinate axes, assigning the number 1 to the quadrant in which we would find a point of the curve close to the origin and traveling toward the origin in the direction of traversal specified (Fig. 183), and assigning the numbers 2, 3, and 4 to the other quadrants in such a way that the tangent separates the quadrants 1, 2 from the quadrants 3, 4 and the normal separates 1, 4 from 2, 3. Then we may distinguish four different cases (I to IV in Fig. 183) according to whether the location of the moving point just after passing through the origin is in the second, third, fourth, or first quadrant. The point at which we are examining the curve is called *regular* only in the first case; in the three remaining cases it is called *singular*. Practically all the points of a curve are regular, and singularities can occur only at isolated points.[1] In the case II, the curve is said to have a *point of inflection*. In the two remaining cases, the curve is said to have a *cusp* of the first kind and a cusp of the second kind, respectively. It may be seen that the classification is independent of the direction in which the curve is traversed.

We shall now form a picture of the way in which the tangent changes its direction as the curve passes through each of these four types of points. To this end, we shall use a method due to Gauss that is of fundamental importance, particularly in the study of surfaces. As before, we choose a sense

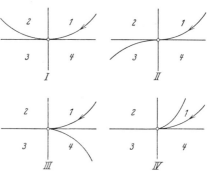

FIG. 183

of traversal on the curve. In the plane of the curve we draw a unit circle. Then we represent every tangent to the curve by the radius of the circle parallel to the tangent and having the same sense as the curve at the point under consideration (Fig. 184). To every point P of the curve this construction assigns a point Q of the circle, viz. the point where the radius meets the circle. The points of the circle occurring in this representation constitute what is called the "tangential image" or "tangent indicatrix" or "Gaussian image" of the curve. Since the radius of the circle is always perpendicular to the corresponding tangent of the circle, the tangent to the curve

---

[1] The straight line is the only curve for which this statement is not true. In the case of the straight line, the procedure outlined above is not applicable at all. Considered from a higher point of view, the case I may also assume a singular character, namely when the circle of curvature at the point degenerates into a straight line or a point (cf. p. 177).

and the corresponding normal to the tangent indicatrix are always parallel, while the tangents to the tangent indicatrix are parallel to the normals of the curve.

We know that this Gaussian representation assigns exactly one point of the circle to each point of the curve. On the other hand, a single point of the circle does not as a rule correspond to one point of the curve but to several, in fact, to all the points of the curve at which the tangents have the same direction (e.g. the points P_1 and P_3 in Fig. 184).

Consider a point that moves along a curve on which there are points of the various types illustrated in Fig. 183. The direction of motion is reversed at points of type III and IV but is left

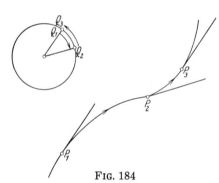

FIG. 184

unchanged in the cases I and II. How does the corresponding point of the Gaussian image behave? In the cases I and III its direction of motion is unchanged, and in the cases II and IV, reversed. For in the neighborhood of a point of type II or IV there are parallel tangents, but not so in the other two cases. Since the direction in which the point of the Gaussian image moves reproduces the change in direction of the tangent to the curve, we may characterize the four types of points on the curve as follows:

I. Regular point: The point on the curve and its tangential image both continue in their old directions.

II. Point of inflection: The point on the curve continues in the old direction while the image reverses its direction.

III. Cusp of the first kind: The point on the curves reverses its direction, while the image continues in the old direction.

IV. Cusp of the second kind: The point on the curve and the tangential image both reverse their directions.

This classification does not exhaust all the possibilities. Even if we limit ourselves to arcs that admit a simple analytic representation, there are three additional cases; there may be "double points" where the curve intersects itself, there may be points where the curve suddenly ends, and finally, the curve may have "isolated points," i.e. points that are completely separated from all the other points of the curve (cf. pp. 198-199). Strangely enough, there are other phenomena which are simple graphically, but relatively complicated in their analytic representation, e.g. corners with angles different from zero.

We proceed to introduce *curvature*, a concept of fundamental importance throughout the theory of curves and surfaces. As we shall see in the sequel, it is intimately connected with Gauss's tangential representation. Let t_1 and t_2 be the tangents, n_1 and n_2 the normals, at two neighboring points P_1 and P_2 on a curve. Let the point of intersection of the two normals be at M (Fig. 185). Clearly, the angle between the tangents is equal to the angle between the normals:

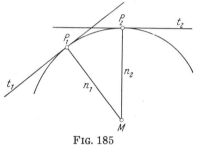

FIG. 185

$$\angle (t_1 t_2) = \angle (n_1 n_2).$$

Let P_2 approach P_1 along the curve, and consider the ratio between the angle $n_1 n_2$ and the distance between the two points of the curve. In general, this ratio approaches a limit,

$$\lim_{P_1 P_2 \to 0} \frac{\angle (n_1 n_2)}{P_1 P_2} = k.$$

This limiting value k is called the *curvature* of the curve at the point P_1.

k is equal to the reciprocal of the length r of the line-segment that is the common limit of the two segments $M P_1$ and $M P_2$ of the normals. This is a consequence of the following transformation, whose analytic justification we shall omit:

$$k = \lim_{P_1 P_2 \to 0} \frac{\angle (n_1 n_2)}{P_1 P_2} = \lim_{P_1 P_2 \to 0} \frac{\sin (n_1 n_2)}{P_1 P_2} = \lim_{P_1 P_2 \to 0} \frac{P_1 P_2}{M P_1 \cdot P_1 P_2}$$

$$= \lim_{P_1 P_2 \to 0} \frac{1}{M P_1} = \frac{1}{r}.$$

The quantity r is also obtained in another way, as follows. We draw a circle through P_1 and two neighboring points of the curve. If the two neighboring points approach P_1, the circle approaches a limiting position. From the construction we should expect that the center of the limiting circle is at the limiting position of the point of intersection M of the normals, and that its radius is therefore equal to r. A study by analytic methods confirms this. This circle is called the *circle of curvature* of the curve at P_1, its center is called the *center of curvature*, and its radius r, the *radius of curvature*. Because of the above construction, it is usual to say that the circle of curvature has three coincident points in common with

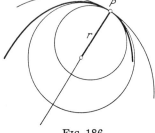

FIG. 186

the curve. Similarly, we may say that the tangent has two coincident points in common with the curve.

There is another method for obtaining the circle of curvature. Consider all the circles through a point P of the curve (Fig. 186) which are tangent to the curve at P, so that their centers lie on the normal to the curve at P. In the neighborhood of P the curve divides the plane into two parts, which we shall call the two sides of that piece of the curve. Of the circles we are considering, there are some that lie entirely on one side of the curve in the neighborhood of P, others that lie entirely on the other side. Now the circle of curvature generally has the property that it separates these two kinds of circle, which it does in the following manner: If r is the radius of the circle of curvature, all the circles with radius greater than r lie on one side of the curve

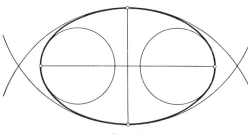

FIG. 187

in the neighborhood of P and all the circles with radius smaller than r on the other. The circle of curvature itself in general occupies opposite sides of the curve on the two sides of the normal; in other words, it crosses the curve at the point of contact. Like the singular points of a curve, the points at which the circle of curvature does not cross the curve can occur only as isolated points of the curve except if the curve itself is a circle. The four vertices of an ellipse furnish an example of this (see Fig. 187); it is evident from considerations of symmetry that the circle of curvature cannot cross the curve at these points. More generally, the same is true at all points where a curve is met by an axis of symmetry.

The fact that the circle of curvature usually crosses the curve is made plausible by the way the circle was obtained in the first place. For in general a circle passing through a point of a curve crosses the curve at this point. Hence a circle passing through three consecutive points on a curve crosses from side A to side B at the first point, from B to A at the second, and from A to B at the third; and if the three points move into coincidence this behavior of the circle is not in general changed in the process, whence it is seen that the circle of curvature does indeed have to cross from one side of the curve to the other.[2]

We have already mentioned that there is a connection between curvature and the tangential image of a curve. Let Q_1 and Q_2 be the tangential images of the two points P_1 and P_2 of the curve (Fig. 188). Then

$$\angle (t_1 t_2) = \angle (Q_1 O Q_2) = Q_1 Q_2.$$

Hence the radius of curvature is the limit of the ratio between the length of a short arc of the curve and that of its tangential image.

At individual points the radius of curvature may become infinite; at such points the circle of curvature degenerates into a straight line and is thus

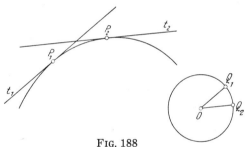

FIG. 188

identical with the tangent. At such a point the tangent usually crosses the curve, so that the point is a point of inflection. There are exceptional cases however, in which the curvature vanishes but the tangent does not cross the curve; this is analogous to the behavior of the circle of curvature at the vertices of an ellipse (cf. footnote, p. 173).

From the relation between the curvature of a curve and the tangential image we can deduce, moreover, that the curvature generally becomes infinite at a cusp of the first kind, i.e. that the circle of curvature at such a point shrinks down to its point of contact. In the case of a cusp of the second kind, we cannot make any general statement.

---

[2] For analogous reasons, the tangent *does not* as a rule cross the curve at its point of contact.

There are a number of important questions arising in connection with the concepts we have introduced. For example, we may try to define a curve by expressing its curvature as a function of arc length. It is plausible, and may be proved analytically, that this function determines the form of a curve uniquely and that, conversely, every function of this type actually yields a curve (provided certain continuity conditions are satisfied by the function). This method of defining a curve has the advantage that it does not make reference to a particular system of coordinates. For this reason, arc length and curvature are called the "natural" or "intrinsic" coordinates of the curve. The simplest case is that in which the curvature k is everywhere constant. This is the case for circles of radius $1/k$ and, by the foregoing remarks, for them only. For $k = 0$, we get the straight lines; thus straight lines and circles are the only plane curves of constant curvature.

Furthermore, there is a variety of ways in which we can derive one curve from another. For example, the set of all the centers of curvature of a given curve forms a new curve, called the *evolute* of the given curve. Conversely, the first curve is called the *involute* of the second. The involutes of a curve can always be obtained by a thread construction: a thread attached to the curve at one end is stretched along the curve; as we unwind the thread, keeping it taut all the time, the free end describes a section of the involute. The involutes of the circle were already constructed in this way on page 6. The underlying reason for this peculiar relation between the involute and the evolute will be explained in the next chapter (pp. 276, 277).

§ 27. Space Curves

Most of the discussion of the last section can be adapted to apply to curves in space (sometimes called twisted curves).

To start with, we again get the tangent as the limiting position of the secant when one point of intersection moves into coincidence with the other. But the three-dimensional case differs from the case of plane curves by the fact that there are infinitely many perpendiculars to the tangent at the point of contact; these perpendiculars fill out a plane which is called the *normal plane* at the point of the curve.

We shall try to find a plane lying as close to the curve as possible in the neighborhood of the point under consideration. To this end, we draw the plane passing through the tangent at the given point and through a neighboring point of the curve and let the second point move along the curve toward the point of contact of the tangent, which we hold fixed. In this process the plane approaches a limiting position. The limiting plane satisfies our requirement; it is called the *osculating plane* of the curve at the point under consideration. Using a mode of expression introduced earlier, we say that the osculating plane has three coincident points in com-

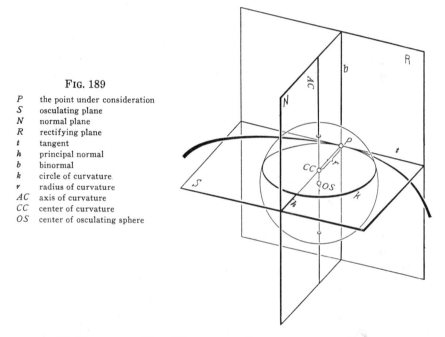

Fig. 189

P	the point under consideration
S	osculating plane
N	normal plane
R	rectifying plane
t	tangent
h	principal normal
b	binormal
k	circle of curvature
r	radius of curvature
AC	axis of curvature
CC	center of curvature
OS	center of osculating sphere

mon with the curve. For this reason, the curve generally crosses its osculating plane at the point of contact, although it lies on one side of any other plane containing the tangent.

Since it contains the tangent, the osculating plane is perpendicular to the normal plane. Finally, let us consider that plane through the given point of the curve which is perpendicular both to the normal plane and to the osculating plane. It is called the *rectifying plane*.

The three planes just considered may be interpreted as coordinate planes in a three-dimensional Cartesian coordinate system which proves to be particularly well suited for describing the course of the curve at the point under consideration. One of the coordinate axes in this system is the tangent; the other two axes, which must lie in the normal plane, are called the *principal normal* and the *binormal*. The principal normal lies in the osculating plane, the binormal in the rectifying plane (see Fig. 189). This coordinate system, depending as it does on the point of the curve, is called the *moving trihedron* of the curve. It is the analogue of the coordinate system formed by the tangent and normal in the case of plane curves. In space, a coordinate system defines eight regions, called *octants*, as against four quadrants in the case of the plane. Thus the moving trihedron serves to distinguish eight types of points on a curve in much the same way as four types of points were distinguished, on page 174, for plane curves. Once again, only one of the cases is regular, and the others can occur only at isolated points (provided our curve is really a space curve, i.e. provided it does not lie wholly in a plane). At a regular point the curve intersects the osculating plane and the normal plane and remains on one side of the rectifying plane. We shall not discuss the other cases here. It may be mentioned, incidentally, that the twisted curves having a simple analytic structure, may, just like the plane curves, exhibit three additional types of singularities, namely double points, terminal points, and isolated points.

Let us generalize the Gaussian representation of plane curves to the case of three-dimensional curves. For this purpose, we use a sphere of unit radius. To every tangent of the curve (which we assume to be oriented, i.e., to have a definite sense of traversal), we draw the radius of the sphere parallel to the tangent and pointing in the same direction. Its extremity on the surface of the sphere is called the tangential image of the point on the curve. In this way the entire curve is represented by a definite curve on the sphere. If the principal normal or the binormal is used instead of the tangent, we get two more curves on the sphere. Referred to their respective moving trihedra, these three "spherical images" are connected with each other and with the original curve by certain simple relations. For example, the tangential indicatrix and the binormal indicatrix together characterize the eight above-mentioned types of point of a curve: the point on the original curve, the tangent, and the binormal may each either move on continuously or reverse its course, and the combination of the various possibilities give us just those eight cases.

We shall next extend the concept of curvature to space curves. Let t_1 and t_2 be the tangents at two neighboring points P_1 and P_2 of the curve. Consider the quotient $\angle\,(t_1 t_2)\,/P_1 P_2$ as P_2 approaches P_1. The quotient in general approaches a limiting value, which is called the *curvature* (or *first curvature*) of the curve at P_1. We saw how the curvature of plane curves is related to the limiting position of the point of intersection of two normals. The analogous argument for space curves yields not a point, but a straight line—the limiting position of the line of intersection of two normal planes. This line is called the *polar axis* of the curve at the point under consideration. It is in the normal plane, and, as may be seen from the limiting process, parallel to the binormal (see Fig. 189). The point of intersection of the polar axis and the principal normal is called the center of (first) curvature. The distance r between this point and the corresponding point of the curve is called the radius of (first) curvature; as in the plane, r is the reciprocal of the curvature. The circle through three neighboring points of the curve approaches a limiting position when the points move into coincidence. The limiting circle lies in the osculating plane, and its center and radius are the center and radius of curvature.

The Gaussian tangential indicatrix is related to the curvature in the same way as in the plane: the radius of curvature is the limit of the ratio between the length of a short arc of the curve and that of its tangential image. The proof is the same as in the plane.

In place of the angle between two tangents, we may start with the angle between two osculating planes, or, what amounts to the same, the angle between the binormals at two points of the curve. This leads to another concept of fundamental importance in the theory of space curves. We divide the angle by the distance between the corresponding points of the curve and then let the points move into coincidence. The limit t of the quotient is called the *torsion*, or sometimes the *second curvature*, of the curve at the given point of the curve. Evidently the reciprocal of the torsion is the limit of the ratio between a small arc of the curve and its binormal image.

We were able to obtain the first curvature by a limiting process involving three neighboring points on the curve. To obtain an analogous interpretation for the second curvature, we need to start with four neighboring points. Four points in general define a sphere. We may now consider the limiting position of the sphere passing through four neighboring points of the curve as they move into coincidence. The sphere that assumes this limiting position is called the *osculating sphere*. We see from the limiting process that the tangent to the curve is also tangent to the osculating sphere at the point of contact and that the center of the osculating sphere lies on the polar axis (see Fig. 189). For the distance of this center from the center of curvature, a calculation gives us the value $\frac{1}{t} \cdot \frac{dr}{ds}$, where ds and dr are the differentials of arc length and of radius of curvature, respectively. Furthermore, we may infer from the construction that the curve of intersection of the osculating sphere with the osculating plane is identical with the circle of curvature. By Pythagoras' theorem we therefore get the value

$$\sqrt{r^2 + \left(\frac{dr}{ds}\right)^2 \cdot \frac{1}{t^2}}$$

for the radius of the osculating sphere.

Like the quantities s and r in the plane, the quantities s, r, and t in space are called the *intrinsic*, or *natural*, parameters of a space curve. In analogy with the plane case, we have the following important theorem: We can always find one, and only one, shape for a curve in space in order that r and t be given functions of s on that curve. If $1/r$ is identically zero, we get the straight lines. The plane curves are characterized by the identical vanishing of t. If r and t are constants different from zero, we get the circular helices.

The curves on a sphere are characterized by a slightly more complicated condition. Evidently the sphere that carries the curve has to coincide with the osculating sphere at all the points of the curve. Hence the radius of the osculating sphere, as computed above, has to be constant:

$$r^2 + \left(\frac{dr}{ds}\right)^2 \cdot \frac{1}{t^2} = \text{const.}$$

It can be proved analytically that this condition is also sufficient.

Some further questions relating to twisted curves will be considered later in connection with the theory of surfaces.

§ 28. Curvature of Surfaces. Elliptic, Hyperbolic, and Parabolic Points. Lines of Curvature and Asymptotic Lines; Umbilical Points, Minimal Surfaces, Monkey Saddles

In beginning our study of surfaces, we shall confine our attention to a small portion of a smooth surface on which the surface does not intersect itself, and leave the boundary points out of consideration. Consider a point P of the surface together with all the curves through P that lie on the surface. It is a remarkable fact that in general the tangents to these curves at the point P all lie in a common plane, which is therefore called the *tangent plane* to the surface at P. The points of the surface at which the tangent plane exists are called *regular*, the other points, *singular*. The singular points of a surface can not fill up more than some individual curves on the surface.

The perpendicular to the tangent plane at a regular point P of a surface is called the *normal* to the surface at P. The term *normal sections* is used to denote the curves in which the planes containing the normal intersect the surface. The normal sections at a regular point P are either regular at P or have points of inflection at P.

Our next task is to adapt the concept of curvature to surfaces. In the case of curves, curvature was an index of the deviation of a curve from its tangent in the immediate vicinity of the point of tangency. Analogously, we are now interested in the behavior of a surface relative to its tangent planes. If we look at actual examples of surfaces, we are led to distinguish between two essentially different cases, viz., points at which the surface is cup-shaped, and points at which it is saddle-shaped.

A point of the first type is characterized by the property that its tangent plane does not intersect the surface (in the immediate vicinity of the point under consideration) but remains on one side of the surface. It is thus possible to rest the surface on a flat table top at such a point. We have met examples—viz., spheres and ellipsoids—of surfaces that are cup-shaped at every one of their points. An alternative name for a point of this type is *elliptic* point.

The behavior of a surface at a point of the second type, or *saddle point* is best illustrated by a surface that looks like a mountain pass (Fig. 190). At the highest point P of the pass, the tangent plane is horizontal. To the right and to the left of P the terrain rises, whereas in front of P and in back of P it falls off. Accordingly, the tangent plane at P meets the surface in a curve consisting of two branches that intersect at P (in other words, there are two horizontal paths that cross at the highest point of the pass). This behavior is characteristic of saddle points; thus at such a point a surface can not be placed on a plane table top. Examples of surfaces that are saddle-shaped at all their points are the hyperboloid of one sheet and the hyperbolic paraboloid. An alternative name for a saddle point is *hyperbolic* point.

Between the cases of elliptic points and hyperbolic points there is a transitional case, the *parabolic* points. One way of obtaining such points is as follows: Let F and G be two surfaces that are mutually tangent at a point P (by which we mean that they have the same

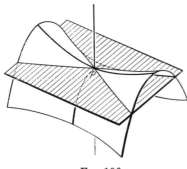

tangent plane at P), such that F is elliptic and G hyperbolic at P. If F is transformed into G by a continuous deformation in the process of which P and the tangent plane at P are not moved, then there is one stage in the course of the transformation at which the surface is parabolic at P. For example, we may begin with Fig. 190 and lower the mountains on both sides of the

FIG. 190

pass P until the ridge of the mountain chain just touches the horizontal tangent plane everywhere; at this stage P is a parabolic point, for, a continued lowering of the terrain to the right and left will transform the former pass into a peak, i.e. into an elliptic point of the surface. However, this example does not give us all the possible types of parabolic points. On the contrary, there are several types of parabolic points that look quite different; we shall treat them in some detail later on (pp. 197, 198, 200). They include types that can not be so readily construed as transitional cases between elliptic and hyperbolic points.

In order to describe curvature in numerical terms, we may begin with the curvatures of the normal sections at a point P of the surface. The center of curvature of such a normal section at the point P is bound to lie on the normal to the surface passing through P, because this is the normal to all the curves that are normal sections at P. By rotating a plane passing through the normal about this normal, we get all the normal sections. In the course of the rotation, the center of curvature performs a definite motion along the normal, which provides a description of the way in which the surface is curved at the point P.

At an elliptic point (see Fig. 191) the center of curvature always remains on one of the two halves into which the surface divides the normal. In general the radius of curvature will change in the course of the rotation of the normal plane and will assume a maximum value r_1 for a definite normal section s_1 and a minimum r_2 for another normal section s_2. r_1 and r_2 are called the *principal radii* of normal curvature of the surface at P; the reciprocals $k_1 = 1/r_1$ and $k_2 = 1/r_2$ are called the *principal* (normal) *curvatures*; and the directions of the tangents to s_1 and s_2 at P are called the *principal directions* of the surface at P. It can be shown that the principal

FIG. 191

directions at a regular point are always mutually perpendicular and that, furthermore, the curvature of *every* normal section is completely determined by the principal curvatures and the angle which the normal section makes with the principal directions.

At a hyperbolic point (Fig. 192), the locus of the center of curvature is not confined to the normal ray on one side of the surface. For if the normal section passes through the two mountains of the surface (which we again interpret as a mountain range with a pass at P), the center of curvature is located above the point P, while a section passing through the two low parts has a center of curvature lying below P. Among the normal sections with centers of curvature lying above P there is one whose curvature k_1 exceeds

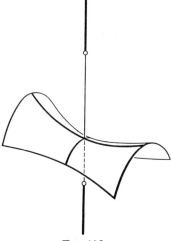

FIG. 192

that of all the other normal sections of this kind. As the normal plane is rotated out of this position, the curvature decreases, and the length of the radius of curvature increases continuously. When the normal plane has finally moved into the direction of one of the horizontal paths through P marked out in Fig. 190, the value of the curvature becomes zero, and the center of curvature recedes to infinity in the upward direction. If the rotation is then continued, the center of curvature jumps over to the lower half of the normal and begins to move upward, approaching P from infinity; thus the radius of curvature decreases and the curvature increases. Finally, the curvature attains a value k_2 that exceeds all the other values of the curvature for normal sections having a center of curvature below P. As in the elliptic case, k_1 and k_2 are called the principal curvatures, and the directions of the corresponding normal sections are called the principal directions. Here again, the principal direc-

tions are mutually perpendicular. Furthermore, they bisect the supplementary angles formed by the two branches of the curve in which the surface intersects its tangent plane. The directions of these two branches are called the *asymptotic directions* of the surface at P.

At a parabolic point there are also, in general, two mutually perpendicular principal directions such that the values k_1 and k_2 of the curvature of the corresponding normal sections are respectively greater than and less than the values for all the

Fig. 193

other normal sections. The parabolic points are characterized by the property that one of these two principal values of the curvature is equal to zero. The other value is in general different from zero, in which case the center of curvature recedes from the position corrsponding to the non-zero principal curvature to infinity along a normal half-line (see Fig. 193). In general, there is thus exactly one normal section with vanishing curvature at a parabolic point. The direction of this section is one of the principal directions but must be regarded at the same time as an asymptotic direction.

Let any surface be given. By analytic methods it is possible to find every curve on the surface that lies along one of the principal directions at all the points of the curve. In this way we obtain a "net" of curves on the surface, i.e. a system of two families of curves such that each family covers the surface simply and completely. These curves are called the *lines of curvature* of the surface. From the foregoing discussion it follows that the two lines of curvature through any given point P of the surface are mutually perpendicular at P, so that an orthogonal net is formed on the surface.

There are points, however, to which our whole discussion does not apply. This is due to the following fact. Our argument was based on the assumption that the curvature of a normal section undergoes change in the course of a rotation of the normal plane in which the normal section lies. Yet it may happen that the curvature has the same value for all normal sections at a point. In this case the principal directions are indeterminate, and we speak of an *umbilical point* (or *umbilic*). An obvious example of a surface consisting entirely of umbilical points is the sphere. As a matter of fact, the spheres and the planes are the only surfaces all of whose points are umbilics. In general, the umbilical points of a surface are isolated points. The net of lines of curvature may have singular properties at umbilical points, and at them only.

Concerning the lines of curvature, there is a remarkable theorem, due to Dupin. On page 5 we introduced the concept of orthogonal families of curves in the plane. The three-dimensional analogue is the concept of families of surfaces such that the tangent planes of the surfaces passing through any given point in space are mutually perpendicular. Through any point in the plane we can draw only two mutually perpendicular straight lines. But at any point in space we can draw three mutually perpendicular planes, and we shall therefore be concerned with orthogonal families of surfaces with three representatives, one from each family, passing through every point of space. The confocal quadrics mentioned in the first chapter are an example of such an orthogonal system.

Given any family of curves in the plane (or on any curved surface for that matter), we can find a family that is orthogonal to it. By analogy, we might be led to think that we can always find a third family of surfaces orthogonal to any two given orthogonal families in space. As a result of Dupin's theorem, however, this conjecture is seen to be false. The theorem asserts that the surfaces of any triply orthogonal system must intersect along their lines of curvature. Consequently a necessary condition for the existence of a third family of surfaces orthogonal to two given orthogonal families is that the two families intersect along their lines of curvature.

Incidentally, the condition is also sufficient. According to Dupin's theorem, the lines of curvature on the ellipsoid are the curves in which it intersects the confocal hyperboloids of one sheet and of two sheets (see Fig. 194). The net of curves thus determined (Fig. 195) is singular at the points of intersection of the focal hyperbola with the ellipsoid. And in fact, these four points are the umbilical points of the ellipsoid.

The pattern formed by the lines of curvature around the umbilical points of the ellipsoid resembles a plane system of confocal ellipses

and hyperbolas around their common foci (cf. Fig. 7, p. 6). This resemblance is not accidental but expresses an intrinsic relation between the two families of curves. For, the lines of curvature on the ellipsoid can be generated by the same thread construction as could the ellipses in the plane, by the use of two umbilical points in place of the foci. The four umbilical points of the ellipsoid come in pairs of diametrically opposite points. Hence there are two different rela-

Fig. 194

tive positions in which a pair of umbilical points not diametrically opposite can be chosen (see Fig. 196). Choosing such a pair F_1 and F_2, we attach the ends of a thread of sufficient length to them and pull it taut at a point P on the ellipsoid. Then the entire length of the thread will automatically lie snug on the ellipsoid. The various positions that P can assume on the ellipsoid trace out a line of curvature. By changing the length of the thread we can get all the lines of curvature of one family. The other family is obtained in the same way by using the other pair of umbilical points. In a plane system of confocal conics we had one family of ellipses and one family of hyperbolas; on the ellipsoid, on the other hand, both families may be regarded as generalized ellipses.

The thread itself forms certain curves on the ellipsoid analogous to the pairs of straight lines that are the focal radii of the ellipse. Like a straight line in the plane, such a curve is characterized by the property that of all the paths on the surface connecting any two points of the curve, the shortest is the curve itself. Such curves are called *geodesic curves*, or *geo-*

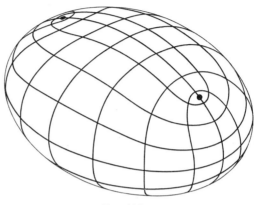

FIG. 195

desics, of a surface. They will be discussed later (pp. 220-224).

At hyperbolic points we distinguished two other exceptional directions besides the principal directions, namely the asymptotic directions. In much the same way as we defined the lines of curvature, we may define a net of curves whose directions at every point are the asymptotic directions. These curves are called the *asymptotic lines* of the surface.

It may happen at hyperbolic points also that the principal curvatures are equal in magnitude. The points where this happens have certain proper-

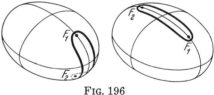

FIG. 196

ties in common with umbilical points. A surface consisting entirely of such points is called a *minimal surface*. A minimal surface is also characterized by the property that its asymptotic lines form an orthogonal net. While the class of all surfaces consisting entirely of umbilical points contains only spheres, the class of minimal surfaces is much more inclusive. This follows from the fact that the soap film which results when a closed wire of whatever shape is dipped in soap solution assumes the form of a minimal surface (cf. Figs. 220 a and b, p. 210). The law of surface tension governing the soap film tends to minimize the surface area of the film. Accordingly, we can characterize a minimal surface in purely mathematical terms as the surface of smallest area among all the surfaces bounded by a given closed curve in space. Here it is noteworthy that this characterization by a property defined in terms of the entire surface (a property *in the large*) gives us the same surfaces as the first property, which is concerned only with the immediate neighborhood of each point (a property *in the small*). This interconnection can be made plausible as follows. Let a minimal surface be given that is bounded by the closed curve S. We choose a small closed curve s on the minimal surface and restrict our attention to the region in the interior of s. This region has an area smaller than that of any other surface bounded by s. For otherwise we could alter the part of our surface lying inside s in such a way as to diminish its area; but this would entail a diminution of the total area bounded by S, in contradiction to the definition of a minimal surface. If the little curve s is now shrunk until it becomes a point of the minimal surface, it is fair to expect that the limiting process will yield some properties of the minimal surface that refer only to the immediate vicinity of a point.

The problems concerned with the characterization of a surface by minimal properties are called *variational problems*. An argument like the one we have just stated for minimal surfaces shows that the minimal property may be replaced by a local property in all other variational problems also. The limiting processes that this involves form the subject matter of the calculus of variations. Thus differential geometry and the calculus of variations proceed in opposite directions: In differential geometry we begin with properties affecting the vicinity of a point on a surface and deduce properties governing the overall structure of the figure under consideration; in the calculus of variations we deduce local properties from properties relating to the overall structure.

The calculus of variations is of fundamental importance in the field of theoretical physics, since all the states of equilibrium and motion occuring in nature are distinguished by certain minimal properties.

By means of soap films we may also generate minimal surfaces that are defined by more than one boundary curve. For example, we may start with two closed wires having the form of circles, bring them into superposition inside the solution, and then, after taking them out, separate them while keeping them perpendicular to the line joining their centers. The resulting soap film connecting the two circles resembles a hyperboloid (see Fig. 197, and Fig. 220b, p. 210). For reasons of symmetry we should expect that it is a surface of revolution. It may be verified by a calculation that this is so and that the meridian of this minimal surface of revolution is a catenary, i.e. has the shape assumed under the influence of gravity by a chain suspended from two fixed points. For this reason, the surface is called a catenoid.

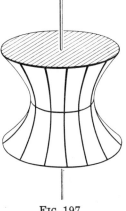

Fig. 197

The points that are simultaneously endowed with the defining properties of umbilical points and those of the points of a minimal surface are the parabolic points at which both principal curvatures vanish. At such a point the curvature of all the normal sections vanishes. Clearly, all the points of a plane fit this description; conversely, the planes are the only surfaces consisting entirely of parabolic umbilics. An example of an isolated parabolic umbilic is easily obtained by a construction analogous to that of the ordinary saddle (Fig. 190, p. 184) but in which we form three mountains and three valleys instead of two, so that the surface can be brought into self-coincidence by a rotation through the angle $2\pi/3$ (see Fig. 198). Obviously each mountain lies diametrically opposite a valley. As a result of this, every normal section has a point of inflection, which means that the

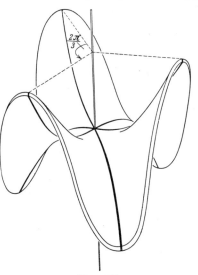

Fig. 198

curvature of every normal section is zero. The surface is called a *monkey saddle*, a term which stems from the fact that a human rider needs two depressions but a monkey requires a third for his tail.

We may characterize the difference in the form of a surface at elliptic points and at hyperbolic points in yet another way, which will at the same time justify the terms "elliptic" and "hyperbolic." Let us draw a plane close to the tangent plane and parallel to it and examine its intersection with the surface. At an elliptic point, only the planes on one side of the tangent plane have a curve of intersection with the surface. If the distance of the parallel plane from the tangent plane is made to approach zero, the curve will shrink

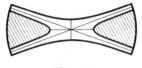

FIG. 199

down to the point of contact. If the distance approaches zero but the curve is suitably magnified on an ever-increasing scale, it is found that the magnified curve of intersection approaches an ellipse lying in the tangent plane and having the point of contact as center and the principal directions as axes. The ratio between the lengths of the axes is equal to the square root of the ratio between the principal radii of curvature.

If the same limiting process is applied to a plane lying on one side of the tangent plane at a hyperbolic point and parallel to the

FIG. 200

tangent plane, the result is a hyperbola, the directions and relative lengths of whose axes are the same functions of the principal directions and principal curvature as in the elliptic case (Fig. 199). Applied to the parallel planes on the other side of the tangent plane, the process gives rise to a second hyperbola having the same axes and same asymptotes as the first. The directions of the asymptotes are, in both cases, identical with the asymptotic directions of the surface at the point under consideration. At any elliptic or hyperbolic point of a surface the ellipse or the pair of conjugate hyperbolas constructed in this manner is called the *Dupin indicatrix*. At a parabolic point the corresponding process may lead to any one of several types of curves. At an umbilical point the Dupin indicatrix is a circle, as may be verified without difficulty in the case of the sphere and the ellipsoid. At a monkey saddle the Dupin indicatrix has a form like that in Fig. 200.

§ 29. The Spherical Image and Gaussian Curvature

So far we have characterized the curvature of a surface by two numbers, the principal curvatures. Gauss originated a method of representing the curvature at a point of a surface by a single number, which is analagous to what we have done for curves in space. This number, of course, will depend on the principal curvatures at the point of the surface.

Through the center of a unit sphere we draw the diameters that are parallel to the various normals of the surface we are studying. At one point of the surface we choose one of the two directions on the normal arbitrarily and then extend this choice of a normal direction continuously to all the neighboring points of the surface, thus obtaining a definite sense on all the normals. By choosing the same sense on the corresponding diameter of the sphere, we assign a definite point on the sphere—the end-point of the directed diameter—to every point of our surface. Thus we have a mapping of the surface onto the sphere. This process, due to Gauss, is called the *spherical representation* of the surface. Since the diameter of the sphere is perpendicular to the tangent plane at its extremities, the normal direction at every point is parallel, under Gauss's mapping, to the normal at its spherical image, and in addition the two tangent planes are parallel. For this reason, the spherical representation is occasionally referred to as the mapping by parallel normals, or as the mapping by parallel tangent planes. A surface may be mapped by parallel tangent planes not only onto the sphere, but onto any other closed surface. These generalized mappings find application in modern differential geometry.

In the spherical representation of a surface, a single point of the sphere corresponds to several points of the surface if and only if there exist on the surface distinct parallel normals having the same sense. As is readily apparent to the intuition, and as we shall see when we go into the matter more thoroughly later, there do not exist distinct parallel normals in the neighborhood of an elliptic or a hyperbolic point on a surface (cf. Figs. 202, 203, p. 196), whence it follows that the spherical mapping of such a neighborhood is one-to-one.

Any closed curve k on the original surface is represented by a closed curve k' on the sphere. We divide the area G enclosed by k'

on the sphere by the area F enclosed by k on the surface and then shrink the curve k down to a point P of the surface. F and G then approach zero and their quotient approaches a definite limit K:

$$\lim_{F \to 0} \frac{G}{F} = K \,.$$

The number K defined in this way is called the *Gaussian curvature* (or *total curvature* or *second curvature*) of the surface at P. It is found by analytical methods that the Gaussian curvature equals the product of the two principal curvatures at the point:

$$K = k_1 k_2 \,.$$

The Gaussian curvature has the highly important property of remaining invariant if the surface is subjected to an arbitrary bending. A bending is defined as any deformation for which the arc lengths and angles of all curves drawn on the surface are left invariant. We may illustrate what a bending is by using a surface made of a material, such as paper or tin foil, that is approximately unstretchable.[1] Being an invariant under bending, the Gaussian curvature must be intimately connected with those properties of a surface that depend only on the arc lengths and angles of the curves lying on it. For this reason, the Gaussian curvature and its higher-dimensional analogue is of fundamental importance in the theory of relativity, since this theory is concerned with just such "intrinsic" properties of higher-dimensional curved manifolds.

Since the definition of Gaussian curvature makes essential use of the position of the surface in space, the fact that it is an invariant under bending is rather surprising. The following argument is to give an indication of why it is nevertheless true. Let several flat triangular plates of rigid material be put together in space in such a way that any two adjacent plates can be rotated relative to each other about their common edge. Fig. 201 shows the setup with four triangles a, b, c, and d. Provided there are more than three sides, the three-dimensional corner constituted by the triangles allows of certain changes in its shape. All the possible changes

---

[1] Two surfaces that can be transformed into each other by bending are called "applicable" (they can be "applied") to each other. Thus the invariance under bending of Gaussian curvature may be expressed by the statement that any two applicable surfaces have the same Gaussian curvature at any two corresponding points. [*Trans.*]

leave the lengths and angles of all the curves drawn on the surface of the corner unaltered, and may therefore be regarded as bendings. By drawing the normals (l, m, n, etc.) to the faces of the corner and choosing the normal pointing to the outside in each case, we get a spherical image of the corner consisting of individual points (l', m', n', etc.) of the sphere. In order to relate this to the spherical representation of surfaces, we connect the points that represent adjacent faces of the corner by arcs of great circles, thus obtaining a spherical polygon on the sphere. We shall see that the area of this spherical polygon is unchanged by the bendings just defined, a fact that is obviously analogous to the invariance under bending of the Gaussian curva-

ture of a surface.

The truth of our contention follows from elementary theorems of spherical trigonometry. It is a well-known theorem that the area of a spherical triangle, and likewise the area of any polygon composed of great circles, depends

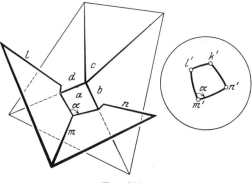

FIG. 201

only on the sum of its angles. Hence all we need to show is that the angles of the spherical polygon representing the corner are unchanged by the above bendings of the corner. But from Fig. 201 it is clear that each of the angles is the supplement of an angle between two adjacent edges of the corner, and by our assumption, these angles cannot be changed.

The discussion just given may be supplemented by a limiting process to yield the invariance of Gaussian curvature, at any rate in the case of convex surfaces. In preparation for this passage to the limit we have to approximate the surface by inscribed polyhedra with small triangular faces and then apply the above argument to each vertex of the polyhedron.

Let us see how the classification of points of a surface into elliptic, hyperbolic, and parabolic points may be expressed in terms of spherical representation and Gaussian curvature. If we move around an elliptic point along a small closed curve that lies on the

surface, its spherical image—assuming that the curve has no
double points—will also be a closed curve without double points
(see Fig. 202), and this curve is traversed in the same sense as the
original curve. A small curve without double points about a hyperbolic point is also mapped into a curve without double points on the
sphere, but in this case the sense is reversed (see Fig. 203). It is
customary in analytic geometry to attach the same sign or opposite

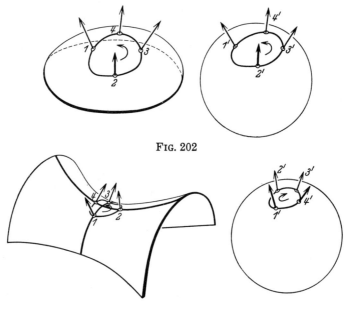

Fig. 202

Fig. 203

signs to the areas of two regions according to whether they are
enclosed by curves having the same sense or opposite senses. In
conformity with this convention, the Gaussian curvature is called
positive at convex parts of a surface, *negative* at saddle-shaped
parts. These are the same signs as we obtain by expressing the
Gaussian curvature in terms of the two principal curvatures. For,
the two principal centers of curvature lie on the same normal half-
line at an elliptic point and on opposite normal half-lines at a hyperbolic point; and if one ray is regarded as positive and the other as
negative, it follows that the product of the two principal radii of
curvature—and therefore also the product of the principal curvatures, i.e. the Gaussian curvature—is positive at elliptic points and
negative at hyperbolic points. Since the image of a sufficiently small

closed curve without double points is also free from double points, the spherical representation of sufficiently small regions that are everywhere cup-shaped (called surfaces of positive curvature), or everywhere saddle-shaped (called surfaces of negative curvature), must be one-to-one.

The parabolic points assume a role intermediate between that of the elliptic and the hyperbolic points. We should therefore expect that the Gaussian curvature at parabolic points is equal to zero. This is readily verified by referring to the definition of parabolic points; at these points one of the principal curvatures vanishes and therefore the

Fig. 204

product of the principal curvatures, which is to say, the Gaussian curvature, vanishes as well.

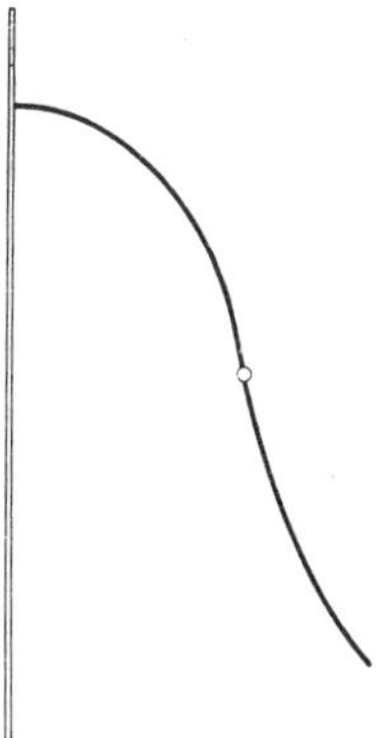

The plane consists entirely of parabolic points. Because the Gaussian curvature is an invariant under bending, it follows that a plane sheet of paper can never be applied to a surface having positive or negative curvature. Indeed, it is intuitively clear that the paper would have to wrinkle in the first case and tear in the second.

Let us consider a given surface that does not consist entirely of parabolic points and that moreover contains points of positive as well as points of negative Gaussian curvature. Since the variation of the Gaussian curvature on the surface is

Fig. 205

continuous, there must be points on the surface at which the Gaussian curvature vanishes, and these points have to form continuous curves separating the regions of positive Gaussian curvature from the regions of negative Gaussian curvature. These curves, consisting of parabolic points, are called the *parabolic curves* of the surface.[2] Of course the presence of parabolic curves is inevitable only on those surfaces on which the Gaussian curvature assumes both signs. This does not happen on any of the surfaces we have thus far studied: on any second-order surface the curvature is either positive everywhere, as on the ellipsoid, or negative everywhere, as on the hyperboloid of one sheet, or everywhere zero, as on the cylinder and the cone, which can, after all, be formed from a plane sheet of paper. On the minimal surfaces, moreover, the curvature is nowhere positive.

We shall now give some examples of surfaces having parabolic curves and examine their spherical images. A particularly simple surface of this type is the surface of a bell. It is obtained by rotating a plane curve having a point of inflection, about an axis in its plane (Fig. 205). Let us use a vertical axis. In the case illustrated in Fig. 205, the part of the curve above the point of inflection generates a surface all of whose points are elliptic, while the lower part of the curve generates a surface all of whose points are hyperbolic. Accordingly, the circle (parallel) of latitude on this surface of revolution traced out by the point of inflection of the curve is the parabolic curve of the bell surface. This can also be seen from the behavior of the tangent planes. The tangent planes at the hyperbolic point intersect the bell in a curve that has the form of a loop with two branches passing through the point of contact (see Fig. 206). As the point of contact approaches the parabolic curve from below, the closed part of the loop becomes smaller and the angle between the two branches intersecting at the point of contact becomes more acute. Finally, when the point of contact lies on the parabolic curve (Fig. 207), the loop is contracted into the point of contact, and the intersection has a cusp at this point. If the point of contact moves on into the elliptic part of the surface (Fig. 208), the intersection

---

[2] F. Klein used the parabolic curves for a peculiar investigation. To test his hypothesis that the artistic beauty of a face was based on certain mathematical relations, he had all the parabolic curves marked out on the Apollo Belvidere, a statue renowned for the high degree of classical beauty portrayed in its features. But the curves did not possess a particularly simple form, nor did they follow any general law that could be discerned (see Fig. 204).

becomes a curve consisting of an isolated point at the point of tangency together with a curve that has continuous curvature and is confined to the hyperbolic part of the surface. As a byproduct, this discussion has provided us with examples of the types of singular points of plane curves listed on page 174.

Let us examine the spherical image of the bell surface in the

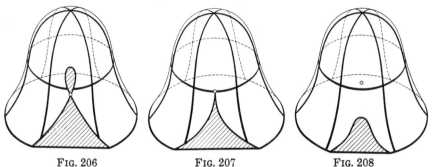

FIG. 206   FIG. 207   FIG. 208

vicinity of the circle of latitude consisting of parabolic points (see Fig. 209). We shall pick an arbitrary point on the parabolic curve and draw a small closed curve 1 2 3 4 5 6 7 8 1 around it. Let the points 1 and 5 be respectively the highest and the lowest point of the region F of the surface enclosed by the curve. Let 3 and 7 be points of intersection of the curve with the circle of latitude forming the parabolic curve. The meridian, whose rotation gene-
rates the bell surface, has parallel tangents in the neighborhood of its point of inflection (cf. p. 174). Clearly, the bell-surface has parallel normals at the corresponding points, so that these points have the same spherical image. Hence every circle of latitude im-

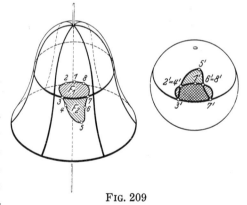

FIG. 209

mediately above the parabolic curve is matched by a circle immedi-
ately below the parabolic curve which has the same spherical image. Thus it is clear that the spherical mapping of the region F cannot be one-to-one. To get a picture of this, we do the following. Choose the points 2, 4, 6, 8 in such a way that the normals at 2 and 4 are

parallel and the normals at 6 and 8 are parallel. The parabolic curve divides F into two regions F_1 and F_2 whose interior consists entirely of elliptic points and of hyperbolic points respectively and which are therefore mapped one-to-one into two regions of the sphere. Both of these regions border on the image of the parabolic curve, and this image, on the unit sphere, is obviously itself a circle in a horizontal plane. But whereas F_1 and F_2 lie on opposite sides of the parabolic curve, their image regions on the sphere both border on the image circle from above and must therefore overlap. The boundary of F is represented by a curve $1'2'3'4'5'6'7'8'1'$ which intersects itself at the points $2'=4'$ and $6'=8'$.

We thus see that the spherical image of the bell must be folded over on itself along the image of the parabolic curve. As a general rule, this folding over occurs along the images of any parabolic curves that may exist on any given surface. However, there is a characteristic exception,

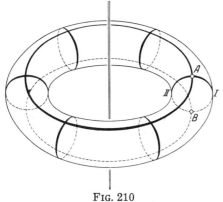

Fig. 210

which we shall explain by means of a second example.

In a vertical plane we draw a circle and a vertical axis that does not intersect the circle. Rotation of the circle about the axis produces a surface of revolution called a torus (see Fig. 210). The highest point A and the lowest point B of the circle divide it into two semicircles I and II. Clearly, the part of the torus generated by I has positive Gaussian curvature and the part generated by II, negative Gaussian curvature. The two parts are separated by the two parallel circles traced by A and B. These circles are the parabolic curves of the surface. Any plane tangent to the torus at a point lying on one of these circles meets the torus in a curve consisting of a single branch through the point of contact, for evidently it is tangent to the torus along the entire length of the circle and does not meet the surface anywhere else. Thus we have found an example of parabolic points the intersection of whose tangent plane with the surface does not have a cusp. Fig. 211 exhibits the curve in which the tangent plane at a hyperbolic point near the parabolic curve intersects the torus. The tangent plane at an elliptic point has only its point of contact in common with the torus.

Let us study the spherical image of the torus. We shall choose a direction, say the direction pointing to the outside, on all the normals. All the normals to either one of the two parabolic circles are parallel; hence each of the parabolic circles is mapped into a single point of the sphere, in fact the images are the highest and the lowest point of the sphere respectively. The part of the torus where the curvature is positive has no two parallel normals, and it is easy to see that its image covers all of the sphere, except for the highest and the lowest points, exactly once. The same is true for the

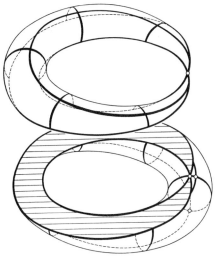

FIG. 211

part of the torus where the curvature is negative. Hence the spherical image of the torus covers the whole sphere, with the exception of the highest and lowest points, exactly twice, and the two layers are connected at these two exceptional points. In order to visualize the way in which the layers are connected, we proceed as in the previous example. Around a parabolic point we draw a small closed curve 12341 without double points. Fig. 212, in which the torus and the sphere are viewed obliquely from above, should make the choice of the points

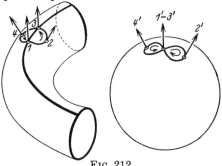

FIG. 212

on the curve and the shape of its image clear without the need of detailed explanation. That the spherical image is a figure eight is in agreement with the fact that the sense is preserved on curves in the elliptic part of the torus and reversed on curves in the hyperbolic part.

Our example is typical for the case of a surface that is tangent to the same plane along the entire length of a (necessarily parabolic) curve. The example of the bell surface, on the other hand, illustrates the case where the tangent plane changes as we move along the parabolic curve. In both examples the parabolic curve separates a region of positive Gaussian curvature on the surface from a region of negative Gaussian curvature.

As a final example, we shall consider a surface that has an isolated parabolic point surrounded by a region of negative curvature (Fig. 213). This is the monkey saddle, described on page 191.

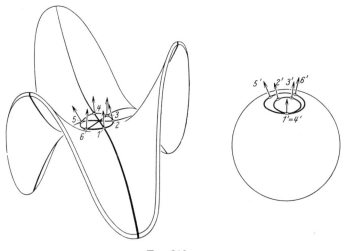

Fig. 213

Evidently the points of the surface where the normals are parallel are the points which have diametrically opposite positions with respect to the parabolic point. Hence the spherical image of a closed curve without double points enclosing the parabolic point is a closed curve that goes two times around the image of the parabolic point.[3] Similarly, it is obvious that we may also construct an isolated parabolic point with saddle-shaped neighborhood such that a closed curve surrounding it once is mapped into a curve making three, four, or any arbitrary number of turns around its image. On the other hand, the Gaussian representation of a parabolic point surrounded by a region of positive curvature behaves as if the

---

[3] Thus the representation by parallel normals of the monkey saddle is a Riemann surface with a branch point at the point representing the parabolic point (see p. 271). Notice also that the sense is reversed in Fig. 213.

curvature on the original surface were positive throughout and the parabolic point did not exist.

In conclusion, we shall describe the behavior of the lines of curvature and of the asymptotic lines of a surface under the spherical mapping of the surface. The principal directions are completely characterized as being the only directions that are parallel to their image directions. Only at the umbilical points does this criterion break down; here every direction is parallel to its image direction. Furthermore, we may observe, in the case of an elliptic point, that either both principal directions have the same sense as their images or both have the opposite sense, depending on the initial choice of the sense of the normals. At a hyperbolic point, on the other hand,

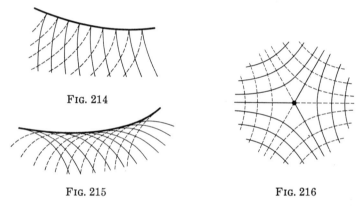

Fig. 214

Fig. 215

Fig. 216

one of the principal directions has the same sense as its image and the other has the opposite sense.

This criterion gives us a very easy way to find all the lines of curvature on any surface of revolution. In fact, it tells us that the lines of curvature of any such surface are the parallels of latitude and the meridians, for it is clear that these curves are represented by a system of parallels of latitude and meridians on the sphere, and that the direction of any such curve, furthermore, is parallel at every point to the direction of its image at the corresponding point. It follows that the two poles of a convex closed surface of revolution are umbilical points.

The asymptotic directions have a different characterization: they are perpendicular to their spherical images, and furthermore they are the only directions with this property. The sense in which the asymptotic line has to be rotated in the tangent plane to get the direction of its image is always clockwise for one asymptotic direction and counterclockwise for the other. This.is connected with the fact that the spherical representation invariably reverses the sense for surfaces of negative curvature.

Since the asymptotic lines cover only the hyperbolic part of a surface, their behavior in the vicinity of a parabolic curve must be singular. If the parabolic curve has a variable tangent plane, as in the case of the bell surface, then the asymptotic lines have cusps along the parabolic curve (Fig. 214). If, on the other hand, all the points of a parabolic curve have a common tangent plane, as they do on the torus, then the curve envelops the asymptotic lines, i.e. it is tangent to one of them at each point (Fig. 215). Fig. 216 shows what the asymptotic lines look like in the neighborhood of a monkey saddle. The number of asymptotic lines passing through such a point is exactly n, if the spherical image of a single closed curve about the point makes $n-1$ turns about the image of the point.

§ 30. Developable Surfaces. Ruled Surfaces

In the foregoing examination of the parabolic points of a surface we have omitted the case of a surface consisting of nothing but parabolic points. Because of its special importance we shall now discuss this case in full detail.

We have encountered examples of such surfaces already, to wit, the surfaces that result from bending a plane region. Now there is a general theorem which states that a surface of *constant* Gaussian curvature can be transformed, by bending, into any other surface of the same constant Gaussian curvature.[1]

It follows from this theorem that every surface whose curvature vanishes at every point, can be constructed by bending some plane region. This is why these surfaces are also called *developable surfaces*.

There are two other ways, entirely different from the first, of obtaining the developable surfaces. First, every surface enveloped

---

[1] In the case of surfaces of *variable* Gaussian curvature we do not have such a simple sufficiency condition for two surfaces to be applicable. A necessary condition is that it be possible to map the surfaces onto each other in such a way that their Gaussian curvatures are equal at corresponding points. But this condition is not sufficient, as may readily be seen by using some surfaces of revolution as counter-examples.

by a one-parameter family of planes is a developable surface. The variable plane is tangent to such a surface along an entire straight line that is obtained as the limiting position of the line in which two neighboring planes intersect. Since the surface has one and the same tangent plane at all the points of this straight line, the straight line is composed of parabolic points of the surface. And since the totality of these straight lines covers the entire surface (for this reason we call them *generators* of the surface), it follows that all the points of the surface are parabolic. It is a remarkable fact that the converse theorem—that every developable surface can be obtained in this way—is also true. Consequently all the developable surfaces are ruled surfaces.[2]

Because three planes always have a point of intersection,[3] it is plausible that any two neighboring generators of a developable surface should have a common point, a conjecture that can be proved analytically. This fact leads us to the third method of constructing the developable surfaces. The points of intersection of consecutive straight lines describe a curve. Intuitively, we are inclined to suspect that the generators do not intersect this space curve but meet it tangentially, and this can be confirmed. Thus we may also define a developable surface as the surface swept out by the tangents of an arbitrary twisted curve. (Considered in this light, the developable surface is known as the *tangential developable* of the curve.) At the same time, the surface is also enveloped by the osculating planes of the curve. Only for the cones and cylinders does this representation fail, while the preceding method of generation obviously applies to them as well as to the other developable surfaces.

From the second method of representation we can immediately find the spherical images of all the developable surfaces with the exception of the plane. For, the enveloping planes constitute the totality of planes tangent to the surfaces; hence all the tangent planes, and likewise all the normals, constitute a family depending on only *one* variable parameter. Hence the spherical indicatrix of a developable surface is always a curve; more specifically, it is the binormal indicatrix of the space curve whose tangents sweep out the surface. The fact that the spherical image of a surface of

---

[2] In four-space, however, there are developable surfaces that are not ruled surfaces. (Cf. the second appendix to Chap. VI).

[3] Provided that parallel planes are regarded as planes that intersect at infinity.

vanishing curvature degenerates into a curve was to be expected from the original definition of Gaussian curvature, since this implies that the spherical image of every region of such a surface has zero area.

Let us develop the tangential developable of any space curve upon the plane. The space curve becomes a plane curve, the generators of the surface become the tangents to the plane curve, and to every portion of the space curve there corresponds a portion of equal length on the plane curve. But over and above this, it may also be shown that at corresponding points of the two curves the curvature is the same.[4]

If we proceed the other way around, starting with a convex arc s in the plane, and removing the portion of the plane lying on the concave side of the arc, then we can bend the remaining part of the plane in such a way that the curvature at every point of the space curve into which s is transformed is the same as the curvature at the corresponding point of s. As can be proved analytically, we can, at the same time, give the space curve any torsion we wish. This type of deformation of a space curve, in which arc length and first curvature are preserved while torsion is changed, will be referred to simply as a *twisting* of the curve in question.

In the course of the above bending of the plane region, all the straight lines tangent to s obviously remain straight, while all the other straight lines become curved.[5] It is found, however, that the surface that results from the bending of the plane region is by no means all of the tangential developable of the twisted curve t obtained from s. For, the surface we have thus constructed contains of every tangent to t only one of the two rays emanating from the point of contact. If we produce the tangent rays so as to complete the tangent lines, we get a second surface. The two surfaces together constitute the tangential developable of t. They meet in in a sharp edge called *cuspidal edge* or *edge of regression* (Fig. 217)

---

[4] Intuitively, this is evident from the fact that the bending leaves the angle between neighboring tangents unchanged, and that curvature is defined as the limit of the ratio between this angle and the corresponding arc.

[5] Of course a completely arbitrary bending of a plane region may also change the curvature of s. For the curvature of s to be preserved, it is not only necessary, but also sufficient, that the tangents to s remain straight lines. Hence we can get a usable model by cutting the plane region out of a piece of paper and reinforcing some tangent rays of s by means of rods pasted to the paper.

of the surface. If t is changed back into the curve s by a continuous twisting, the two parts move continually closer to each other until they finally unite to form the plane of s. The whole tangential developable of t can be obtained by tacking together along s two sheets having the form of a part of the plane outside s, and then pulling the sheets apart in the course of the twisting of s. In this

process it is essential that the curvature of s be everywhere different from zero. If, on the other hand, the initial curve s has a point of inflection, then the tangential developable consists in general of four sheets that meet at the point of inflection, two of which are connected along the tangent to s at the point of inflection.

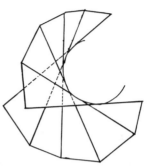

Let us now turn to the study of the ruled surfaces that are not develop-

FIG. 217

able. From the foregoing discussion, it follows that they are the ruled surfaces on which two neighboring rulings are mutually skew; for, as we have seen, the surface is developable if and only if neighboring generators meet.

We have associated with every developable surface a space curve lying on it that we called the edge of regression. We may generalize this idea so as to define a correspond-

ing curve, the *line of striction*, for the other ruled surfaces. To this end, we select two generators a and b from the family of generators on the surface and draw their common perpendicular (see Fig. 218). As is well known, this perpendicular is the

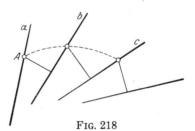

FIG. 218

shortest line connecting a and b. Let A be the point where the perpendicular meets a. If b approaches a through lines of the family of generators, A approaches a limiting position which is called the *central point*, or *point of striction* of a. The central point corresponds to the point of a developable where a generator intersects the neighboring generator and the edge of regression.

The *line of striction* is defined as the locus of the central point as a varies over all the generators of the surface. It would be erroneous to conclude that the line of striction has to intersect all the generators at right angles. For if a, b, and c are three neighboring generators (see Fig. 218), then the common perpendicular of b and c does not in general intersect b at the same point as does the common perpendicular of a and b. Hence the line through the central points need not have the same direction as the common perpendiculars, and therefore it need not meet the generators at right angles. On the hyperboloid of rotation of one sheet, for example, the line of striction is the equatorial circle, and obviously this does not meet any of the rulings at right angles.

The ruled surfaces are one-parameter manifolds of straight lines. For this reason, there are certain analogies between the ruled surfaces and the space curves, the latter being one-parameter manifolds of points. Thus, for example, it is possible to introduce a concept for the ruled surfaces that corresponds to the concept of curvature; this is the so-called *pitch*, or *striction*. We divide the angle between two generators by the shortest distance between them and call the limit of this quotient as the generators approach a common position, the pitch of the surface. (The reciprocal of the pitch is called the *parameter of distribution* of the ruled surface.)

The pitch is a measure of the variation of the tangent plane along a ruling. If the point of contact moves along a ruling, the tangent plane can obviously only change by a rotation about the ruling, since it always has to contain this straight line. It may be demonstrated analytically that the position of the tangent plane at a point P of the generator a is uniquely determined by the following three things: The position of the tangent plane at the central point A of a, the distance PA, and the pitch of the ruled surface on the ruling a. The distribution of the tangent planes may be described as follows: If P travels along a, moving in one direction from A to infinity, then the angle between the tangent plane at P and the tangent plane at A increases continuously and in the limit becomes a right angle. On the other side of A the behavior of the tangent planes is analogous and is symmetrical with respect to the central point A; if the points P and Q on opposite sides of A have the same distance from A, the tangent plane at A bisects the angle between the tangent planes at P and Q.

This leads us to the following result. Suppose we are given two ruled surfaces having the property that there is a certain generator on one of them at which the pitch has the same value as on a certain generator of the other. Then we can put the surfaces together in such a way that the two generators in question are coincident and that furthermore the surfaces are mutually tangential along this line. All that is necessary in order to accomplish this, is to make sure that the tangent planes at the respective central points coincide, with the two central points themselves coinciding, after which we may still have to rotate one of the surfaces relative to the other through two right angles, keeping the central points and their tangent planes together. The fact that the two surfaces can be put together in this way is of importance in the field of kinematics (cf. p. 286).

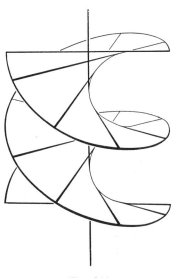

The developable surfaces may be characterized in various ways by their pitch. The cylinders are obviously the same as the surfaces of vanishing pitch, since the angle between neighboring generators is zero. The cones and the tangential developables of space curves, on the other hand, have infinite pitch, since neighboring generators have distance zero.

We have already found the spherical image of the developable surfaces. For ruled surfaces of finite pitch, as well,

Fig. 219

the spherical images have a simple property. The normals at all the points of a given ruling are parallel to a fixed plane, the normal plane of the straight line. We see, therefore, that first of all, the spherical image of a ruling has to be an arc of a great circle. Furthermore, the normal at a point that moves along a ruling rotates continuously through a right angle each time the point travels from the central point to infinity in either direction, whence it follows that the spherical image of the straight line is a semicircle. The extremities of the semicircle correspond to the ideal points of the straight line, and the image of the central point bisects the semicircle.

In conclusion, we shall construct a particularly simple ruled surface of constant pitch (Fig. 219). Here the obvious choice for the line of striction is a straight line that meets all the generators of the surface at right angles. Let d be the (constant) pitch of the surface. If a and b are two generators making an angle α with each other, and if A and B are the points where they intersect the line of striction, then

$$\alpha = AB \cdot d.$$

Hence the surface, which is called a *helicoid*, is transformed into itself by a screw motion of pitch d with the line of striction as axis. The most general helicoid is the surface swept out by an arbitrary space curve performing a uniform screw motion about a fixed axis. Thus our particular ruled helicoid is obtained when the generating curve is a straight line intersecting the axis at right angles. This surface is called a right helicoid.

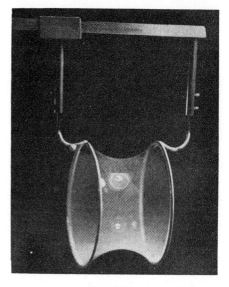

Fig. 220a   Fig. 220b

An examination by analytic methods reveals that the right helicoid is a minimal surface (Fig. 220a). On page 191 we have already seen an example of a minimal surface, the catenoid. There is an intimate connection between the catenoid and the right helicoid, for, the latter can be transformed into the catenoid by bending. This is accomplished by wrapping the helicoid infinitely many times around the surface of revolution in the same way as a plane can be wrapped around a circular cylinder; the line of striction has to cover the equator (i.e. the smallest circular section) of the catenoid, and the rulings are transformed into the meridians.[6]

---

[6] Note that the axis of the helicoid, far from being transformed into the axis of revolution, becomes a circle perpendicular to it. This is why Figs. 220a and 220b show the axis of the helicoid in a vertical position but that of the catenoid in a horizontal position.

A general discussion of the helicoids and the way in which they are related to the surfaces of revolution will be given later.

§ 31. The Twisting of Space Curves

The theory of developable surfaces has given us access to a method of deforming a space curve in such a way as to leave its arc length and curvature unchanged and to vary only its torsion. We called such a transformation of space curves a *twisting*. In particular, every space curve t can be transformed into a plane curve s by a twisting; the shape of s is uniquely determined by t, since the curvature of s is a given function of its arc length, and, by § 26, this completely determines the shape of s. There is a peculiar relation between s and t, as we shall see presently.

From the theory of geodesic curvature—a concept we shall not

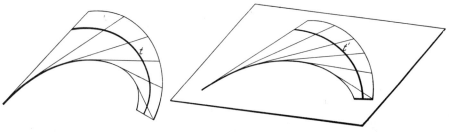

FIG. 221a   FIG. 221b

discuss here—we can get the following simple inequality, which we shall need in the sequel (see Figs. 221a and 221b) : If t lies on a developable surface and is transformed into a plane curve t' by unrolling the surface on the plane, then the curvature k' of t' can never be greater than the curvature k at the corresponding point of t, and in general it is actually smaller. For if α denotes the angle between the osculating plane of t and the corresponding tangent plane of the developable surface, then

$$k' = k \cos \alpha.$$

From this lemma we can deduce the following peculiar theorem: *Whenever a convex plane arc is subjected to twisting, all the chords become longer.*

In order to prove this, we consider the convex plane arc s with the end-points A, B (see Fig. 222a). Let a twisting of s yield the arc t of a space curve, with end-points C and D. Then we have to

prove that the straight-line segment CD is longer than the segment
AB. To this end, we construct a conical surface with C as vertex
which contains the arc t (Fig. 222b) and develop this cone in the
plane of s. Then t becomes a plane curve t' with end-points E and F
(Fig. 222c). The straight-line segment CD is on a generator of

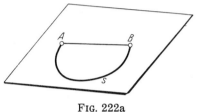

FIG. 222a

the cone; therefore it remains a
straight line under the above development and is mapped without
change in length onto the segment
EF. Hence the straight-line segments EF and CD are equal, and
it only remains to be proved that
EF is longer than AB. Now, the curves s and t' are equal in
length, and by our lemma, the curvature at every point of t' is
smaller than the curvature at the corresponding point of t and

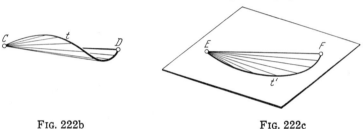

FIG. 222b   FIG. 222c

therefore of s also. Hence s can be transformed into t' by keeping
the point A fixed and diminishing the curvature at all the points
of s without changing the arc lengths. As a result of the convexity

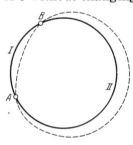

FIG. 223

of s it is intuitively evident that our deformation keeps moving B further away from a,
which may also be confirmed analytically
without difficulty. This completes the proof
of the inequality $EF > AB$, and hence of
our theorem.

We shall apply the result to the simple case
of the curves obtained by twisting a circular
arc, that is, to the curves of constant curva-
ture. By magnification or reduction of the figure, we can always
ensure that the value of the curvature shall be 1; hence we may
confine our attention to the case of curvature unity. Consider all
the space curves of curvature unity that connect two fixed points

A and B. In order to ensure the presence of circular arcs in this set, we shall assume that the distance AB is less than 2. Then it is indeed possible to pass a circle of unit radius through A and B. The two points divide the circle into two unequal arcs; let us call them I and II, where I denotes the shorter arc (see Fig. 223). Now we have the following paradoxical fact: The shorter arc I is longer than all the neighboring arcs of our family; the longer arc II is shorter than all neighboring arcs of the family; the only exceptions are the arcs obtained from I and II by rotation about AB, as their lengths are obviously equal to those of I and 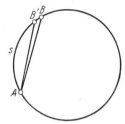 II respectively. We are concerned, then, with the curves that are obtained from I and II by twisting.

We shall prove the above fact in the following more general form: If a twisted arc t of constant curvature unity connects the points A and B and if it is not longer than II, then it

FIG. 224

is shorter than I. Let us transform t into a circular arc s by a twisting and superimpose s on the circle through A and B in such a way that one of the extremities of s falls on A (see Fig. 224). Then the other extremity of s is a point B' on the circle. By the theorem we proved earlier in this section, the chord AB' is shorter than the chord AB. But the length of the arc t has to be equal to the length of one of the arcs into which A and B' divide the circle. One of these arcs is longer than II and is therefore excluded by our assumption; hence t is equal to the other arc of the circle and is therefore shorter than I.

We have thus proved that no curve of curvature unity connecting A and B has a length between those of I and II. Let us now inquire whether there are any further limitations on the length of such a curve.

To begin with, it is easy to see that the arc may be arbitrarily long. For, the curves of constant curvature

FIG. 225

include, in particular, the circular helices (cf. p. 182). The pitch of such a helix may be chosen arbitrarily small. Therefore the number of turns on a helix between two points of distance AB, may be made arbitrarily large. But for sufficiently small pitch, the length of every turn of the helix of curvature unity is approximately equal to that of the circumference of the unit circle. Hence it is clear that the curve connecting A and B may indeed be arbitrary long (see Fig. 225).

On the other hand, our curve can not be arbitrarily short, since its length necessarily exceeds that of the straight-line segment AB. It is possible, however, to get arbitrarily close to this lower bound. For if we take a helix of curvature unity whose pitch is very large, then the tangent to the helix is nearly parallel to the axis and the distance of this helix from the axis can be made arbitrarily small. Thus an arc of such a helix can be made to differ arbitrarily little from its chord (see Fig. 226), and this proves our result. We thus see that the problem of connecting two fixed points by a curve of curvature unity having the smallest possible arc length, has no solution. An apparently similar minimal condition was seen earlier to characterize minimal surfaces. Similarly, Riemann showed that certain important theorems of the theory of functions were reducible to minimal properties. The present example shows that the assumption that every minimal problem has a solution, though apparently self-evident, is false in some cases and must therefore be checked in each individual case. To date, these existence proofs rank with the most laborious problems in the whole field of analysis (cf. §§ 38, 39).

FIG. 226

There is a very simple example of a minimal problem without a solution. It is the problem of connecting two points A and B by the shortest possible curve subject to the condition that the curve makes a right angle with the straight line AB at A. Here, too, we can get arbitrarily close to the straight-line segment AB but cannot reach it because the segment itself does not satisfy our condition (see Fig. 227).

FIG. 227

In conclusion, we mention a minimal problem for which the question of whether or not a solution exists had long been the subject of controversy. It is required to move a rod AB in the plane in such a way that the final effect is that of a rotation through two right angles and that the area swept out in the course of the motion is as small as possible. Only quite recently, Besicovitch proved that this problem has no solution (see *Math. Zeitschrift*, Vol. 27, 1928). By using a zig-zag motion we can make the area swept out arbitrary small (cf. p. 280).

§ 32. Eleven Properties of the Sphere

We have already become acquainted with the surfaces of vanishing Gaussian curvature. We shall now look for the surfaces of constant positive or negative curvature. By far the simplest and most important surface of this type is the sphere. A thorough study of the sphere would in itself provide sufficient material for a whole book. We shall here present only eleven properties that have a particularly strong appeal to the visual intuition. We shall at the same time become acquainted with several properties that are of importance not only for the geometry of the sphere but also for the general theory of surfaces. With regard to each property to be described we shall inquire whether it defines the sphere uniquely or whether there are other surfaces having the given property.

1. *The points of a sphere are equidistant from a fixed point. Also, the ratio of the distances of its points from two fixed points is constant.*

The first of these two properties constitutes the elementary definition of the sphere and consequently defines the sphere uniquely. The fact that the sphere has the second property as well, can be ascertained very easily by analytical methods. On the other hand, the second property defines not only the sphere but the plane as well. For, a plane is obtained if, and only if, the constant ratio is equal to unity. The plane obtained in this case is the plane of symmetry of the two fixed points.

2. *The contours and the plane sections of the sphere are circles.*

In the discussion of the second-order surfaces we mentioned the theorem that all the plane sections and contours of such surfaces are conics. In the case of a sphere, all these conics are circles. This property defines the sphere uniquely. From the observation that the shadow of the earth at a lunar eclipse is always a circle we may therefore infer that the earth is spherical.

3. *The sphere has constant width and constant girth.*

The term *constant width* denotes the property, of a solid, that the distance between any pair of parallel tangent planes is constant. Thus a sphere can be rolled arbitrarily between two parallel tangent planes. It would seem plausible that the sphere is uniquely defined by this property. In actual fact, however, there are numerous other closed convex surfaces, some of them without any singularities, whose width is also constant and which therefore can also be rotated between two fixed parallel plates to which they remain tangent throughout. Fig. 228 illustrates two different positions of such a surface.

The concept of constant width can also be applied to curves. A closed convex curve in the plane is said to have this property if the distance between two parallel tangents is always the same. The circle is a curve with this property, but is by no means the only one. Indeed, one of the two arcs into which the points of contact of a parallel pair of tangents divide a closed convex curve of constant width can be given quite arbitrarily, and then the other arc can always be (uniquely) determined in such a way that the condition of

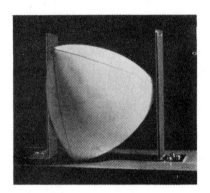 

Fig. 228a   Fig. 228b

constant width is satisfied for the resulting curve. This can be easily made plausible. For, the tangents of the given arc uniquely define the tangents of the second arc, since the latter are obtained by drawing the parallels to the given tangents at a fixed distance on the appropriate side. The second arc is then simply the envelope of this set of straight lines.

Obviously, the solids of constant width w are characterized by the property that all their contours obtained by parallel orthogonal projection are curves of the constant width w. Now there is a theorem to the effect that all curves sharing the same constant width are equal in circumference. And since a girth of a solid is defined as being the perimeter of one of its orthogonal parallel projections, it follows from the above theorem that the solids of constant width have constant girth as well. Consequently any surface of constant width. around which a paper cylinder has been firmly wrapped, is free to turn in all directions inside the cylinder without becoming loose or tearing the cylinder.

Conversely, it has been proved by Minkowski that all convex surfaces of constant girth also have constant width, so that each of these two properties implies the other.[1]

4. *All the points of a sphere are umbilics.*

We have mentioned this property earlier, pointing out at the same time that the plane is the only other surface sharing this property with the sphere (see p. 187). One of the ways in which we can recognize that all the points of a sphere are umbilics is from the fact that all plane sections of a sphere are circles. Let a plane that intersects the sphere be moved, keeping it parallel to its original position until it is tangent to the sphere at a point P; then we see that the Dupin indicatrix at the point P is a circle (see p. 192). Hence P is an umbilical point.

5. *The sphere does not have a surface of centers.*

We have seen earlier (p. 184 ff.) that the centers of curvature of all the normal sections at a point on a surface in general fill out a segment of the normal at this point. The extremities of this segment are the centers of curvature belonging to the principal directions. These two points are sometimes called the *foci* of the normal. They coincide if and only if the point of the surface is an umbilic. A focus is at infinity if and only if the Gaussian curvature vanishes at the point of the surface.

If the point of the surface assumes all the positions possible on the surface, then the two foci on its normal in general take on all possible positions on a certain pair of surfaces which are jointly called the *evolute* or *surface of centers* (or *focal surface*) of the original surface. In the case of a sphere, the evolute, or surface of centers, consists of the center of the sphere alone, since all the foci are at this point. The sphere is the only surface for which one sheet of the surface of centers degenerates into a point. Let us now find out what surfaces have the property that both sheets of their surface of centers degenerate into curves. It is found that the only

---

[1] If we had set the condition that all the projections of a solid have the same area instead of the same circumference, we would have obtained a different class of surfaces, the so-called *surfaces of constant brightness*. The sphere is one of these surfaces, but by no means the only one. (Cf. W. Blaschke, *Kreis und Kugel*, p. 151, New York, Chelsea Publishing Company.)

surfaces with this property are the surfaces called *Dupin's cyclides*, after their discoverer (some of them are shown in Fig. 229). These surfaces may also be defined as the envelopes of the family of spheres tangent to three fixed spheres. Furthermore, the Dupin cyclides

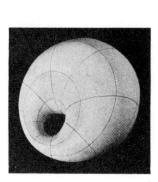

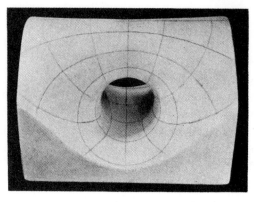

Fig. 229a

Fig. 229b

are the only surfaces all of whose lines of curvature are circles. Some of the lines of curvature are marked out on the five plaster models whose photographs appear in Fig. 229. Incidentally, each sphere of the family of spheres that envelops a cyclide is tangent to the latter along a line of curvature, and every line of curvature

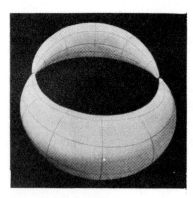

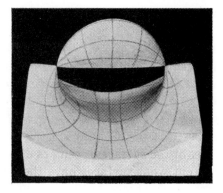

Fig. 229c

Fig. 229d

on a cyclide can be obtained in this way. An example of a cyclide with which we are already familiar is the torus. Its surface of centers consists of the axis of rotation together with the circle traced out by the center of the generating circle during the rotation.

Furthermore, all the cones and cylinders of revolution are cyclides; one part of the surface of centers is the axis of rotation, and the other part is at infinity. In the case of all the other cyclides, the surface of centers consists of two conics, which are in general an ellipse and a hyperbola having the same relative positions as the focal curves of a quadric surface.[2]

If we require only one sheet of the surface of centers to degenerate into a curve, we get a much more inclusive class of surfaces. Every surface of revolution has this property; one part of its surface of centers always consists of the axis. The most general class of surfaces satisfying our condition is the class of *canal surfaces*. A canal surface is defined as the envelope of a family of spheres of variable radius with centers lying on a fixed curve. The fixed curve itself always forms one of the two parts of the surface of centers of the canal surface. In the special case where this curve is a straight line, the result is a surface of revolution; thus the surfaces of revolution are a special case of canal surfaces. As in the

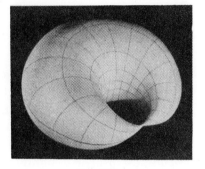

Fig. 229e

case of surfaces of revolution, one of the two families of lines of curvature on every canal surface consists of circles. These circles occupy the limiting positions of the circles of intersection of neighboring spheres. (They are called the characteristics of the spheres of the family.)

For all other curved surfaces, the surface of centers consists of a pair of two-dimensional sheets. It can be proved that, at its foci, a normal never cuts these two sheets, but is always tangent to them. Thus if the two sheets of the surface of centers of a surface are given, the normals of the surface are characterized as being the common tangents of the two sheets. This raises the question of

---

[2] The surfaces illustrated in Figs. 229a and 229b are obtained from the torus by inversion in a sphere (see p. 268). In Fig. 229b the center of the inversion lies on the torus; in Fig. 229a it does not. The surfaces of Figs. 229c and 229d are obtained by inversion from a circular cone, the center of inversion lying on the cone in the case of Fig. 229d. Fig. 229e illustrates a surface obtained by inversion from a circular cylinder, where the center of inversion does not lie on the cylinder.

under what circumstances it is possible to reverse the order of derivation. We begin with two arbitrary surfaces and consider the family S of all straight lines tangent to both. Then the question is whether there is a surface (the *involute*) whose normals consist of the straight lines of the family S, i.e. whether the two given surfaces constitute the surface of centers, or evolute, of another surface. For this to be the case there is a single condition that is both necessary and sufficient: the tangent planes to the two surfaces at the two points where any given straight line of the family S touches the surfaces, have to be mutually perpendicular. A system of confocal quadrics gives us an example of such surfaces, for it may be shown that every pair of confocal quadrics of unlike type satisfies our condition.

6. *All the geodesics of the sphere are closed curves.*

The geodesic lines, or geodesics, of a surface are a generalization of the straight lines of the plane. Like the straight lines, they are endowed with several important properties distinguishing them from all other curves on the surface. Hence they may be defined in various ways. We shall discuss the three definitions of geodesics as *shortest* lines, as *frontal* lines, and as *straightest* lines.

The first property signifies that every sufficiently small portion of a geodesic curve is the shortest path on the surface connecting the end-points of the portion. It follows that the geodesic lines of a surface continue to be geodesic if the surface is subjected to bending. Hence the geodesics are of fundamental significance for the intrinsic properties of a surface (cf. p. 194), and all the intrinsic properties of a surface (such as its Gaussian curvature) can be determined by drawing geodesics and measuring their arc lengths. This is analogous to the fact that the geometry of the plane can be fully characterized by the drawing of straight lines and the measuring of linear distances. Analogous to the fact that there is one and only one straight line through any two points in the plane, is the fact that one and only one geodesic arc can be drawn through any two points of a surface if they are not too far apart. Obviously, the geodesic arc is obtained by pulling taut a thread that passes through the two points on the surface.[3]

---

[3] On the outside of a convex surface the thread will automatically lie on the surface. For other surfaces, it is necessary to ensure that the thread does not leave the surface.

The second property of geodesic lines, that they are *frontal*, is also an intrinsic property of the surface. Here the geodesics are defined by the condition that they always move an infinitesimal arc of the surface "straight ahead." Let a small finite arc AB be moved along the surface in such a way that the paths of A and B are equal in length and that both paths are perpendicular to AB throughout; then the locus of the midpoint of AB can be made to approximate a geodesic with any degree of accuracy desired, by choosing the arc AB to be sufficiently short. In the light of this definition of geodesics, it is plausible that there should be exactly one geodesic issuing in each direction at every point of a surface. Furthermore, the definition tells us that we can obtain an approximation to the geodesic lines by moving a very small buggy along the surface on two wheels, the wheels being rigidly fastened to their common axis so that their speeds of rotation are equal. Since the driver of an automobile does not want to drive only along the geodesic lines of the earth, and since it is desirable (for the preservation of the tires and for other reasons) to avoid skidding, the automobile has to be constructed in such a way that the back wheels are free to turn at different speeds.

The third definition of geodesics, as the *straightest lines*, is not an absolute property of the surface but depends on the way the surface is imbedded in space; at each of its points a geodesic line has the smallest curvature among all the curves through the point that lie on the surface and that have the same tangent at the point as the geodesic. The entire course of a geodesic is fully determined by this property if one of its points and its direction at this point are given. The geodesic line can be obtained by attaching a flexible straight knitting needle at the given point in such a way that it points in the given direction, and then bending it onto the surface so that it can only move along the surface. Then the needle will assume the form of a geodesic line because its elastic resistance will always cause it to resist further bending.

The straightest lines may also be characterized by the geometric requirement that the osculating plane of the curve is to contain the normal to the surface at every point of the curve. If this condition is satisfied, it is easy to see intuitively that the angle between the tangents at neighboring points on the curve will be as small as it can be if the curve is to remain on the surface. But this is tantamount to the condition of minimum curvature. It is to the characterization by their osculating planes that the geodesics owe their name. This is the criterion used in staking out the shortest lines on the surface of the earth in a geodetic survey.

The geodesics of the sphere are its great circles. For, the planes of the great circles intersect the sphere at right angles, and from every point on the sphere there emanates a great circle in every direction. Thus all the geodesics on the sphere are closed curves. This, however, is by no means a unique characterization of the sphere; there are a great many other closed convex surfaces all of whose geodesics also are closed curves.[4]

It is now natural to try to find closed geodesic lines on any surface. This is particularly simple in the case of the surfaces of revolution. On these surfaces all the meridians are geodesics, because their planes contain the axis and therefore cut the surface at right angles. (We proved earlier that the meridians are lines of curvature as well.) Thus every closed surface of revolution has a one-parameter family of closed geodesic lines. On other types of surfaces there are only isolated lines of this kind. It may be demonstrated, for example, that the only closed geodesics on the general ellipsoid are the ellipses in which the surface intersects its three planes of symmetry.

On the other hand, there are at least three closed geodesics on every closed convex surface. This theorem had been conjectured for a long time, but was proved only recently by Lusternik and Schnirelmann.

The geodesics play a very important role in physics. Any mass point that is not acted on by any forces but is constrained to remain on a fixed surface moves on a geodesic line of the surface. Each of our definitions of a geodesic line gives us an approach to the laws of the mechanics of points. Thus the definition of geodesics as the shortest lines is embodied in *Jacobi's principle* in mechanics. As the straightest lines they appear in the Gauss-Hertz *principle of least constraint*. The relation of the osculating plane to geodesics plays a role in the Lagrange equations of the first kind.

There is a peculiar relation between the geodesic lines on the one hand and the theory of surfaces of centers and lines of curvature

---

[4] Here and in the following we call a geodesic curve closed if it returns to its starting point without having a corner and without intersecting itself before it reaches the starting point.

on the other. We have mentioned before that the normals of every
surface are tangent to its surface of centers. Thus a certain direction on the surface of centers is assigned to each of its points,
namely the direction of that normal of the original surface that is
tangent to the surface of centers at the particular point under consideration. Like the principal directions and asymptotic directions,
this field of directions on the surface of centers can be integrated,
that is, a family of curves can be found having the given direction
at every point. It is found that the curves of this family are geodesic lines. Of course, the tangential developables of these geodesics
are generated by normals of the original surface. But in addition,
the curves in which the developables intersect the original surface
are identical with its lines of curvature; moreover, each of the two
sheets of the surface of centers corresponds to one of the two
families of lines of curvature.

We mentioned earlier that any pair of confocal quadrics of dif-

FIG. 230

ferent types can be interpreted as the surface
of centers of some surface. This fact furnishes
a method for finding all the geodesic lines of
the general ellipsoid. Let E be the given ellipsoid. Choose some hyperboloid H confocal
with E. The straight lines that are tangent
to E and H at the same time define a field of directions on E, and
by the theorem we have just mentioned, all the integral curves of
this field are geodesics. But this by no means exhausts all the
geodesics on E; through every point of the surface, geodesic lines
run in all directions, and we have only found those geodesics that
lie in certain preassigned directions. It is easy to characterize the
family of the geodesic lines thus far found on E; for, it may be
proved that they are all those geodesics of E, and only those, that
are tangent to the curve in which E and H intersect (see Fig. 230).
They cover the ellipsoid in much the same way as the tangents of
an ellipse cover the plane. The curve of intersection of E and H
(which, incidentally, is a line of curvature of E, as we have already
mentioned), divides the ellipsoid into two parts. One part has no
curves of the family on it, while two curves of the family pass
through every point of the other part.

The totality of the geodesic lines of E can be obtained by simply
letting H run through all the hyperboloids of one sheet and two

sheets of the confocal system defined by E. In this process, it is necessary to include the focal hyperbola as a limiting case of a hyperboloid and to count all the straight lines meeting the hyperbola as tangents to this degenerate surface. The focal hyperbola intersects E in the four umbilical points. A limiting process applied to the above argument shows that the family of geodesic lines of E belonging to the focal hyperbola consists of all those geodesics that pass through an umbilical point of E, and only of those.[5] Furthermore, it is found that every geodesic line through an umbilical point also passes through the diametrically opposite umbilical point.

On the sphere, all the geodesics through a given point P also pass through a second fixed point, the point diametrically opposite P. The behavior of the geodesic lines passing through an umbilical point of the ellipsoid is analogous to this property. On the other hand, it can be proved that the geodesics through any other fixed point of the ellipsoid do not all have a second point in common.

It is natural to ask whether the sphere is the only surface on which all the geodesic lines emanating from an arbitrary fixed point have a second point in common. The answer to this question has not yet been found.

7. *Of all solids having a given volume, the sphere is the one having the smallest surface area; of all solids having a given surface area, the sphere is the one having the greatest volume.*

These two properties (each of which implies the other) define the sphere uniquely. The proof of this fact leads to a problem of the calculus of variations and is extremely laborious. But a simple experimental proof is implicit in every freely floating soap bubble. As was mentioned earlier in connection with the minimal surfaces, the soap bubble, by virtue of its surface tension, seeks to reduce its surface area to a minimum; and since the bubble encloses a fixed volume of air, it follows that the bubble assumes the minimum surface area for a fixed volume. But it is found by observation that freely floating soap bubbles are always spherical unless they are appreciably subjected to the influence of gravity because of adhering drops of liquid.

8. *The sphere has the smallest total mean curvature among all convex solids with a given surface area.*

---

[5] The thread construction described on p. 188 is intimately connected with this fact.

The mean curvature H at a point on a surface is defined as the arithmetic mean of the principal curvatures at the point:

$$H = (k_1 + k_2)/2.$$

In this formula, the principal curvatures must be assigned like signs at elliptic points and unlike signs at saddle points. In contrast with the Gaussian curvature, the mean curvature does not in general remain invariant under bending of the surface. Thus the mean curvature tells us something primarily of the way the surface is imbedded in space.

The minimal surfaces have already given us an idea of the significance of this concept of curvature. The minimal surfaces were defined by the property that the principal curvatures at any point of such a surface are equal in magnitude and opposite in sign; and this means that the mean curvature is everywhere zero.

In order to get the *total* mean curvature of a surface, we proceed as follows. We think of the surface as having mass distributed upon it, the mass density at each point being equal to the mean curvature at that point. Then the total mass spread out over the surface in this way is called the total mean curvature of the surface.

The problem of finding the closed surfaces with minimum total mean curvature for a given surface area leads, like the problem connected with the preceding property of the sphere, to a problem of the calculus of variations, and here again, we find that the sphere is the only surface satisfying the given condition.

The two last-named properties of the sphere are derived from certain inequalities in the general theory of convex bodies. Let us at least indicate the principle involved. A sphere of radius r has surface area $S = 4\pi r^2$ and volume $V = 4\pi r^3/3$. In order to deal with like dimensions, we have to compare the third power of the surface area with the square of the volume. This gives us the equation

$$S^3 = 36\pi V^2,$$

which applies to every sphere no matter what its radius. Since of all surfaces of the same area, the sphere has the greatest volume, we must have

$$S^3 \geqq 36\pi V^2$$

for all the other surfaces. Now if M denotes the total mean curvature of a surface, the following important inequalities can be proved to hold for all convex bodies:

1. $S^2 - 3VM \geqq 0$,

2. $M^2 - 4\pi S \geqq 0$.

In the second formula, the equality holds only in the case of the sphere. But this implies that among all convex bodies having given surface area, the sphere, and the sphere only, yields the minimum value of M. By eliminating M from formulas 1. and 2., we get the above relation between surface area and volume and see that the equality sign applies only in the case of the sphere. The argument we have outlined takes into consideration only convex bodies, whereas the inequality involving the volume and surface area is in fact also true for bodies that are not everywhere convex.

9. *The sphere has constant mean curvature.*

This follows from the fact that all normal sections have the same radius of curvature, namely the radius of the sphere. But the sphere is by no means the only surface of constant mean curvature. Every minimal surface, for example, has mean curvature zero at every point, and hence constant mean curvature. Like the sphere and the minimal surfaces, all the other surfaces of constant mean curvature can also be realized by soap bubbles. Let an arbitrary closed curve in space be given. Take a fixed surface bounded by the curve and in addition stretch a soap film over the curve. This may be accomplished in practice, for example, by giving the rim of the head of a pipe the shape of the desired curve, making a soap bubble with this pipe, and then plugging up the stem so that it is airtight. Then the soap film and the interior wall of the pipe enclose a fixed quantity of air. Under the influence of surface tension, the soap film assumes the shape that makes its surface area a minimum under the given conditions. By use of the calculus of variations it can be shown that every surface determined in this way is a surface of constant mean curvature. The particular value of this constant mean curvature depends on the pressure of the air enclosed (which in turn is controlled by the amount of air blown into the pipe). In the particular case where the pressure of the enclosed air equals, rather than exceeds, the atmospheric pressure, we are back to the case of minimal surfaces.

Thus our soap films furnish us with a multitude of surfaces of the kind we were trying to find. But all these surfaces have the property of ending abruptly at the space curve, that is, they have a boundary. This raises the question of whether there are any surfaces of constant mean curvature other than the sphere that have neither a boundary nor any other singular points. It is found that the answer is in the negative, so that the sphere is defined uniquely by our additional condition. This fact can be made plausible by reference to soap bubbles. We already know that a soap bubble suspended freely in the air always assumes the form of a sphere. If we produce soap bubbles of constant size bounded by smaller and smaller curves, then it is to be expected—and may be verified experimentally—that the shape of the boundary curve has less and less influence on the shape of the bubble, and that the shape assumed by the bubble in the limit is always that of a bubble not having a boundary, i.e. that of a sphere.[6]

10. *The sphere has constant positive Gaussian curvature.*

The answer to the question of whether the sphere can be uniquely characterized by this property is the same as in the case of mean curvature. By itself, the property of constant Gaussian curvature certainly does not characterize the sphere. For, all the surfaces derived from a portion of the sphere by bending share this property, since the Gaussian curvature is unaltered by bending. Let us once again add the condition that the surface have no boundary and no other singularities and then ask whether there are any surfaces of constant positive Gaussian curvature other than the sphere which satisfy this additional condition. It is found that the answer is in

---

[6] It would be easy to fall into the error of thinking that the mean curvature of the soap bubble keeps on increasing as we blow into the pipe. In the beginning, the mean curvature does in fact increase, starting from the value zero which it has for the minimal surface. But if we blow quite hard, it follows from the argument given in the text that the soap bubble (assuming that it does not burst) will take on the approximate shape of a sphere of steadily increasing radius; hence the mean curvature, which is the reciprocal of the radius of the sphere, will steadily decrease, approaching the value zero. Given a definite boundary curve and any sufficiently small number c, we therefore know that there are at least two surfaces bounded by the given curve and having the constant mean curvature c. This phenomenon contrasts remarkably with many other variational problems which invariably lead to only one extremal surface bounded by a given closed curve. If the sign of the mean curvature is disregarded, then we can get two more surfaces of the same constant mean curvature bounded by the same curve; they can be realized in the form of soap bubbles by inflating the original minimal surface from the other side.

the negative, one immediate consequence of which is that the sphere as a whole cannot be bent. To begin with, it can be proved that a surface of constant positive Gaussian curvature having no singularities and no boundary curve can not extend to infinity, like the plane, but must necessarily be a closed surface, like the sphere. An easy calculation reveals, furthermore, that there are no other surfaces besides the sphere and the plane on which both principal curvatures are constant. Hence we shall only have to consider the case of a closed surface on which both principal curvatures vary, but vary in such a way that their product has the given constant value of the Gaussian curvature. On such a surface there would have to be at least one regular point at which one of the principal curvatures assumes a maximum. But it can be proved analytically that no such point can exist on a surface of constant positive Gaussian curvature. In other words: On a bounded region, not spherical in shape, of a surface of constant positive curvature, all the points at which the principal curvatures have maxima are on the boundary. And since the sphere does not have a boundary, it follows that the sphere as a whole cannot be bent, and that there are, other than the sphere, no closed surfaces at all that are free from singularities and have constant positive Gaussian curvature.

Since there are, on the other hand, pieces of the sphere which can be bent, there arises the question of how big a hole we must cut out of the sphere in order to be able to bend the remaining part. It is conceivable that the hole would have to be at least of a certain minimum size, the size of a hemisphere, for example. It can be proved, however, that the contrary is the case: the spherical surface can be bent as soon as any arbitrarily small portion is removed; it is in fact sufficient even to slit the sphere open along an arbitrarily small segment of a great circle. On the other hand, it is not yet known whether the sphere can be bent after the removal of nothing but one or more isolated points.

A remarkable relation exists between the fact that the sphere can be bent once an arbitrarily small hole is cut out of it, and the behavior of soap bubbles. It rests on the following fact, which is readily proved by analytic means. Let F be a surface of constant mean curvature c; on the normals on a certain definite side of F we mark off the points lying at a distance of $1/2c$ from the surface. These points constitute a surface G. To be sure, G does not have constant mean curvature; but it does have the constant Gaussian curvature $4c^2$. G is called the surface parallel to F at the distance $1/2c$. If F is part of a sphere, then G is part of a sphere concentric with F. And conversely, G cannot be part of a sphere unless F is part of a sphere. For, it can be shown that the normals to F are also normal to G at the corresponding points of G. The side of F on which we measure off the normal distances cannot be chosen arbitrarily but has to be determined by a definite rule. It is easy to give a precise statement of this rule if F is visualized as a soap bubble blown up on a pipe: The normals have to be directed towards the interior of the enclosed space.

Consider a sphere of radius $1/c$, whose mean curvature is thus c, and a small closed curve R lying on the sphere. Let us subject the curve to a continuous deformation which is such that the resulting curves can no longer lie on any sphere. It is plausible that, as long as the deformation is not too great, we can find soap bubbles of constant mean curvature c passing through each of the resulting curves. For if a soap film is stretched across the original curve R, the proper amount of blowing will certainly bring it into the form of a surface of mean curvature c; this is so because the sphere on which R lay originally is such a surface, and at a certain stage during the process of blowing up the bubble (from the proper side), we obtain the larger of the two parts into which R divides the sphere. From considerations of continuity it follows that we can ensure, by suitably increasing the amount of air in the pipe in the course of the deformation of R, that the form of the soap bubble—which had originally been spherical—vary continuously in such a way as to keep the value of the mean curvature fixed; but the deformed soap bubbles can no longer be spherical in shape, since by construction the deformed boundary curves do not lie on any sphere. We now construct the interior parallel surfaces to all these soap bubbles at the distance $1/2c$. This gives us a continuous family of surfaces, and, by the theorem cited above, they all have the constant Gaussian curvature $4c^2$. The first of these surfaces is a sphere of radius $1/2c$ with a small hole bounded by a curve similar to R and similarly positioned in space. All the other surfaces of the family can be transformed into the first one by a continuous bending; but they cannot be spherical in shape, since, as we have mentioned above, this would imply that the soap bubbles themselves also are spherical in shape. Thus a sphere with an arbitrarily small hole can indeed be bent.

The question of whether a surface can be bent has been investigated in much more general cases of both bounded and closed surfaces. Bending is impossible in the case of all closed convex surfaces,
such as, for example, the ellipsoids. It is likewise impossible to
bend any convex surface having boundary curves, provided each
boundary curve has the property that at all of its points the tangent
plane is the same. An example of such a surface (with two boundary
curves) is the convex part of the torus (see Fig. 210, p. 200).

If an arbitrarily small hole is cut out of a convex surface, the
surface becomes bendable. It is not yet known whether it is sufficient
merely to slit the surface open or even to remove merely some
isolated points.

11. *The sphere is transformed into itself by a three-parameter
family of rigid motions.*

Obviously the totality of rigid motions that bring the sphere into
self-coincidence are the rotations about the center. And the totality
of these rotations is indeed dependent on three parameters. For,
two parameters are necessary to define the position of the axis of
rotation (a straight line that has to pass through the center but
that is otherwise arbitrary), and a third parameter is needed to
determine the angle of rotation. This enumeration may also be
based on other considerations, as follows. An arbitrary point on
the sphere can evidently be carried to any other point of the sphere
by a rotation belonging to the family, and in addition, a direction
on the sphere through the initial point can be transformed into
any direction through the image point. This uniquely determines
a transformation of the family. And it involves exactly three
parameters; for, the freely chosen image of the given point depends
on two parameters, and the directions on the sphere at this image
point constitute another one-parameter family.

The latter of these enumerations can be applied not only to the
sphere but also to the plane; hence the plane as well has a three-
parameter family of rigid motions into itself. On the other hand,
there are no further surfaces of this kind, so that the property
characterizes the spheres and the plane.

Let us now look into the question of what other surfaces admit
any family at all of rigid motions into themselves. In each case
the family is necessarily a two-parameter or one-parameter family.
The only surfaces admitting a family of motions with exactly two

parameters are the circular cylinders. A circular cylinder is brought into self-coincidence by an arbitrary rotation about its axis or by an arbitrary translation along the axis. The rigid motions of this type form a two-parameter family, and there are no further rigid motions that will bring the circular cylinder into self-coincidence. By a motion of this kind we can map any given point on the cylinder into any other point on the cylinder. But directions can no longer be mapped arbitrarily, because the straight lines which are generators of the cylinder are always mapped into each other by the above rigid motions.

The surfaces of revolution suggest themselves as obvious examples of surfaces that admit just a one-parameter family of rigid motions. All of these surfaces are transformed into themselves by all the rotations about the axis of rotation and (leaving aside the sphere, the plane, and the circular cylinder) by no other rigid motions. Thus any given point can be moved into any other point on the same circle of latitude, and once such a displacement of one point is given, the mapping is fully determined.

But the totality of surfaces having a one-parameter family of rigid motions is by no means exhausted by the surfaces of revolution. Indeed, the surfaces characterized by this property comprise all the helicoids; these include as limiting cases the surfaces of revolution on the one hand and the cylinders on the other. As was already pointed out on page 210, every helicoid can be generated as follows: An arbitrary space curve is subjected simultaneously to a rotation at some constant rate about any fixed straight line and a translation at constant speed in the direction of this straight line. It follows from this definition that every helicoid has a one-parameter family of motions into itself, namely the same family of motions by which the surface is generated from the space curve. The limiting cases mentioned above are obtained by setting either the angular velocity or the translational velocity equal to zero. In the first case the screw motion becomes a translation, and the curve sweeps out a cylinder; in the second case we get a rotation, and the curve sweeps out a surface of revolution.[7]

---

[7] That the helicoids are the only surfaces with one-parameter families of rigid motions, follows from the fact that the rigid motions of a surface into itself form a group. The screws with fixed axis and fixed pitch constitute the most general one-parameter groups of motions in space, if the rotations about the axis and the translations along the axis are again counted in as limiting cases.

Leaving aside the limiting cases, an individual point of the generating curve traces out a helix. Thus the motions of the one-parameter family of the helicoid move every point of the helicoid into an arbitrary point of its helix. In the limiting cases, the helices reduce to the generators of the cylinder and the circles of latitude of the surface of revolution, respectively.

§ 33. Bendings Leaving a Surface Invariant

The eleventh property of the sphere led us to the question of what surfaces are transformed into themselves by rigid motions. We shall now generalize this question and consider the surfaces that can be transformed into themselves by some bending. Let us suppose that we have a model of such a surface and a perfectly flexible but unstretchable piece of brass foil of such shape that it can be placed snug against some part of the model in some position. Then it must be possible to push the piece of foil along the model in some suitable manner so as to keep it snug against the surface without tearing, although it may change its shape.

While the possibility of transforming a surface into itself by a rigid motion depends on the way it is imbedded in space, the property of being bendable into itself is an intrinsic property, which can neither be destroyed nor created by bending the surface.

Since the rigid motions are special cases of bending, the class of surfaces with which we are now concerned certainly includes the surfaces listed in the last section. Now it turns out that the surfaces of the last section and those derived from them by bending already constitute the most general surfaces that admit bending into themselves; in other words, our generalization of the condition does not yield any essentially new class of surfaces. But the types of surfaces previously set up now acquire a different meaning. Thus we must obviously adopt the point of view that the cylinders are not essentially different from the plane, since every cylinder can be obtained from the plane by bending. Similarly, the second limiting case of helicoids, the case of surfaces of revolution, also loses its special character. For, a portion of any helicoid can always be bent into the form of a portion of a surface of revolution; this can be achieved by simply bending the helicoid in such a way that one of the helices on it becomes a circle—of course the helix, being infinite in length, has to make infinitely many turns on the circle.

Then the other helices also go over automatically into circles, and all these circles have the same axis, so that the resulting surface is indeed a surface of revolution whose circles of latitude are the images of the helices on the original surface. An example of this phenomenon is the way in which the right helicoid can be wrapped around a catenoid, as described on page 210.

Leaving aside the analytic proof, we can easily give a heuristic indication of why all the surfaces admitting a one-parameter family of bendings into themselves can be brought into the form of helicoids or surfaces of revolution, and why the helices and the circles of latitude correspond to each other.

The intuitive argument runs as follows. Through every point of a surface admitting a one-parameter family of bendings, there must be a curve that consists of the totality of the images of the point under all the bendings of the family. Hence the surface is covered simply and completely by a definite family of curves that are transformed into themselves by the bendings in question. If any two of these curves are chosen at random, all the points on one of these curves must have the same geodesic distance from the other curve, since geodesic distance is not changed by bending. It follows that every geodesic line perpendicular to one curve of the family must also meet all the other curves of the family at right angles, because the shortest distance measured along the surface from a point of the surface to a curve on the surface is the geodesic that passes through the point and meets the curve at right angles. Hence every surface of the type under consideration contains an orthogonal net of curves of which one family is the family of curves described above while the other consists of geodesics. Moreover, along each curve of the first family the Gaussian curvature must remain constant, because every point of the curve can be moved to every other point of the same curve by the bending, and all bendings leave Gaussian curvature invariant. In order to describe the distribution of the Gaussian curvature over the whole of our surface it is therefore sufficient to describe it as a function of arc length along one of the geodesic curves of the second family.

But it is easy to construct surfaces of revolution for which the Gaussian curvature is a prescribed function of the arc length of a meridian. Since the meridians of the surfaces of revolution are geodesics intersecting the circles of latitude at right angles, it is plausible, and is verified by computation, that the given surface we have been studying can be transformed into all those surfaces of revolution by bending and that the orthogonal net on the surface constructed above goes over into the net of meridians and circles of latitude in the process.

On the helicoids, the helices obviously have the same property as do the circles of latitude on the surfaces of revolution: each helix is the path traveled by a point when a length-preserving (isometric) transformation of the surface into itself is carried out. If, therefore, a given helicoid and a given surface of revolution are mutually applicable at all, the helices on the helicoid must necessarily correspond to the circles of latitude on the surface of revolution.

A calculation shows that from any given helicoid we can obtain, by bending, a two-parameter family of other helicoids and a one-parameter family of surfaces of revolution.

Let us now consider the surfaces that are invariant under a family of bendings with two or more parameters. The stipulation that the family of bendings have at least two parameters is equivalent with the condition that every point of the surface be moveable to every neighboring point of the surface. As a result, the Gaussian curvature of such a surface must be constant. But all the surfaces of constant positive Gaussian curvature (provided we confine our attention to a sufficiently small portion of the surface), can be applied to the sphere (cf. p. 204). Like the sphere, they must therefore be invariant under a family of bendings with not just two, but three, parameters. The same is true for the surfaces of vanishing Gaussian curvature, since they can be developed into the plane. It can be proved analytically that the surfaces of constant negative Gaussian curvature also admit of three-parameter families of bendings into themselves.

Thus all surfaces of constant Gaussian curvature have an important intrinsic property in common with the plane. We shall devote a detailed study to this in the sequel. The geometry of the plane can be developed in such a way that its foundations and its most general theorems apply not only to the plane but to all surfaces of constant curvature. Then the distinction between the plane and the surfaces of constant positive or negative Gaussian curvature only makes its appearance at a later stage of the development, at which geometry divides into Euclidean geometry and the two non-Euclidean geometries.

§ 34. Elliptic Geometry

The geodesic lines of the curved surfaces must be regarded as the analogue of the straight lines of the plane. We proceed to examine this analogy more closely. The simplest constructions of plane geometry are based on the drawing of straight lines and the marking off of lengths and angles. But in attempting to adapt such constructions to curved surfaces, we encounter a basic difference at the very outset: In the plane constructions we used the plane as a whole; but on the general curved surface we always considered only small regions, in accordance with the point of view of differential geometry. Accordingly, we have to limit ourselves to constructions which do not extend beyond the boundaries of the region of the surface and which are thus analogous to constructions confined to a small region of the plane.

On a sufficiently small portion of a curved surface, two points not too close to the boundary can be connected by one and only one geodesic line; this is analogous to the fact that in any region of the plane, two points not too close to the boundary can be connected by exactly one straight line lying in the region.[1]

Angles having geodesic lines as sides can be drawn and laid off on any portion of a curved surface in the same way that angles with straight lines as sides can be laid off in a plane region.

The marking off of geodesic segments of given lengths is also subject to the same laws as that of straight-line segments in a plane region.

But even in one of the simplest constructions consisting of all three of these operations (the connecting of two points, the marking off of angles, and the laying off of distances) —namely the construction of congruent triangles—the analogy in general breaks down. Two plane triangles are called congruent if the vertices of one of them can be paired off with those of the other in such a way that corresponding angles and sides are equal. This concept can clearly be applied to geodesic triangles in a region of a curved surface. Suppose, now, that we are given a triangle $A_0 B_0 C_0$ in a region of the plane as well as a point A, and that we construct two

---

[1] Except for regions whose boundary is everywhere concave toward the inside, part of the segment connecting two points sufficiently close to the boundary may lie outside the region.

points B and C which are such that $AB = A_0B_0$, $AC = A_0C_0$, and $\angle\, BAC = \angle\, B_0A_0C_0$; then by the appropriate (side-angle-side) theorem on congruent triangles, the triangle ABC is congruent to the triangle $A_0B_0C_0$; the only assumption we need to make here is that the point A is far enough from the boundary of the region to make it possible for all the constructions to be effected inside the region.

But if the analogous construction is made on a region of a curved surface, then the geodesic arc BC will in general have a length different from that of B_0C_0, so that the triangles ABC and $A_0B_0C_0$ cannot possibly be congruent.

There is one case, however, in which the above theorem on congruent triangles can be applied to geodesic constructions; this is the case where the surface is of constant Gaussian curvature. In this case the portion of the surface can be bent in such a way that A_0 coincides with A and that the geodesic sides of the angle $B_0A_0C_0$ coincide with the corresponding sides of the angle BAC.[2] Owing to the invariance under bending of lengths and angles, B_0 then coincides with B, and C_0 with C. Hence the triangles $A_0B_0C_0$ and ABC must be congruent.

Now the axiomatic analysis of the geometrical constructions in the plane reveals that all the theorems dealing with congruence of figures are logical consequences of the above congruence theorem. Therefore as far as the constructions referred to at the beginning of this section are concerned, the geometry of surfaces of constant curvature is completely analogous to the geometry of a region of the plane.

In proving that the above congruence theorem remains true on any surface of constant curvature, we made use of the three-parameter group of bendings of these surfaces. But the logical connection may also be reversed. If the side-angle-side congruence theorem is true for the geodesic triangles of a given surface, it follows that this surface admits of a three-parameter family of isometric (length-preserving) maps into itself and hence that its Gaussian curvature must be constant. To show this, we proceed as

---

[2] This can not always be accomplished by a *continuous* transformation, either on curved surfaces or in the plane. We know that in the plane the mappings that transform figures into congruent figures include the *reflections*. On the surfaces of constant curvature different from zero, also, there are isometric (length-preserving) mappings corresponding to the reflections (see the footnote on p. 257).

follows. By virtue of the construction of triangles given above, we can construct ∞^3 triangles congruent to any given geodesic triangle of sufficiently small dimensions. But if one triangle is given, all measurements on the surface can be completely determined by the marking off of lengths and angles and repeated application of the side-angle-side congruence theorem, in accordance with the same principles surveyors use in measuring the earth. To every congruent displacement of the fundamental triangle there corresponds, therefore, a length-preserving mapping of the surface under consideration.

This proves that the surfaces of constant Gaussian curvature are the only ones on which the above congruence theorem applies to all the geodesic triangles.

In order to pursue this analogy with the plane a step further, we shall try to do away with the restriction to small portions of the surface. We begin with surfaces of (constant) positive Gaussian curvature. The most obvious choice for such a surface is the sphere. But by considering the sphere in its entirety we destroy the analogy with the plane at a decisive point. We recall that the

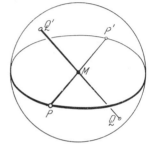

FIG. 231

geodesics of the sphere are the great circles; now through two diametrically opposite points there are infinitely many great circles, whereas any two points in the plane have just one straight line connecting them. Furthermore, while two straight lines in the plane have at most one point of intersection, two great circles of the sphere always intersect in two (diametrically opposite) points. Yet no surface of constant positive curvature other than the sphere can be taken as an analogue of the plane—if only because all the other surfaces of constant positive curvature have boundaries or singular points (cf. pp. 227-228).

However, a simple abstraction enables us to eliminate this disturbing property of the sphere. We limit ourselves to the surface of a hemisphere on which we regard every diametrically opposite pair of points of the boundary circle as a single point. In dealing with a spherical figure that extends beyond the boundary circle we shall, moreover, replace all the points lying outside our hemispherical surface by the points diametrically opposite to them; then the latter points will lie on the given hemisphere (see Fig. 231).

In this way, we get a set of points having all the desired properties. First, every sufficiently small region can be mapped isometrically onto a portion of the sphere. Second, the possibility of laying off lengths and of connecting pairs of points by geodesic lines is not limited by the existence of a boundary. Third, two distinct points can be connected by one and only one geodesic line, and no two geodesic lines have more than one point of intersection; both of these last statements follow from the fact that every pair of diametrically opposite points contained in our domain was treated as a single point.

Our surface is referred to as a model of the *elliptic plane*, and the analogue of plane geometry that governs this model is called *elliptic geometry*. A second model of elliptic geometry is obviously obtained if the whole surface of the sphere is used and every pair of diametrically opposite points on it is treated as a single point.

We shall now study elliptic geometry. We shall refer to the great circles simply as straight lines and to arcs of great circles as straight-line segments (or simply segments). Then there are two conspicuous differences between elliptic geometry and ordinary Euclidean geometry. First, the straight lines of elliptic geometry are closed curves, while the Euclidean straight lines extend to infinity. Second, two elliptic straight lines always intersect in a common point, while every Euclidean straight line has straight lines parallel to it, i.e. straight lines that do not intersect it.

A complete understanding of the way in which elliptic geometry is related to Euclidean geometry can be obtained only by beginning with the axioms of Euclidean plane geometry and ascertaining for each axiom whether it is valid in elliptic geometry or requires replacement by a modified axiom. We have mentioned earlier the axioms of incidence (pp. 114-115) and of continuity (pp. 129 and 130). Euclidean plane geometry can be built up on five groups of axioms in all—the axioms of incidence, of order, of congruence, of parallels, and of continuity. Underlying each group of axioms there are certain concepts; for example, the axioms of incidence are based on the concepts of point, straight line, and incidence. Some additional concepts are, in turn, only made possible by certain axioms; for example, the concept of a segment or of a half-line is made possible only by the axioms of order. The concept of a straight-line segment forms, in turn, the basis for the axioms of congruence;

thus the formulation of the axioms of congruence presupposes certain of the axioms of order. We proceed to list the axioms of Euclidean plane geometry.[3]

I. Axioms of Incidence

1. *Two points have one and only one straight line in common.* 2. *Every straight line contains at least two points.* 3. *There are at least three points not lying on the same straight line.*

II. Axioms of Order

1. *Of any three points on a straight line, one and only one lies between the other two.* 2. *If A and B are two points, there is at least one point C such that B lies between A and C.* 3. *Any straight line intersecting a side of a triangle (i.e. containing a point lying between two vertices) either passes through the opposite vertex or intersects a second side.*

The axioms of order enable us to define the concepts of "segment," "angle," "being on different sides of a point on a straight line," "half-line (ray)," and "being on different sides of a half-line in the plane."

III. Axioms of Congruence

1. *On a straight line a given segment can be laid off on either side of a given point; the segment thus constructed is called congruent to the given segment.* 2. *If two segments are congruent to a third segment, then they are congruent to each other.* 3. *If AB and A′B′ are two congruent segments and if the points C and C′ lying on AB and A′B′ respectively are such that one of the segments into which AB is divided by C is congruent to one of the segments into which A′B′ is divided by C′, then the other segment of AB is also congruent to the other segment of A′B′.* 4. *A given angle can be laid off in one and only one way on either side of a given half-line; the angle thus drawn is called congruent to the given angle.* 5. *If two sides of a given triangle are equal respectively to two sides of another triangle, and if the included angles are equal, the triangles are congruent.*

---

[3] Cf. D. Hilbert, *Grundlagen der Geometrie* (7th ed.: Berlin, 1930). (English translation *in prep.*, New York, Chelsea Publishing Company.)

IV. Axiom of Parallels

Through any point not lying a given straight line there passes one and only one straight line that does not intersect the given line.

V. Axioms of Continuity

The way in which these axioms are formulated varies a great deal. We may state them, for example, as follows:

1. (*Axiom of Archimedes*, cf. p. 130). *Every straight-line segment can be measured by any other straight-line segment.* 2. (*Cantor's axiom*). *Every infinite sequence of nested segments* (i.e., a sequence of segments such that each contains all the following ones) *has a common point.*

In elliptic geometry, the axioms of incidence are obviously valid. On the other hand, the axioms of order are not satisfied; for since

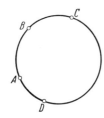

FIG. 232

the straight lines in elliptic geometry are closed curves (like circles), we cannot say of three points on a straight line that one and only one of them lies between the other two. But in place of the relation of *between*-ness for three collinear points, we can introduce into elliptic geometry a relation of *separation* between four points, which is subject to a group of axioms quite analogous to the axioms of order. We cite the first of these axioms of separation: Any four points on a straight line can be broken up in one and only one way into two pairs that separate each other. (For example, the points A, B, C, D in Fig. 232 break up into the mutually separating pairs AC and BD.)

Like the corresponding Euclidean axioms, the elliptic axioms of separation also lead to the definition of a straight-line segment and of the other concepts used in the axioms of congruence. But these definitions must be based on the fact, analogous to the fact that any circle is divided into two segments by any two points on it, that two points A and B always define two segments rather than just one. Only by recourse to a third point C of the straight line AB can we distinguish between the two segments defined by A and B; one segment consists of all those points that are separated from C by A and B, and the other segment consists of the remaining points of the straight line AB. Furthermore, it is necessary to stipulate that none of the interior angles of a triangle shall exceed a straight angle, as two sides and the included angle would otherwise determine not one triangle but two non-congruent triangles (Fig. 233), so that the side-angle-side theorem on congruence would be violated. If these restrictions are observed, it is found that the analogy with a region of the Euclidean plane, which was our starting point, is preserved on every sufficiently small portion of the elliptic plane, and that the Euclidean axioms of congruence, and the axioms of continuity as well, remain valid in the elliptic plane.

The parallel axiom, on the other hand, does not remain valid, but has to be replaced by the axiom of incidence for the projective plane that has already been mentioned on page 116: Two straight lines have one and only one point of intersection.

With respect to ordering also, elliptic geometry behaves like projective geometry. In order to make this clear, we choose as our model of the elliptic plane the whole sphere with every diametrically opposite pair of points treated as a single point. If the sphere is projected from its center onto a plane, then every point of the plane corres-

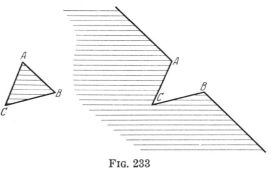

FIG. 233

ponds to one pair of diametrically opposite points of the sphere, that is, to one point of the elliptic plane. To every great circle on the sphere, that is, to every straight line of the elliptic plane, there corresponds one straight line in the image plane. The correspondence becomes one-to-one if the infinitely distant line of the image plane is adjoined—if, in other words, the image plane is considered as a projective plane.

Accordingly, the projective plane may be used directly as a model for the elliptic plane, provided the equality of lengths and angles is interpreted, not in the Euclidean sense, but in the sense indicated above, that is, using the spherical trigonometry of an auxiliary sphere. It follows that all the theorems of projective geometry dealing with points of intersection, such as the theorems of Desargues and Pascal, remain valid in elliptic geometry.

Let us consider the isometric mappings of the elliptic plane. As in the Euclidean case, we may study the discontinuous groups of these mappings. Every group of this kind is associated with a discontinuous group of isometric mappings of the sphere, and hence with one of the regular polyhedra discussed in §§ 13 and 14. Conversely, every regular polyhedron gives rise to a discontinuous symmetry group of the elliptic plane, and the central projections of regular polyhedra shown in Figs. 160 to 163 and 165 to 168 provide some solutions of the problem of "tiling" connected with those groups, which was formulated on page 81 for the Euclidean plane.

Elliptic geometry can be defined not only in the plane but also in three-dimensional space. As a model for the points, straight lines, and planes of the elliptic space, we may use the points, straight lines, and planes of projective space. Comparison of lengths and angles must again be carried out in a way different from that of Euclidean geometry, and can only be described in analytic terms—for example by central projection of a hypersphere in four-dimensional space. The discontinuous symmetry groups of elliptic space are connected with the regular polytopes in four-dimensional space, and Figs. 173 to 176 may be interpreted as "tilings" of the elliptic space.

§ 35. Hyperbolic Geometry, and its Relation to Euclidean and to Elliptic Geometry

We shall now turn our attention to the surfaces of constant negative curvature. They do not include any such simple shapes as the

FIG. 234a   FIG. 234b   FIG. 234c

sphere. The surfaces of revolution of constant negative curvature can assume the three different forms illustrated in Fig. 234. We note that all three of these surfaces have singular boundaries beyond which they cannot be extended continuously.[1] It has not been found possible to date to give an explicit description for the totality of surfaces of constant negative curvature, but it can be proved that none of these surfaces can be free of singularities.

There are thus no surfaces in space which can be mapped isometrically in the small onto a surface of constant negative curvature and on which the drawing of geodesic arcs is nowhere obstructed by boundary points. But in the plane it is possible to construct models of such abstractly defined surfaces by these conditions in the same way as it was possible to use the projective plane as a model of the elliptic plane. In constructing our model, we have to introduce the measurement of distances and angles in a way different not only from those followed in Euclidean Geometry but also from those followed in elliptic geometry. The surface which it is our aim to represent by our model is called the *hyperbolic plane*, and the geometry on this surface is called *hyperbolic geometry*.

We shall take as points of the hyperbolic plane the points in the interior of a circle in an ordinary plane, and as hyperbolic straight lines we shall take the chords of this circle (end-points excluded).

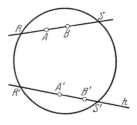

Fig. 235

These definitions will serve our purpose, since any portion of an arbitrary surface F of constant negative curvature $-1/c^2$ can be mapped into a plane region G in the interior of the circle in such a way that all the geodesics of F are mapped into the straight-line segments lying in G. Since the curvature of G is zero, while F has negative curvature, the map can not, of course, be isometric. If A, B (Fig. 235) are the images of two points P, Q of F and if R and S are the extremities of the chord that passes through A and B, then the geodesic distance s between the points P and Q is given by the formula

$$(1) \qquad s = \frac{c}{2} \cdot \left| \log \frac{AR \cdot BS}{BR \cdot AS} \right|$$

We shall use the right-hand side of equation (1) as the definition of "hyperbolic distance" for all pairs of points AB in our model.

---

[1] In Fig. 234b only the lower boundary is singular. In the upward direction the surface extends to infinity, the circles of latitude at the same time becoming smaller and smaller.

Similarly, the map $F \to G$ gives us a definite way of measuring "hyperbolic angles," which differs from the Euclidean way of measuring angles. For example, the perpendicular h from a point A of the hyperbolic plane to a straight line g is obtained by connecting A with the auxiliary point P constructed in Fig. 236. It is clear

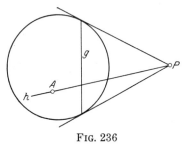

that the Euclidean angle between h and g is, in general, not a right angle.

Let us check to see which of the axioms of Euclidean geometry remain valid in the hyperbolic plane. First of all, it is evident that the axioms of incidence hold. Furthermore, we see that the axioms of order will also hold if we simply define the relation of

Fig. 236

"between-ness" for three points to be the same as in the model. We now define as the segment AB, the points of the Euclidean straight-line segment joining A and B in the model. Then we base the definition of congruence for segments on formula (1). Now consider the side-angle-side axiom of congruence. We might get the impression that the possibility of laying off segments at will would sometimes

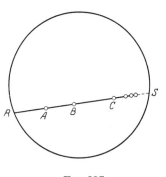

be obstructed by the circumference of the circle, so that the axiom would not hold. In actual fact, however, the circumference is never reached if we lay off segments in accordance with the definition (1) for distances. For, given a straight-line segment AB and a half-line h issuing from the point A' in the interior of the circle (see Fig. 235), the point B' on h for which $A'B'$ is to be equal to AB must, by (1), satisfy the relation

Fig. 237

$$\frac{AR}{BR} \cdot \frac{BS}{AS} = \frac{A'R'}{B'R'} \cdot \frac{B'S'}{A'S'}$$

or

(2)
$$\frac{B'S'}{B'R'} = \frac{A'S'}{A'R'} \cdot \frac{AR}{AS} \cdot \frac{BS}{BR}.$$

Since the three points A', A, and B lie in the interior of the circle, all three ratios on the right-hand side of (2) are negative. Hence $B'S'/B'R'$ is negative too, which means that B' is inside the circle, as stated. If we keep laying off the same length repeatedly along a straight line, then we approach the circumference of the circle, getting nearer and nearer to it without ever reaching it (see Fig. 237). In our model of hyperbolic geometry, the circumference of the circle plays a role analogous to that of the infinitely distant line in Euclidean geometry.

From the foregoing argument it follows that the side-angle-side axiom of congruence holds in the hyperbolic plane. It is clear that the second, third, and fourth axioms of congruence are also valid.

As we have mentioned in § 34, the fifth axiom of congruence is equivalent to the existence of a sufficiently inclusive group of mappings that transform the interior of the circle into itself in such a way that straight lines are mapped into straight lines and that distances and angles are preserved. In plane projective geometry it is proved that such a group really exists.

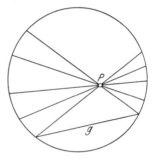

(Our maps are among the projective transformations of the plane and may be obtained graphically by a repeated application of central projection.) Thus all the axioms of congruence are valid in hyperbolic geometry. It is easy to see that the axioms of continuity are satisfied as well.

Only one axiom of Euclidean geometry is not valid in the hyperbolic plane: The axiom of parallels. That this axiom does

FIG. 238

not hold is apparent from Fig. 238. If P is a point and g is any straight line not incident with P, there is a whole pencil of straight lines through P that do not intersect g. Thus while in elliptic geometry not only the axiom of parallels but also the Euclidean axioms of order are not valid, the only way in which hyperbolic geometry differs from Euclidean geometry is that the axiom of parallels is not valid.

For this reason, our model is of fundamental importance. Throughout the middle ages and up to the beginning of the 19th century, efforts were made in vain to prove the axiom of parallels on the basis of the other axioms of Euclid. The discovery of a model of hyperbolic geometry revealed the inherent impossibility of such a proof. For in our model all the geometrical axioms with the exception of the axiom of parallels are satisfied. If the axiom of parallels could be deduced logically from the other axioms, then it would also have to hold true in our model, which is not the case.

Hyperbolic geometry and elliptic geometry are referred to as the two *non-Euclidean* geometries. As regards the distribution of values of the Gaussian curvature, it is found that Euclidean geometry plays the role of a transitional case between elliptic and hyperbolic geometry, which it does in other respects as well. Thus the hyperbolic plane was obtained from the Euclidean plane by removing the points of the circumference and exterior of a circle, whereas the points of the ideal line had to be added to the Euclidean plane in order to complete the elliptic plane. Furthermore, if a straight line and a point not on the line be given, there is no line passing through the point and parallel to the fixed line in elliptic geometry; there is just one in Euclidean geometry; and there are infinitely many in hyperbolic geometry. An especially neat characterization of the three geometries is found by considering the sum of the angles in a triangle. In Euclidean geometry, this sum is equal to π; in elliptic geometry, it is greater than π; this follows from certain well-known theorems of spherical trigonometry. In the hyperbolic plane, on the other hand, the sum of the angles is always less than π. We shall give a heuristic proof for this last result later on.

According to this result, the theorem of Euclidean geometry that the angles of any triangle add up to π, can not be proved without recourse to the axiom of parallels; for otherwise the theorem would also have to be true in the hyperbolic plane. On the other hand, any theorem of Euclidean geometry that is true in hyperbolic geometry as well, can certainly be proved without the Euclidean axiom of parallels. An example of such a theorem is the theorem that every exterior angle of a triangle is greater than each of the two opposite interior angles. On the other hand, it is readily seen from a consideration of spherical triangles that this theorem is not true for elliptic geometry. It follows that the proof of this theorem involves the Euclidean axioms of order.

An example of a theorem that is true in all three geometries is the theorem that the base angles of an isosceles triangle are equal. The proof of this theorem requires neither the Euclidean axioms of order nor any assumptions about parallelism.

We have mentioned that the projective theorems on incidence, such as Desargues' theorem, are valid in the elliptic plane. In the

Euclidean plane, Desargues' theorem, like all the other theorems on incidence, is true only if the ideal points are included. In the hyperbolic plane, a unified formulation of the theorems on incidence is possible only if two kinds of ideal points are adjoined—points corresponding in our model to the points of the circumference of the circle and points corresponding to the points in the exterior of the circle. For example, it is clear that, if a Desargues configuration in the plane is given, we can always draw the fundamental circle of our model of the hyperbolic plane in such a way that nine points of the configuration are interior to the circle and that the tenth point is on the circumference of or exterior to the circle. Because the configuration is regular, we may regard the tenth point as the Desargues point; the figure can then be interpreted as a pair of hyperbolic triangles with pairs of corresponding sides intersecting at points of one hyperbolic straight line. By Desargues' theorem, the lines connecting pairs of corresponding points pass through a common point, and yet we know that these straight lines do not have an interior point of the circle in common.

If we attempt to give a direct proof of Desargues' theorem in the hyperbolic plane, without recourse to our model, then we are faced with difficulties similar to those in Euclidean and projective geometry. The theorem can be proved with the use of the axioms of congruence. To prove it without them requires auxiliary three-dimensional constructions. This rests on the fact that there is also a hyperbolic geometry of space: A model of the "hyperbolic space" can be obtained by using the points, straight-line segments, and plane regions in the interior of a sphere as points, straight lines, and planes, respectively, and defining the distance between two points in a way analogous to what we did in the plane model.

We mentioned above that the sum of the angles of any triangle in the hyperbolic plane is less than π. This theorem is not evident from observation of our model, because the hyperbolic angles are not the same as the Euclidean angles. In the next section we shall remedy this weakness by constructing another model of the hyperbolic plane from the first model in such a way that the new model reproduces hyperbolic angles without distortion. The construction is based on a simple technique of elementary geometry: the theory of stereographic projection and circle-preserving transformations.

§ 36. Stereographic Projection and Circle-Preserving Transformations. Poincaré's Model of the Hyperbolic Plane

Consider a sphere resting on a horizontal plane (Fig. 239). Let us project the sphere onto the plane from the highest point N ("north pole") of the sphere. The map of the sphere ($P' \rightarrow P$ in

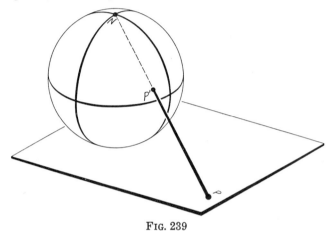

Fig. 239

Fig. 239) produced in this way is called a *stereographic projection*. The entire surface of the sphere with the exception of the point N is mapped onto the entire plane. The image plane is parallel to the

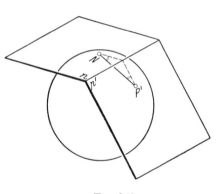

Fig. 240

plane n tangent to the sphere at N. Furthermore, if p' is the plane tangent to the sphere at P' (Fig. 240), then it follows, from the perfect symmetry of the sphere, that the two planes n and p' form equal angles with the straight line NP' joining their points of contact, and that the line of intersection of n and p' is perpendicular to NP. Since n is parallel to the image plane, the image plane also forms the same angle as does p' with the projecting ray PP', and it intersects p' in a straight line perpendicular to PP'. This gives rise to several visually evident properties of stereographic projection. First, if r' is a tangent to the sphere at P' (see Fig. 241) and r is the image of r', then r and r' form equal angles with PP'. For, r is obtained as the intersection of the image plane with the plane containing r' and NP'; but if two straight lines r and r' are the respective intersections of a plane e with two planes

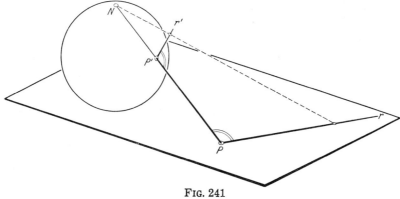

FIG. 241

p and p' where e contains PP' and where p and p' form equal angles with the straight line PP' and intersect in a straight line perpendicular to PP' (see Fig. 242), then r and r' also form equal angles with PP'. The same consideration of symmetry gives us the following additional result: If s' is another tangent to the sphere at P' and if s is its image, then the angle formed by r and s is equal to the angle formed by r' and s'. *Thus stereographic projection reproduces the angles on the sphere without distortion.*

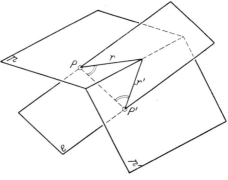

FIG. 242

For this reason, the mapping is called *angle-preserving*, or *isogonal*; another term is *conformal*.

Now let k' be an arbitrary circle lying on the sphere and not passing through N (Fig. 243). The planes tangent to the sphere at the points of k' envelop a circular cone, whose vertex we shall call S. Since k' does not pass through N, NS is not tangent to the sphere at N and is therefore not parallel to the image plane; let M be the point at which NS intersects the image plane. We shall prove that the curve k that is the image of k', is a circle with M as center.

The proof is apparent from Fig. 243. If P' is an arbitrary point of k' and P is its image, then $P'S$ is tangent to the sphere at P' and PM is the image of $P'S$. Hence $\angle PP'S = \angle P'PM$. Through S we draw the line parallel to PM; let P'' be the point at which it intersects NP. Then either P'' coincides with P', or the triangle $P'P''S$ has equal angles at P' and P'' and is thus isosceles: $SP' = SP''$. But now $PM/P'S = PM/P''S = MN/SN$, so that $PM = P'S \cdot MN/SN$. $P'S$ is constant, because S has the same distance from all the points of K'. Hence it follows from the last formula that PM is constant too. In other words, k is a circle with center M.

Thus the stereographic projection of the sphere onto the plane

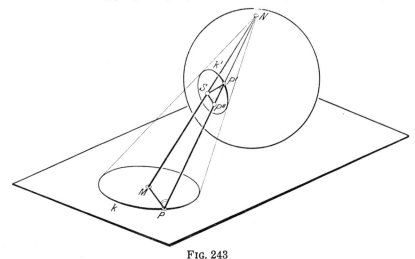

FIG. 243

maps those circles on the sphere that do not pass through N onto circles in the plane; and by reversing the preceding argument we can see that every circle in the image plane is the image of a circle on the sphere. If a circle that is free to move on the sphere approaches a circle passing through N, then NS approaches a tangent to the sphere at N, and thus M recedes to infinity. It follows that the images of the circles on the sphere that pass through N are straight lines of the image plane. This fact is obvious even without the limiting process, since the projecting rays of a circle that lies on the sphere and passes through N lie in the plane of the circle, so that the *straight line* forming the intersection of this plane with the image plane is the image of the circle. Thus we see that under stereographic projection the set of all circles on the sphere corresponds to the set of all circles and straight lines in the plane. Stereographic projection is *circle-preserving*.

Now consider any mapping a' of the sphere onto itself that maps all the circles of the sphere into circles; for example, a' may be a rotation of the sphere about any diameter (not necessarily one that passes through N). As a result of the stereographic projection, the mapping a' gives rise to a mapping a of the image plane into itself which maps the set of all circles and straight lines into itself. Any such map of the plane into itself is called a *circle-preserving transformation*.

In the Euclidean plane, the circle-preserving transformations are not in general one-to-one, since under stereographic projection no point of the plane corresponds to the point N of the sphere. Now, the mapping a' of the sphere will not in general leave the point N fixed but will transform some other point P', whose stereographic image we shall call P, into N. Then the point P of the plane has no image under the circle-preserving transformation a corresponding to a'. In order to avoid having to make exceptions under the mapping process, we proceed as in projective geometry, by making an abstract extension of the Euclidean plane. But while the projective plane was constructed by supplementing the Euclidean plane with a whole family of "infinitely distant" points, the extension made in the theory of circle-preserving transformations consists in supplementing the Euclidean plane by a single "infinitely distant" point U which is regarded as the image of N under the stereographic projection. As a result of this extension, the relation between the plane and the surface of the sphere becomes one-to-one and continuous, and the circle-preserving transformations become one-to-one mappings; in the example given above, the point P is mapped by the circle-preserving transformation a into U. The corresponding mapping a' of the sphere into itself obviously transforms the circles passing through P' into the circles passing through N; hence a maps the circles passing through P into the straight lines of the plane. Accordingly, it is found expedient to regard the straight lines as "circles passing through the infinitely distant point." The images of parallel straight lines under a circle-preserving transformation are either themselves parallel straight lines, or mutually tangent circles.

We have some trivial examples of circle-preserving transformations in the rigid motions, reflections, and similarity transformations of the plane; these transformations map the Euclidean plane one-to-one into itself; hence if we enlarge the plane by adjoining U, we may say that these transformations are circle-preserving transformations leaving U fixed. But it may also be proved, conversely, that the three types of plane transformation just mentioned are the only circle-preserving transformations leaving U fixed. On the basis of this theorem, we may readily obtain an exhaustive description of all the circle-preserving transformations of the plane. Consider a given circle-preserving transformation a_0. Let P be

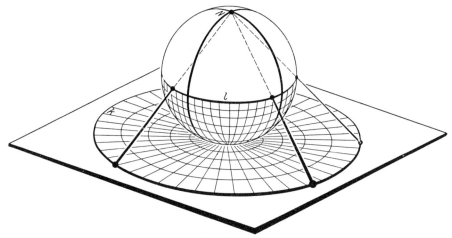

Fig. 244a

the point of the plane whose image under a_0 is U, and let P be the stereographic image of the point P' of the sphere. We now subject the sphere to a rotation a' transforming P' into N. There corresponds to the rotation a' a certain circle-preserving transformation, and the properties of this transformation are connected with the properties of a' in a way that is easy to describe in graphical terms. Like a, the given transformation a_0 moves P to U, so that the transformations a_0 and a can differ only by a circle-preserving transformation that leaves U fixed. It follows, by the theorem we have just cited, that a_0 is identical with a except for a possible rigid motion, reflection, or similarity transformation.

We have mentioned earlier that stereographic projection is angle-preserving. Also, the rotation a' is an angle-preserving transformation of the sphere, and since a is obtained from a' by a stereographic projection, a must therefore be an angle-preserving transformation of the plane. Since a_0 and a differ at most by an angle-preserving transformation, it follows that *all circle-preserving transformations are angle-preserving.*

Figs. 244a and b elucidate the relation between the maps a and a' by exhibiting prominently a circle k in the plane that passes through P and is the stereographic image of a great circle l of the sphere. Under a', l is transformed into a great circle n that passes through N and has the straight line g as its image. Thus a transforms k into g. From the figures it is plain, moreover, that the interior and

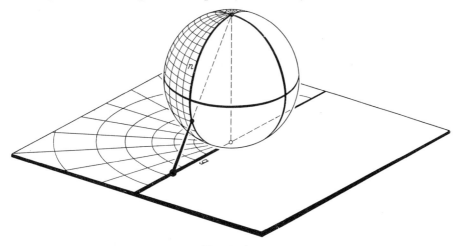

Fig. 244b

the exterior of k are transformed respectively into the two half-planes bounded by g, which is in any case evident from considerations of continuity.

The reflection u of the plane in g is a circle-preserving transformation. Hence the mapping $i = aua^{-1}$ is a circle-preserving transformation that leaves every point of the circumference of k fixed and interchanges the interior with the exterior of the circle. The map i is called an *inversion* in the circle k, or a *reflection* in the circle k, or a plane transformation by reciprocal radii. This transformation is particularly important, and we shall therefore discuss it in some detail.

Let h be a circle intersecting k at right angles at a point R (see Fig. 245). Then h and k have a second point S of intersection at which they are also perpendicular. Then the tangents to h at R

and S are radii of k intersecting at the center M of k, which is therefore exterior to h. The inversion i transforms h into a circle h', and this circle must also pass through R and S, because R and S remain fixed. Since the inversion is angle-preserving, h' intersects the circle k at R and S at right angles. But this is possible only if h' is identical with h. Hence every circle h that intersects k at right angles is transformed by i into itself. Since the interior and exterior of k are interchanged, the two arcs into which k divides h must also be interchanged.

Consider a straight line l passing through M, for example the straight line RM. Let its second point of intersection with k be R'

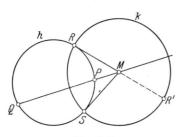

Fig. 245

(see Fig. 245). Then l must be transformed into a circle or straight line l' meeting k at right angles at R and R'. This is possible only if l' is identical with l. Accordingly, the inversion transforms each diameter of k into itself. Since the only points that these straight lines have in common in the enlarged plane are M and the infinitely distant point U, it follows that the inversion interchanges M with U. The totality of straight lines not passing through M is therefore interchanged with the totality of circles passing through M.

Now let P be a point of h different from R and S. The image of P under the inversion i can only be at the second point Q of intersection of the straight line MP with h, because MP and h are each mapped into themselves. By the elementary theorem about intersecting chords of a circle, we have $MP \cdot MQ = MR^2$. Q is called the *inverse point* of P with respect to the circle k. Thus we have found a method of determining the inverse of any point P with respect to k without the use of the auxiliary circle h: If r is the radius of k, the inverse Q of the point P is that point on the ray MP for which $MP \cdot MQ = r^2$.

It may be proved that every circle-preserving transformation can be expressed as the resultant of at most three inversions. We shall consider, in particular, the totality of circle-preserving transformations that transform a given circle k into itself and also the interior of k into itself. Evidently these maps constitute a group, which we shall call H. If n is a circle cutting k at right angles, the inversion in n certainly belongs to H. It can be proved that every map of the group H can be produced by three inversions in circles perpendicular

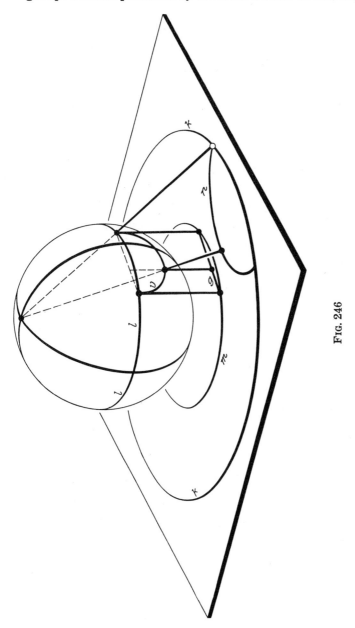

Fig. 246

to k, that is, by three inversions which themselves belong to H.

We now proceed to tie this discussion in with the model of the hyperbolic plane constructed in the previous section. Let the hyperbolic plane be represented by the interior of a circle m lying in a horizontal plane. Let us place on the plane a sphere having the same radius as m and touching the plane at the center of m (see Fig. 246). We now project the circumference and the interior of m *by vertical parallel projection* onto the lower hemisphere bounded by the great circle l congruent to m. By virtue of this projection, the hemisphere has become a new model of the hyperbolic plane. Every chord g of m is projected into a semicircle v of the sphere meeting l at right angles, so that these semicircles now are to be considered as images of the hyperbolic straight lines. We now map the hemisphere back into the plane by *stereographic* projection.

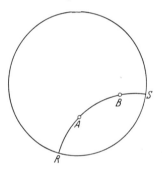

FIG. 247

The image of the hemisphere under this projection covers the interior of a circle k, which thus becomes a new model of the hyperbolic plane. Because of the angle-preserving and circle-preserving nature of the stereographic projection, the semicircles v have in this model be-become circular arcs n perpendicular to the circle k. Here and in what follows we have to include the diameters of k as limiting cases in this class of circular arcs.

This new model is due to Poincaré. Let us examine it in a little more detail. From our derivation it follows that there is a one-to-one correspondence between the set of all circular arcs perpendicular to k and the set of all chords of another circle m. Hence any two points A and B in the interior of k can be connected by one and only one circular arc perpendicular to k. If R and S are the points where this arc connecting A and B meets k (Fig. 247), the hyperbolic distance between A and B can be obtained from formula (1) of page 243. For if A', B', R', S' are the points of the original model that give rise to A, B, R, and S under the construction described above, then it can be deduced **from theorems** of projective geometry that the following relation holds:

$$\frac{AR \cdot BS}{BR \cdot AS} = \sqrt{\frac{A'R' \cdot B'S'}{B'R' \cdot A'S'}}.$$

This gives us the following formula for the hyperbolic distance s of A and B in our new model:

$$(2) \qquad s = c \left| \log \frac{AR \cdot BS}{BR \cdot AS} \right|.$$

Now every rigid motion of the hyperbolic plane into itself must be associated with a mapping a of the interior of k into itself transforming into itself the set of circular arcs perpendicular to k. It is plausible, and it is easy to prove rigorously, that this mapping is a circle-preserving transformation, which means that it belongs to the group H considered above. In addition, it can be proved that the group H is even identical with the group of all hyperbolic rigid motions.[1]

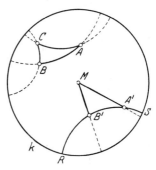

FIG. 248

Being circle-preserving, the transformations belonging to H leave angles invariant; but at the same time they are hyperbolic rigid motions and therefore leave hyperbolic angles invariant. Consequently, the Euclidean angles in Poincaré's model are equal to the hyperbolic angles multiplied by a fixed proportionality factor, and since the angle 2π of a full rotation is obviously reproduced in the hyperbolic plane without change, the factor must be unity. Thus *Poincaré's model preserves angles.*

By means of analytic methods, a formula can be set up by which an angle-preserving mapping can be effected directly from a given portion of a surface of constant negative curvature to a portion of the plane interior to k such that the geodesic lines are mapped into the circular arcs perpendicular to k.

We are now in a position to fill in the proof of the theorem stated on page 246, that in hyperbolic geometry the sum of the angles of any triangle is less than π. We begin with an arbitrary triangle ABC in Poincaré's model of the hyperbolic plane (Fig. 248). We know that the axioms of congruence are valid in the hyperbolic plane.

---

[1] Here the category of rigid motions is taken to include all maps of the hyperbolic plane that preserve distances, even if they cannot be effected continuously. A simple rigid motion that cannot be effected continuously, is represented by any inversion contained in H; this is a "reflection" of the hyperbolic plane in a straight line. By the remark on page 254, every hyperbolic rigid motion can be expressed as the resultant of at most three reflections.

According to these, we can draw a triangle $A'B'M$ congruent to ABC, in which the point corresponding to C is the center M of k. On page 253 we saw that every circle perpendicular to k that passes through M is bound to degenerate into a diameter of k and that M is exterior to all the other circles that meet k at right angles. In our model, therefore, the hyperbolic straight lines $A'M$ and $B'M$ are represented by Euclidean straight lines, while the hyperbolic straight line $A'B'$ is represented by a circular arc to which M is exterior. The *Euclidean* angles at A' and B' are therefore smaller in the triangle $A'B'M'$ formed by two straight lines and a circular arc than they are in the rectilinear triangle $A'B'M$, and it follows that the sum of the angles in the former triangle falls short of π. Since the model preserves angles, the same is true for the sum of the hyperbolic angles in the hyperbolic triangle $A'B'M$ and in the congruent triangle ABC.

In considering the hyperbolic rigid motions, it is natural to look for discontinuous groups of such motions. In the case of elliptic geometry we saw that the study of this problem boiled down to the study of the regular polyhedra and that there are only a few discontinuous groups in the elliptic plane. In Euclidean geometry it was already more difficult to obtain all the discontinuous groups. In the hyperbolic plane we find that the discontinuous groups are far more numerous than even in the Euclidean plane. All these discontinuous groups of hyperbolic rigid motions are represented in Poincaré's model by groups of circle-preserving transformations contained in H as subgroups.

These groups play a role in the theory of functions. Of special importance among them are the groups of "hyperbolic translations." By hyperbolic translation is meant any hyperbolic rigid motion that can be obtained continuously from the identity and that leaves no point fixed. In plane elliptic geometry there are no rigid motions analogous to this, since every rigid motion in the elliptic plane has a fixed point. In Euclidean geometry, the analogue of the hyperbolic translations are the ordinary translations. But the composition of hyperbolic translations does not follow any such simple law as does the composition of Euclidean translations, since uniqueness of parallels is lacking in the hyperbolic plane.

We shall limit our attention to those discontinuous groups of hyperbolic translations that have closed unit cells. Their Euclidean analogues are the translation groups having parallelograms as unit cells. In a hyperbolic translation group with closed unit cell, the unit cell can never be a quadrangle. On the other hand, the number of corners of the cell can be any number divisible by four, except four itself. Fig. 249 indicates the tiling of the hyperbolic plane by unit cells in the case where they are octagonal, the hyperbolic plane being represented by Poincaré's model. Of course, we cannot depict the tiling of the whole plane, since the octagons composed of circular arcs get more and more crowded as we approach the boundary of the circle. In our unit cell, as in the case of the fundamental parallelogram of a Euclidean translation group, the sides come in pairs that are equal in length and equivalent; in Fig. 249 this division into pairs is indi-

cated for one of the unit cells. The vertices of all the unit cells drawn in the figure have been numbered, corresponding vertices of different unit cells being identified by the same numbers. It is seen that we come across each of the numbers exactly once in going around any vertex. It follows that the sum of the angles of a unit cell must be 2π. In the representations of all the

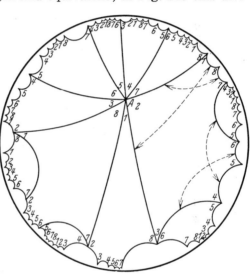

FIG. 249

other groups too, the arrangement of the unit cells is analogous. Hence the sum of the angles of a unit cell is 2π in every case. Furthermore, the sides must be equal in pairs, the arrangement into pairs being made according to a certain rule which we shall not discuss here; in all other respects, the fundamental region may be formed arbitrarily. The fact that the angles always add up to 2π is the reason why the unit cells can never be quadrangles. For, the sum of the angles of a hyperbolic quadrangle is always less than 2π, as is easily seen by dividing the quadrangle into two triangles.

A far greater variety yet is that of the groups of hyperbolic translations with open unit cell. One of these groups is made use of in the theory of the elliptic modular function.

§ 37. Methods of Mapping. Isometric, Area-Preserving, Geodesic, Continuous, and Conformal Mappings

We have on various occasions mapped surfaces onto each other using various types of mappings—for example, central projection or mapping by parallel normals. It is our object in this section to survey and compare the most important kinds of mappings.

The most faithful image of a surface is obtained by an *isometric*, or *length-preserving*, mapping. Here the geodesic distance of any two points is equal to the geodesic distance of their image points,

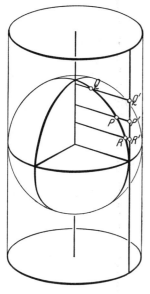

all angles remain unchanged, and geodesic lines are mapped into geodesic lines. As was mentioned somewhat earlier, two arbitrary surfaces can not, as a rule, be mapped into each other isometrically, because the Gaussian curvatures at corresponding points of two surfaces related by an isometric mapping must be equal. Hence the only surfaces that can be mapped isometrically into a part of the plane are surfaces whose Gaussian curvature is everywhere zero; this excludes, for example, any portion of a sphere. Every geographical map, consequently, can not be free of distortions.

Less accurate—but also less restrictive— are the *area-preserving* mappings. They are defined by the condition that the area

Fig. 250

enclosed by every closed curve be equal to the area enclosed by the image of the closed curve. It is plausible, and may be proved without difficulty, that this condition will be satisfied for all closed curves if it is satisfied for all "infinitesimal" closed curves. Hence the area-preserving maps can be easily characterized in terms of differential geometry.

Area-preserving maps are frequently used in geography. There is a simple method of producing area-preserving mappings of portions of the sphere into portions of the plane. Around the sphere we construct a cylinder of the same radius (Fig. 250). Then we project the points of the sphere onto the cylinder along the normals of the cylinder. If the cylinder is now slit open along a generator and developed into the plane, the result is an area-preserving image of the sphere in the plane, as may be verified by calculation. The image is obviously more distorted the further we are from the circle along which the cylinder touches the sphere.

Another type of mapping of importance for geography, and especially for charts used in navigation, are the *geodesic* maps. In this case it is required that the geodesics of one surface be mapped into the geodesics of the other. Thus the isometric mappings are a special case of geodesic mappings. Another case of a geodesic mapping was considered in the study of elliptic geometry: If a sphere is projected from its center onto the plane, then the great circles are mapped into the straight lines of the plane, and the map is therefore geodesic. At the same time, this gives us a geodesic mapping of all surfaces of constant positive Gaussian curvature into the plane, because all of these surfaces can be mapped isometrically into spheres. All the surfaces of constant negative Gaussian curvature can also be mapped into the plane by a geodesic mapping. This is effected by means of the model of the hyperbolic plane described in § 35.

It can be proved that no surface other than the surfaces of constant Gaussian curvature can be mapped geodesically onto the plane. However, the general problem of when two curved surfaces can be mapped geodesically *onto each other* involves more difficult calculations. The generalization of this problem from surfaces to spaces of three and more dimensions plays a certain role in modern physics, because the trajectories of material points are regarded in the general theory of relativity as geodesic lines of a four-dimensional continuum.

The most general mappings that are at all comprehensible to visual intuition are the *continuous* mappings. The only condition here is that the mapping be one-to-one and that neighboring points go over into neighboring points. Thus a continuous mapping may subject any figure to an arbitrary amount of distortion, only it is not permitted to tear connected regions apart or to stick separate regions together. This great generality notwithstanding, the continuous mappings do not make it possible to map any two arbitrary surfaces into each other. An example of two surfaces that can not be mapped into each other continuously are the circular disk and the plane annulus bounded by two concentric circles (Fig. 251).

Indeed, we cannot even map the boundaries of these two surfaces onto each other continuously, since the circular disk is bounded by one connected curve while the annulus has two separate curves as its boundary.

The question of when two surfaces can be mapped onto each other by a continuous mapping is one of the problems of topology, a subject we shall treat of in the last chapter. Clearly, the class of continuous mappings embraces all the types of mappings we have been discussing. Thus a geometrical mapping will yield useful results only to the extent that it is continuous. For example, the mapping given in Fig. 250 maps portions of the surface of the sphere into regions in the plane in such a way as to preserve areas. Evidently the entire surface of the sphere is mapped onto a rectangular region. Here it is seen that the mapping ceases to be meaningful visually on the boundary of the rectangle, since it is no longer continuous there. It is true that in the modern development of topology some even more general mappings have been considered that are not one-to-one but are single-valued, and continuous, in one direction only; for example, mappings of a portion of a surface into a segment of a curve.

A type of mapping that has been the subject of a more thorough investigation than any other mapping mentioned so far, is that of the *angle-preserving* (or *conformal*) mappings. The defining con-

FIG. 251

dition for such mappings is that the angle at which two curves intersect be reproduced without distortion. The simplest example of conformal mapping, apart from the isometric mappings, are stereographic projection and the circle-preserving transformations. An angle-preserving transformation that maps surfaces of negative Gaussian curvature into the plane is represented by Poincaré's model of the hyperbolic plane.

The angle-preserving transformations have a certain property in common with the isometric transformations: It can be proved analytically that very small figures suffer hardly any distortion at all under angle-preserving transformations. Specifically, not only are angles preserved, but the ratios of distances—although not the distances themselves—are preserved approximately, and as the size of the figure under consideration decreases, the accuracy of approximation increases. The term *conformal* stems from this property. In the small, the conformal mappings are thus the nearest thing to isometric mappings among all the types of mappings we have been describing; for it is clear from our examples that, even in arbitrarily small figures, area-preserving and geodesic mappings may bring about arbitrarily great distortions.

Whereas isometric mappings are very limited in their applicability, conformal mappings are highly adaptable as regards applicability. And it is mainly its great applicability that has made conformal mapping central in many fertile geometrical investigations. The simplest problem in this connection, namely the problem of when two *plane* regions can be mapped conformally into each other, leads to a geometric interpretation of the complex numbers. This question is treated of in *geometrical function theory*.

§ 38. Geometrical Function Theory. Riemann's Mapping Theorem. Conformal Mapping in Space

Let a Cartesian coordinate system in the plane be given. With every point P having coordinates x, y, we associate the complex number $z = x + iy$. This yields a one-to-one correspondence between the complex numbers and the points of the plane. It is found expedient to complete this correspondence by adjoining to the plane a point at infinity P_∞ in the same way as we did in the theory of circle-preserving transformations, and to associate the "number" ∞ with this point. This graphical model of the complex numbers is called the *complex plane*.

In this way, all mappings from one region of the plane into another become correspondences between complex numbers. As a simple example, let us consider the relation $w = az + b$, where a and b are any complex constants subject only to the condition $a \neq 0$. Given any complex number z, we consider the point associated with $w = az + b$ as the image of the point associated with z. The mapping of the plane into itself obtained in this way turns out to be nothing but a similarity transformation. Conversely, all those similarity transformations that can be generated continuously from the identity transformation can be obtained by assigning to the numbers a and b all complex values except $a = 0$. The similarity transformations that cannot be continuously generated from the identity transformation in the plane itself but involve a reflection (or folding over) of the plane, correspond to the equation

$w = az + b$, where $\bar{z}$ denotes the complex conjugate $x - iy$ of $\bar{z} = x + iy$. The proof of these theorems is elementary.

The circle-preserving transformations that do not leave P_∞ fixed are represented by the *fractional linear transformations*

$$(1) \qquad w = \frac{az + b}{cz + d} \qquad (c \neq 0, \quad ad - bc \neq 0),$$

provided we take only those circle-preserving transformations that can be continuously generated in the plane from the identity transformation. The remaining circle-preserving transformations are obtained by replacing z by $\bar{z}$ in (1). For example, the inversion in the circle k with center at the origin and radius 1 is represented by the formula $w = 1/\bar{z}$. For,

$$w = u + iv = \frac{1}{\bar{z}} = \frac{1}{x - iy} = \frac{x + iy}{x^2 + y^2},$$

and therefore

$$(2) \qquad u = \frac{x}{x^2 + y^2}, \quad v = \frac{y}{x^2 + y^2}.$$

If M, P, Q are the points whose coordinates are $(0, 0)$, (x, y), and (u, v), so that P and Q are the points associated with the numbers z and w, then it follows from (2) that P and Q both lie on the same ray emanating from M and that the distances MP and MQ satisfy the condition $MP \cdot MQ = 1$. This proves that P and Q are indeed inverse points with respect to k.

Let us now take a more general function $w = f(z)$, say, a fractional rational function of z. Such a function also will invariably effect a *conformal* mapping of the plane. We have only to limit ourselves to regions of the plane not containing certain points determined by the function.

Every function $f(z)$ which is such that $w = f(z)$ defines a conformal mapping of the complex plane, is called an *analytic function*.[1] Not only are the rational functions analytic, but practically all the functions ever encountered in practice are analytic. In working with complex analytic functions we can apply most of the same rules that govern real functions of a real variable. This

---

[1] This geometrical definition is equivalent with the condition that $f(z)$ be *differentiable*, i.e. that the quotient $[f(z) - f(z_0)]/[z - z_0]$ converge to a complex number $f'(z_0)$ at every point z_0 of the region as z approaches z_0 within the region. The important part of this condition is that the number $f'(z_0)$ be independent of the path along which z approaches z_0 in the region of the complex plane.

reduces the two-dimensional problem of conformal mapping to a one-dimensional type of investigation.

By such considerations from the theory of functions of a complex variable, it is possible to prove the important theorem that the circle-preserving transformations, or in other words, the integral and fractional linear functions, represent the only conformal transformations that map the interior of a circle into the interior or exterior of another (or the same) circle. It follows that the hyperbolic rigid motions of the Poincaré model represent all of the conformal transformations of a circular disk into itself. Thus any conformal mapping is defined to within a hyperbolic rigid motion as soon as we know the region into which a circular disk is mapped. Accordingly, the analytic functions can be characterized to within an unessential transformation by the region into which they transform a circular disk. It is understood in this that regions that can be obtained from each other by a circle-preserving transformation are considered as not essentially distinct. For example, a circular region may be replaced by a half-plane. Thus, the function $\sqrt{z}$ transforms a half-plane into a quadrant, and the function $\log z$ transforms a half-plane into a strip bounded by two parallel straight lines. By using linear transformations it is thus easy to construct a conformal mapping by which the circular region of Fig. 252 is transformed into one of the other two regions shown in this figure.

Fig. 252

In all these examples and in the ones to be discussed later, the mapping is conformal at all interior points of the regions, but on the boundaries it is conformal only wherever there are no corners. If a smooth arc of a boundary is mapped into an arc having a corner, it is obvious that the mapping cannot be conformal along the whole length of the arc. But at the points where it is not conformal it is found that the mapping preserves the proportions between angles; in other words, all angles are multiplied by the same factor. For example, in the mapping effected by $\sqrt{z}$, the straight line bounding the half-plane under consideration is transformed into the sides of a right angle; and in this case at the point mapped into the vertex of the angle all angles are halved.

Riemann stated the fundamental theorem that every plane region other than the entire Euclidean plane that can be mapped one-to-one and continuously onto a circular disk, can also be mapped onto it *conformally*. This theorem gives us an indication of how great the variety is of analytic functions.

Riemann himself did not give a rigorous proof of his fundamental mapping theorem but only pointed out that it is equivalent with a variational problem, the so-called *Dirichlet problem*, and regarded it as obvious that this has a solution. That Dirichlet's problem has a solution was rigorously proved only much later. But before that, Riemann's theorem was proved by the following simpler method.

Let G be an arbitrary region that can be deformed into a circular disk. In order to construct a conformal transformation of G onto a given circular disk K, we begin with any conformal transformation a_0 mapping G conformally onto a subregion K_0 of K. For a_0 we may choose, for example, a similarity transformation. We shall impose the additional condition that a_0 map some given point P in the interior of G onto the center M of the circle. Now let R_0 be the image of any other interior point Q of G. Then it is possible to prove the following: The mapping a_0 can be changed into a conformal mapping a_1 of such a nature that the image of G under a_1 is a subregion K_1 of K, that P is again mapped into M, *and that Q is mapped into a point R_1 on the radius MR_0 whose distance from M is greater than that of R_0.* The transition from a_0 to a_1 is given, incidentally, by a conformal transformation represented by the square root of a fractional linear function. a_1 can in turn be altered in the same way, and by continuing in this way we get a sequence of conformal mappings a_n of the region G onto subregions K_n of K, which are such that P is always transformed into M and Q is transformed into a sequence of points R_n on the radius MR_0 which keep moving further away from M. It is found that the regions K_n more and more nearly fill out the circular disk K and that the sequence of mappings a_n converges to a conformal mapping a. Then a maps G conformally onto K, as required by Riemann's theorem.

The method we have sketched here is due to Koebe. It shows that the mapping with which we are concerned is distinguished by an extremal property. For evidently the point R of K into which a maps Q is that point of MR_0 towards which the points R_n converge, and hence $MR > MR_n$ for all n. The same inequality holds if instead of measuring the distances in the Euclidean sense, we regard the interior of K as a Poincaré model of the hyperbolic plane and measure distances in the hyperbolic metric. This is true because the hyperbolic distance of a point from the center M is measured along the radius like the Euclidean distance, since the radii represent the hyperbolic straight lines passing through M (cf. pp. 254, 258). Besides a there are other conformal mappings b mapping G onto K. But, by a theorem mentioned earlier, b can differ from a only by a hyperbolic rigid motion of K. If therefore S and T are the images of P and Q under the mapping b, then the hyperbolic distances MR and ST are necessarily equal. Thus we have found the extremal property we were looking for: *The hyperbolic distance between the images of two arbitrary interior points of G under any conformal mapping of G into K exceeds the hyperbolic distance between the two images under any conformal mapping of G into a subregion of K.*

In terms of hyperbolic geometry, we may also describe the process as follows. Suppose we have a conformal mapping from G onto a region K' of the hyperbolic plane. If we now try to alter the mapping continuously in such a way that it remains conformal but that the distance between two arbitrarily chosen points increases all the time, then K' will gradually fill up the entire hyperbolic plane. The distance between the two points increases to a *finite* maximum which is reached when K' fills up the entire hyperbolic plane, and not before.

It would be natural to try mapping the interior of G onto the Euclidean plane instead of onto the hyperbolic plane. A *continuous* mapping of the interior of G into the Euclidean plane obviously exists, since it was assumed that the interior of G can be mapped continuously onto the interior of a circle, and the interior of a circle can obviously be mapped continuously onto the Euclidean plane (for example, we may map the interior H of a circle stereographically onto a hemisphere and then map the hemisphere continuously onto the plane E by projection from the center of the sphere). But it is impossible to find a *conformal* mapping of H onto E. For, by virtue of such a mapping, every conformal mapping of H onto itself would induce a conformal mapping of E onto itself. And the set of all conformal mappings of H onto itself consists of the hyperbolic rigid motions, a three-parameter family. If a conformal mapping $H \to E$ existed, the set of all conformal mappings of E onto itself would therefore also form a three-parameter family. But all the similarity transformations are conformal mappings of E, and they alone form a four-parameter family, as can be seen from their representation in the form $w = az + b$ which involves two arbitrary complex numbers a and b, and consequently four arbitrary real numbers. Hence there is no conformal mapping of H onto E. Incidentally, the similarity transformations are the only conformal mappings of E onto itself.

In three dimensions we can define the conformal mappings in exactly the same way as in the plane. But in three dimensions the variety of conformal mappings is very limited. For, all of these mappings preserve spheres (i.e. transform the set of all spheres and planes into itself). The family of all sphere-preserving transformations has only ten parameters. A particularly simple type of sphere-preserving mappings are the three-dimensional inversions. Their definition is analogous to the definition of inversions in the plane: We choose a fixed point M and a fixed number r at pleasure and then map every point P different from M into that point Q on the ray MP for which $MP \cdot MQ = r^2$. Every sphere-preserving transformation can be resolved into a three-dimensional inversion and a similarity transformation.

§ 39. Conformal Mappings of Curved Surfaces. Minimal Surfaces. Plateau's Problem

An example of a conformal mapping of a curved surface onto the plane is furnished by stereographic projection. Under stereographic projection every conformal mapping in the plane becomes a conformal mapping on the sphere. If the center of the stereographic projection is at a point N, the conformal mappings of the sphere leaving N fixed correspond to the conformal mappings of the Euclidean plane onto itself. As we have mentioned above, the only conformal mappings of the Euclidean plane onto itself are the similarity transformations. It follows that all the conformal mappings of a sphere onto itself leaving a point fixed are circle-preserving transformations. Any conformal mapping of the sphere onto itself can be transformed by a rotation about a diameter into a conformal mapping of the sphere that leaves a point fixed. Hence the totality of conformal mappings of the sphere onto itself must be identical with the totality of circle-preserving mappings on the sphere, i.e. with the transformations derived by stereographic projection from the circle-preserving transformations of the plane. The circle-preserving transformations of the plane are represented by formula (1) on page 264. This formula involves four complex constants, but they are only defined to within a complex common factor. Thus the circle-preserving transformations in the plane, and likewise those on the sphere, form a six-parameter family.

It may be proved that every closed surface that can be mapped continuously onto the sphere, as for example the ellipsoid, can also be mapped onto the sphere conformally. It follows that any two surfaces of this kind can also be mapped conformally onto each other and that every surface of this kind admits of a family of conformal mappings onto itself with exactly six parameters.

The surfaces, such as the hyperbolic paraboloid, that can be mapped continuously onto the interior of a circle or onto the Euclidean plane, certainly can not all be mapped conformally onto each other, since the interior of a circle, for example, can not be mapped conformally onto the whole Euclidean plane. But for these surfaces we have the following important "either-or theorem": Every surface of this kind can be mapped conformally either onto the interior of a circle or onto the Euclidean plane.

For other types of surfaces too, e.g. for the torus, the problem of the existence of conformal mappings of the surface can be solved completely. Since the treatment of this problem requires topological methods, we shall defer it to the chapter on topology.

A particularly interesting example of conformal mappings is provided by the minimal surfaces. The minimal surfaces were defined (p. 189) by the property that the principal curvatures at every point of such a surface are equal in magnitude and opposite in sign. It is readily deduced from this definition that the spherical representation of a minimal surface is conformal, and, conversely, it is readily proved that the minimal surfaces are the only surfaces other than the sphere whose spherical representation (by parallel normals) is conformal. The minimal surfaces are therefore intimately tied up with the theory of functions. Every complex analytic function can be used to define a minimal surface.

As we have mentioned before, a soap film stretched across a

closed wire takes on the shape of a minimal surface. This leads
to the following problem first posed by Plateau: Given any closed
twisted curve, to find a minimal surface bounded by the curve.
For a long time, all efforts to prove even the existence of such a
minimal surface for every preassigned boundary curve, were un-
successful. It was only in 1931 that the solution to the general
Plateau problem was found by Jesse Douglas.[1]

In order to solve Plateau's problem, Douglas substituted a still
more inclusive problem; he set out to find not only the minimal
surface M bounded by the given space curve r but also its conformal
mapping onto a plane circular region K. To this end, he began by
considering the way in which such a mapping maps the curve r
onto the circumference k of K. It is found that this mapping is
distinguished by an extremal property. If s is any chord of r, the
mapping of the end-points of s associates s with a chord s' of k.
Calling the ratio s'/s the magnification of the chord s, let us take
the mean value, over all chords of r, of the reciprocal of the magnification squared. The desired mapping makes the value of this
mean as small as possible.[2] We may thus say that the desired mapping moves all the points of r as far apart, in the mean, as possible.
It can be proved that a mapping with this extremal property always
exists. By means of this mapping $r \to k$, the Cartesian coordinates
of the remaining points of M may then be expressed as point functions on K by well-known analytic formulas.[3]

If we let r be a plane curve, then M degenerates into the plane
region G bounded by r. Then Douglas' procedure gives us a conformal mapping of G into K and thus a solution of Riemann's
mapping problem. It is seen that the method leading to this solution proceeds in a direction exactly opposite to that of the method

---

[1] Trans. Amer. Math. Soc., Vol. 33 (1931). A short time before, Tibor Radó
had solved the Plateau problem under somewhat more special conditions; Math.
Zeit., Vol. 2 (1930).

[2] In formulas, this may be stated as follows. If two points P and Q of r are
mapped into the points P' and Q' of k, let α and β be the amplitudes of the points
P' and Q' respectively, and set $PQ/P'Q' = v(\alpha, \beta)$. Then the double integral

$$\int_{\alpha=0}^{2\pi} \int_{\beta=0}^{2\pi} [v(\alpha, \beta)]^2 \, d\alpha \, d\beta$$

will take on the smallest possible value in the case of the mapping we are
looking for.

[3] Poisson integrals over r.

described earlier. In the earlier construction, we began with a pair of interior points of G; by increasing the hyperbolic distance between images of these points, we eventually brought the boundary of G into superposition with the boundary of K. Douglas' procedure, on the other hand, begins by effecting a suitable mapping, distinguished by an extremal property, of the boundary of G onto the boundary of K, and then the mapping of the interior points is determined automatically.

For certain special space curves r, the minimal surfaces bounded by r can be found by much simpler methods—for example, if r is a closed polygon composed of straight-line segments in space. While in general the resulting minimal surface has a singular boundary at r, it is possible by special choice of r to get a minimal surface that can be extended beyond r without having any singularity. In this way, Neovius[4] succeeded in constructing a minimal surface that extends over the entire space without singularity or self-intersection and has the same symmetry as the diamond lattice.

Nor can the spherical image of this surface have a boundary. Furthermore, it can be shown that a minimal surface cannot contain any parabolic curves, at which the spherical image might return on itself. Yet the spherical image of Neovius' surface cannot cover the whole sphere smoothly, since it would then be possible to map Neovius' surface continuously onto the sphere. This apparent contradiction is resolved by the fact that there are monkey saddles on Neovius' surface. A curve making one complete turn around such a point on the surface is represented by a curve making several turns on the spherical image (see p. 202). The spherical image of Neovius' minimal surface covers the sphere in infinitely many layers that are connected at the points that are images of the monkey saddles. In the case of many other minimal surfaces too, the course of the spherical image is similar to this. Riemann found surfaces that cover the sphere or the plane in this way, by studying in its entirety the conformal mapping effected by a non-linear function, such as $w = z^2$. The points analogous to the spherical images of monkey saddles, where the sheets of a Riemann surface are connected, are called *branch points*.

[4] E. R. Neovius, *Bestimmung zweier speziellen periodischen Minimalflächen.* Akad. Abhandlung, Helsingfors, 1883.

CHAPTER V

KINEMATICS

So far we have been concerned chiefly with the study of entities that are *fixed* in space, since it is such entities that must form the starting point of geometrical investigation. But even the elements of geometry make use of the concept of *motion*. Thus we have called two figures congruent if they can be superimposed by a rigid motion. Furthermore, we have studied movable hyperboloids (see p. 16), we have determined ruled surfaces by means of a moving plane (pp. 204-205), and we have subjected surfaces to bending and distortion (Chap. IV). Kinematics is concerned with the systematic study of motions.

We shall begin with the study of linkages, a part of kinematics that is intimately connected with elementary metric geometry. We shall then proceed to a more general discussion of continuous motions, using the methods of differential geometry.

§ 40. Linkages.

The term "plane linkage" applies to every plane system of rigid rods which are interconnected, or connected with fixed points of the plane about which they are free to turn, in such a way that the system is capable of certain motions in the plane. The simplest mechanism of this kind consists of a single rod with one end attached to a point of the plane; in effect, this is a compass. Just as the free end of a compass traces out a circle, so the points of the rods in all other plane linkages move on algebraic curves, i.e. curves satisfying an algebraic equation in a system of Cartesian coordinates. Conversely, it is possible to find a system of jointed rods that is suitable for the construction (at least piecemeal) of any given algebraic curve no matter how complicated.

The construction by means of a linkage of the simplest algebraic curve, viz. of the straight line, has been a famous problem. We shall study one particular model for tracing out the straight line, Peaucellier's inversor. We begin with the mechanism consisting of six rods illustrated in Fig. 253. The rods a and b are equal in length and so are c, d, e, and f. a and b are connected by a joint at the fixed point O. P and Q are always collinear with O, being on the bisector of the angle AOB. Applying to the circle with center A and radius c a well-known theorem about the secants of a circle, we note in addition that the relation

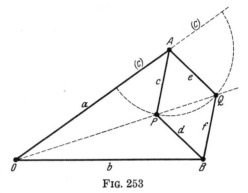

$$OP \cdot OQ =$$
$$(OA + c)(OA - c)$$
$$= a^2 - c^2$$

is valid for all the positions of the mechanism. Hence P and Q are conjugate points with respect to the circle

FIG. 253

with center O and radius $\sqrt{a^2 - c^2}$ (cf. p. 254). Clearly, P is free to move through every point in the ring with center at O having outer radius $a^2 - c^2$ and inner radius $a - c$. Thus the mechanism constructs the inverse to every point in this region with respect to the above circle; for this reason, it is called an inversor. If P now traces out a circle that passes through O, then Q must trace out a straight line (see p. 254). Accordingly, we attach one end of another rod g (see Fig. 254) to P and the other end to a point M the distance of which from O is equal to the length g of the rod. P is then constrained to

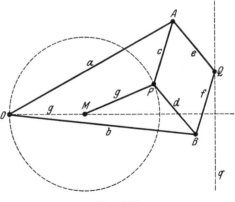

FIG. 254

travel on the circle of radius g with center M. And since $OM = g$, this circle passes through O. Hence Q traces out a straight line q, and our problem is solved. Furthermore, it is readily seen that q is perpendicular to OM, so that in addition, Peaucellier's inversor provides a means for drawing a perpendicular to a given straight line.

In space, the definition of a linkage is analogous. But now the attachment of the rods to each other or to fixed points of space must be done in such a way as to permit rotation in all directions in space rather than just in a plane. Within a certain range this can be realized in practice by the use of ball pivots. The ends of the rods constituting a linkage in space always trace out algebraic surfaces. On the other hand, it has not yet been proved that every algebraic surface can be constructed by means of a linkage, although this theorem is most probably true.

Here again, we shall consider the very simplest construction, that is, the construction of a plane. Our starting point is the collapsible rod model of the hyperboloid of one sheet (see pp. 16 and 29). Let g and g' be two straight lines of the same family and h a variable straight line of the other family intersecting g and g' at the vari-

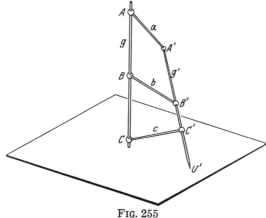

able points H and H'. Let the model be moved, but in such a way as to keep the rod g fixed (see Fig. 255). Then the distance of every point H' on g' from the point H of g which is associated with it, re- mains fixed. As the model is moved, the points of g' therefore move on spheres with

FIG. 255

centers at the corresponding points of g. If the straight line h is now chosen so as to intersect g at its ideal point U, then the point U' associated with U, being the point of intersection of h and g', must be a finite point; for if it were not, then $UU' = h$ would be an ideal straight line lying on the surface, and then the surface would have to be a hyperbolic paraboloid instead of a hyperboloid (cf. p. 120). As the linkage is moved, U' therefore travels on a sphere with infinite radius, i.e. on a plane.

This argument suggests a simple mechanism for constructing a plane. Three rods of one family define the hyperboloid uniquely. Hence we attach three rods a, b, and c to a fixed rod g by ball joints at A, B, and C (see Fig. 255). Then we attach the free ends of a, b, and c to ball joints at the points A', B', and C' of a rod g'. To ensure that a, b, and c generate a hyperboloid and not a hyper-

bolic paraboloid, it is sufficient to choose the points in such a way
that $AB : AC \neq A'B' : A'C'$. For, it is easy to prove that the
distances between three points on small g must be proportional to the
distances between the corresponding points on g' if the rods lie on
a hyperbolic paraboloid.
The movable hyperbo-
loid defined by a, b, and
c can assume ∞^1 different shapes, and each of
these surfaces is free to
rotate about the axis g;
hence every point on
the rod g' of our linkage
has two degrees of free-
dom.[1] We have seen
above that the points of
g' move on spheres hav-

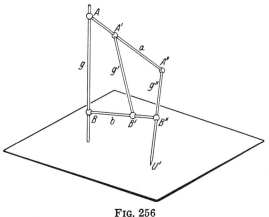

FIG. 256

ing g as a diameter and that a certain point U' of g' traces out part of
a plane which is perpendicular to g'. It is seen that U' passes through
all the points of a plane annulus whose axis is g. Thus the solution
of our problem is complete. Another possible solution is illustrated
in Fig. 256. This is obtained from the mechanism we have described
by interchanging the roles played by the two families of straight
lines on the hyperboloid.

§ 41. Continuous Rigid Motions of Plane Figures

Let a movable plane σ slide over a fixed plane ϱ in any way whatever. It is our aim to characterize this process—which we shall call
a *continuous rigid motion*—as simply as possible geometrically.

In a detailed discussion earlier in the book (p. 60) we saw that
the effect of any given plane rigid motion, in transforming an initial
position into a final position, may always be achieved by a single

---

[1] The number of degrees of freedom may also be obtained as follows: If the
rod g' were not present, then the point triple $A'B'C'$ would have six degrees of
freedom, since each point separately could move on a sphere and would thus
have two degrees of freedom. Now the collinearity of A', B', C' implies two relations, and the conditions that $A'B'$ and $A'C'$ have a given length each yields one
further relation. Thus we arrive at $6 - 2 - 1 - 1 = 2$ degrees of freedom, by
the methods discussed in § 24.

rotation or by a single translation. If the translations are treated as rotations about an ideal point, we may say that every rigid motion of the plane, without exception, can be replaced by a rotation about a definite center.

Now let a definite motion be given. At a given time t, the moving plane σ has a certain position A. At a subsequent time $t + h$ it has another position A_h. The change of position $A \to A_h$ is associated with a center of rotation M_h, and if we make h smaller and smaller, so that the difference between A_h and A also becomes smaller and smaller, M_h moves towards a limiting position M. The point M is called the *instantaneous center of the motion* at the instant t. If P is any other point of the moving plane, the motion of P at the instant t is perpendicular to PM.

By marking the instantaneous center at every moment of the motion, we get a locus which is a curve on the fixed plane. This curve is called the *fixed centrode* of the motion. But in the same motion we may also regard the plane σ, which we had considered movable, as fixed and the plane ϱ, which we had considered fixed, as movable—this is how the motion appears to an observer who accompanies the plane σ. Then we get a curve—called the *moving centrode*—as the locus of the instantaneous centers in the plane σ. Both curves are continuous everywhere. They may extend to points at infinity, but then they have to be closed at infinity in the sense of projective geometry, i.e. the central projections of the curves onto another plane must be curves that are continuous at the points corresponding to the horizon.

A more detailed study shows that the motion is completely determined by the form of the two centrodes together with two points, one on each curve, which coincide at some instant of the motion. For, if the curves are made to touch at the given pair of points, and the moving centrode, accompanied by its own plane, is subsequently caused to roll along the fixed centrode without sliding, then the original motion will be generated. At every instant during the motion the two curves are mutually tangent at the instantaneous center. From the fact that the two curves roll along each other without sliding it follows that the arc bounded by any two points on the fixed centrode has the same length as the arc bounded by the corresponding points on the moving centrode.

We have thus found a simple characterization for the continuous rigid motions analogous to the one we previously found for rigid motions: every continuous motion is generated by rolling one curve on another. It is necessary to include the special case (rotation) where both curves degenerate into points.

Let us consider the special case of an arbitrary curve k in the fixed plane and a straight line g in the movable plane, where it is required that a point P of the straight line traverse k in such a way that g is always perpendicular to k (see Fig. 257). In this case it follows directly from the definition of the center of curvature that the instantaneous center M is always the center of curvature, corresponding to the point P, of the curve k. Hence the fixed centrode is the evolute m of k, and, since M is always on g, the moving centrode is the straight line g itself; thus the motion is

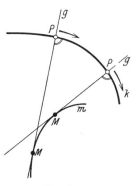

Fig. 257

generated by rolling g on m. In this process the fixed point P on g describes the curve k whose evolute is m. The distance between two points of g is always equal to the arc length cut off by the corresponding points of m. This leads us to the thread construction of any curve from its evolute given on page 178.

Of particular importance are the curves described by the points of the moving plane in the case where both centrodes are circles. Different types of such curves are obtained according to whether the moving circle touches the fixed circle from the inside or from the outside. In the first case, the curves are called hypotrochoids, in the second

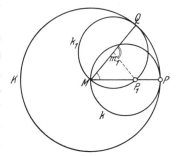

Fig. 258

case epitrochoids. If the point generating the curve is on the circumference of the rolling circle, the curve is called a hypocycloid or epicycloid. The form of the trochoids and cycloids also depends on the ratio between the radii of the two circles.

Let us first take a rolling circle k having a radius just half that of the fixed circle K. Let k be internally tangent to K.

We shall determine the path of a point P of k, that is, a hypo-cycloid.[1] Let us consider first the position in which k is tangent to the fixed circle K at the point P, and then some other position k_1 of the rolling circle in which P has reached P_1 (see Fig. 258). Let the centers of the circles K and k_1 be at M and m_1 and let their point of contact be at Q. Since the circles roll on each other without sliding, the length of the arc QP_1 of k_1 is equal to that of the arc QP of K. Furthermore, since k is half the size of K, it follows that $\angle Q m_1 P_1 = 2 \angle QMP$, and in addition that M lies on k_1. Hence we have, by the well-known theorem about the angles subtended at the circumference and at the center of a circle, that $\angle QMP_1 = (1/2) \angle Q m_1 P_1 = \angle QMP$. Hence the straight line MP_1 coincides with MP, i.e. P_1 travels on the straight line MP during the course of the motion. Thus we have proved the surprising theorem that in

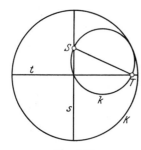

FIG. 259

our particular case the hypocycloids coincide with the diameters of the fixed circle. As a by-product, we get a new mechanism for tracing out a straight line.

We proceed to find the corresponding hypo-trochoids. To this end, we describe the motion in another way, making use of the result just obtained. In the process of rolling, the arc ST, where S and T are the two ends of a diameter of k, corresponds to one quarter of the circumference of K. Therefore S and T move on two perpendicular diameters, s and t, of K (Fig. 259). An easy calculation gives the following result: If a straight-line segment ST is moved in such a way that its extremities travel on two mutually perpendicular straight lines s and t, then the midpoint of ST traces out a circle; every other point P of ST traces out an ellipse whose axes are on s and t and are respectively equal to SP and PT in length. Consequently all the hypotrochoids generated by the rolling circle k are ellipses. For, every point rigidly connected to k lies on a diameter of k, and this diameter is a straight line two points of which slide along two mutually perpendicular straight lines.

---

[1] Which point we choose on the circumference is immaterial; because of the symmetry of the figure, the cycloids generated by different points on the circumference of k differ only by a rotation about the center of K.

Let us now turn to the case where k rolls on the outside of K. The resulting epicycloids are shaped like the curve e in Fig. 260. It can be shown that, like this curve, all hypocycloids and epicycloids have cusps. At such points, the cycloid always meets the fixed circle at right angles. The cusps correspond to the position in which the generating point of the cycloid is at the point of contact of the circles. In our particular case, where k is half as big K, there are exactly two cusps.

The tangents to our curve have a peculiar property, illustrated in Fig. 261. Let the rolling begin at the moment when the generating point P on k is the point of contact with K, i.e. when it just passes through a cusp. The figure shows k in a second position k_1; by the time this position is reached, P has moved along an arc of the cycloid to P_1. We connect M and m_1, the centers of K and k_1. The straight line Mm_1 passes through Q, the point of contact of K and k_1, and meets k_1 again at R. Let t be the tangent to the cycloid at P_1. Since Q is the instantaneous center of the motion in the present position of k, the direction of motion of P_1, and hence also the straight line t, is perpendicular

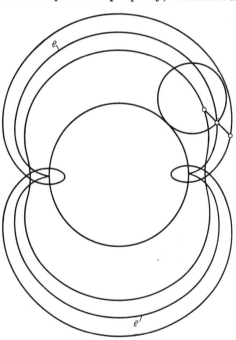

Fig. 260

to QP_1. Hence t is concurrent with P_1R, since the angle QP_1R, being in a semicircle, is a right angle. A similar property is shared by the tangents of all the epicycloids and hypocycloids. In our case, where k is half the size of K, the equality of the arc PQ of K with the arc P_1Q of k_1 leads to the equation

$$\angle PMQ = 1/2 \; \angle P_1m_1Q = \angle P_1RQ.$$

Thus, if s is the line through R parallel to MP, s and t form equal angles with MR. This may be formulated as a theorem of Geometrical Optics as follows: If a beam of parallel light rays (s) falls on a reflecting surface that is in the form of a circle with center M and radius MR, then the reflected rays (t) envelop an

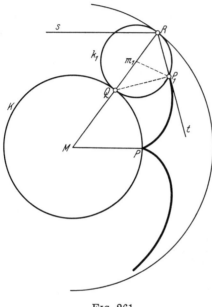

epicycloid with two cusps whose base circle has the center M and radius $(\frac{1}{2})MR$. The straight line connecting M with the cusps of the cycloid is parallel to the direction of the beam (s). Because of this optical property, the curve is sometimes called the focal line (or caustic curve) of the circle. We may observe them every day in cups and tin cans when the light shines on them.

    Two of the epitrochoids associated with this epicycloid are shown in Fig. 260. All the epitrochoids generated by points inside the rolling circle

FIG. 261

are free from singularities. On the other hand, those generated by points outside the rolling circle have loops and double points. The cycloids represent the transition between the two types of trochoids.

    The case next in order of simplicity results when the diameters

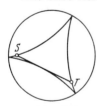

of the fixed circle and the rolling circle are in the ratio 3:1. The hypocycloid with three cusps is shown in Fig. 262. The tangents to this curve have a special property, which may be derived analytically: the segment ST of the tangent which is inside the curve is constant in length, i.e. its length is independent of the point of tan-

FIG. 262

gency with the curve. At one time this fact was believed to be significant in connection with a problem referred to on page 214, the problem of moving a straight-line segment in such a way that the net effect is that of a rotation through 180° about the center and that the plane area swept out during the motion is a minimum.

We have already mentioned that the area can be made arbitrarily small by a suitable choice of the motion, so that there is no solution to the problem. However, it had been conjectured earlier that there is a solution and that it consists of the tangential motion of ST (see Fig. 262) along the three-cusp cycloid in which the extremities of the segment stay on the curve throughout. There was, in fact, some evidence in favor of the conjecture that the area could not be further diminished.

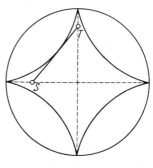

Fig. 263

The tangent of tne hypocycloid with four cusps (Fig. 263), generally called the astroid, has a similar property too: if S and T denote the points where the tangent intersects the axes of symmetry of the curve, the distance ST is constant. Therefore a straight-line segment that moves with its end points on two mutually perpendicular straight lines envelops an astroid. We mentioned earlier that every point of a segment executing this motion traces out an ellipse. From this it may be deduced that the astroid is enveloped by a family of ellipses for which the sum of the axes is constant (see Fig. 264).

Going over to the general case, we note that there is a fundamental difference between those cycloids for which the radii, r and R, of the rolling and the fixed circle are commensurable and those cycloids for which they are not. If r/R is a rational number, which may then be written as a fraction a/b in

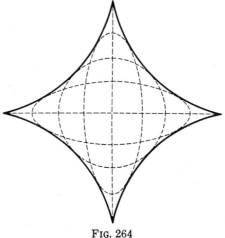

Fig. 264

lowest terms, then the cycloid has b cusps and closes up after the moving circle has rolled a times around the fixed circle. If r/R is irrational, the curve has infinitely many cusps and does not close up. In the latter case it can be proved that we can get arbitrarily close to every point of the region swept out by the rolling circle by following the course of the curve sufficiently long. The limiting cases where $r = \infty$ or $R = \infty$ have a particularly simple meaning. If $r = \infty$, so that the rolling circle is replaced by a straight line, we get the involute of the circle (Fig. 8, p. 6). If it is the fixed circle that is replaced by a straight line, we get the "ordinary cycloid." This is the curve (Fig. 265) traced out by any point on the circumference of a wheel that rolls in a fixed direction on a plane.

The continuous motions we have studied so far involve a single moving plane. But in physics we are led to the study of more general phenomena, the relative continuous motions. Let us consider, in addition to the fixed plane E and the movable plane e (denoted earlier by ϱ and σ respectively), another plane f that slides over E in a different manner than e. Then f also performs a perfectly definite continuous motion relative to e, as seen by an observer attached

FIG. 265

to e. We may think of the continuous motion (fE) of f relative to E as decomposable into the separate motions (fe) and (eE). A complicated motion can frequently be simplified by such a decomposition into two motions. There is, for example, a particularly simple decomposition for the rolling of two circles K and k. Let E be the fixed plane containing K, and f the movable plane containing k. Let M and m be the centers of K and k respectively. All that we need do in order to describe the motion of m relative to E is to introduce a plane e in which m is fixed and which rotates about M. Then the motion of f relative to e can only be a rotation about m. The angular velocities of the rotations about M and m vary inversely as the radii of the circles K and k. It is found, in consequence, that the cycloidal motion is the resultant of two rotations. The important role of the cycloids and trochoids in astronomy is due to this fact. Since all the planets move in approximately circular orbits about the sun with constant velocities and in approximately the same plane (the ecliptic), the path of every planet as seen from the earth appears approximately trochoidal. Thus the pre-Copernican geocentric system of astronomy stimulated a thorough study of these curves.

In our example, M and m are the instantaneous centers of the motions (eE) and (fe), while the instantaneous center Q of the cycloidal motion (fE) is situated, as we have seen, at the point of tangency of the circles k and K. Thus the three instantaneous centers are collinear. The same can be shown to be true quite generally: If the motion (fE) is the resultant of the motions (fe) and (eE), then the instantaneous centers of (fE), (fe), and (eE) at any instant are collinear (Law of Three Centers).

§ 42. An Instrument for Constructing the Ellipse and its Roulettes[1]

Let c and c' be two rods of the same length c. Let a_1 and a_2 be two other rods both equal to $a > c$ in length. Let the extremities F_1, F_2 of c and F_1', F_2' of c' be linked to a_1 and a_2 by pin joints in such a way as to form a self-intersecting quadrilateral with opposite sides equal, as shown in Fig. 266. Let E be the point at which a_1 and a_2 cross. Its position on these two rods will change as the plane linkage assumes its various possible positions. At E we place a joint with two sleeves which are free to turn about E and in which the rods a_1 and a_2

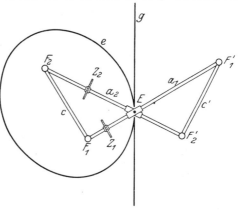

Fig. 266

can slide freely. If the rod c is now held fixed, the curve that the point E is still free to trace out is an ellipse e with F_1, F_2 as foci and with a as the constant sum of its focal distances; this is proved as follows. The triangles $F_1F_2F_2'$ and $F_1F_1'F_2'$ are always congruent because their corresponding sides are equal. Therefore $\angle F_1F_2'F_2 = \angle F_2'F_1F_1'$, so that the triangle $F_1F_2'E$ is isosceles. From this it follows that $F_1E + EF_2 = F_2'E + EF_2 = a$, as was to be proved.

Now let two wheels Z_1 and Z_2 be mounted at any two points of the rods a_1 and a_2 in such a way as to be free to rotate about these rods but not to slide along them (see Fig. 266). Let F_1 and F_2 be

---

[1] This instrument was first described by R. C. Yates (*The description of a surface of constant curvature*, Amer. Math. Monthly, December, 1931).

no longer fixed. Then we can move E along any curve while the wheels roll over the plane of the curve. The presence of the wheels has the effect of restricting the direction of motion of the center of each wheel to the plane of the wheel, at right angles to the rod that carries the wheel. Then all the other points of a_1 and a_2 also move at right angles to their respective rods; this can be rigorously deduced from the fact that the distance between two points of the same rod remains constant. If we now imagine the rod c to be rigidly attached during the motion to a moving plane f that remains parallel to the plane of the curve k, then the instantaneous center of the motion of f is always at E. For since every point of the plane f constantly moves at right angles to the line connecting it with the point that is the instantaneous center at any given moment

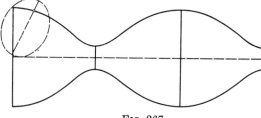

(cf. p. 276), and since F_1 always moves at right angles to a_1, the instantaneous center must lie on a_1 throughout the motion; similarly, it has to lie on

FIG. 267

a_2, and hence it must be at the point of intersection of the rods a_1 and a_2. Thus the fixed centrode of the motion of f is the curve k. On the other hand, the moving centrode must be the ellipse e, since we have shown that e is the curve traced out by E when c is held fixed. Thus our instrument moves the points of the plane f along the same curves on which they travel when the ellipse e is rolled along k. These curves are called the *roulettes* of the ellipse.

Of particular importance among the roulettes of the ellipse is the curve traced out by one of the foci when the ellipse rolls on a straight line. Fig. 267 depicts such a curve. The vertices of the quadrilateral in Yates' apparatus travel on curves of this type if the point E is moved along a straight line g. Since, as we have already mentioned, the rod a_1 is simultaneously perpendicular to the paths of all its points, these curves are all parallel, and this is true, in particular, for the paths of F_1 and F_1'. Thus the study of Yates' apparatus leads to a peculiar geometrical theorem which may be formulated at follows: Given a roulette generated by a focus of an ellipse, on the normals to the roulette draw the points whose distance from the curve, measured in the direction of the center of curvature, is equal to the constant sum of focal radii for the ellipse; then the points thus marked out lie on another roulette generated by a focus of an ellipse; this ellipse is congruent to the first ellipse and rolls on the same curve as the first ellipse but on the opposite side of that curve.

The roulette shown in Fig. 267 crops up as the meridian of the surfaces of revolution of constant mean curvature. The curvature is equal to the reciprocal of half the sum of the focal radii of the generating ellipse. We have mentioned on pages 228-229 that every surface of constant mean curvature is parallel to some surface having constant positive Gaussian curvature. In our case, the latter surface must be another surface of revolution, and the meridians of the two surfaces must be parallel. Hence there is a point on the rod a_1 of our apparatus which traces out a meridian of a surface of revolution having constant Gaussian curvature. From the relation between curvatures given on pages 228-229 it can be deduced that this point is the midpoint of the rod a_1. By assigning all possible values to the lengths c and a of the rods, we obtain the meridians of all the surfaces of revolution having constant positive Gaussian curvature with the exception of the sphere.

§ 43. Continuous Motions in Space

We shall adapt the discussion of the last section to apply to the case of a three-dimensional space or three-dimensional region r moving in a space R that is considered fixed. In space, every rigid motion can be effected by a rotation about a definite axis combined with a translation along that axis, i.e. by a screw motion (see p. 82). This assigns to every rigid motion, except for pure translations, a definite straight line that serves as axis of the screw or rotation. The anomalous role of the translations can be eliminated by treating every translation as a rotation about an infinitely distant axis.

By comparing neighboring positions of the moving space we can construct the *instantaneous axis* of the motion at any given moment; the procedure is analogous to the construction of the instantaneous center in the case of plane motions. As the motion progresses, this axis changes its position continuously, thus sweeping out a ruled surface in R and another in r. These are the analogues of the fixed and moving centrodes of a plane motion and are called the fixed and the moving axode respectively of the three-dimensional motion. A motion in space is uniquely defined by its axodes and the particular rule on either axode that corresponds to one rule on the other. To reconstruct the motion, we begin with the two given straight lines in coincidence and with the surfaces tangent along this line. We then "roll" the movable axode along the fixed axode using a certain type of motion we shall describe below, making sure that the surfaces always have a line in common along which they are tangential.

This contact motion in space is analogous to the rolling of one curve on another in the plane. Yet there is a fundamental difference between these two forms of motion: a plane curve can be rolled along any other plane curve in a variety of different ways, but a given ruled

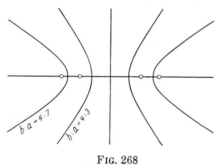

FIG. 268

surface can not be "rolled" on every other ruled surface. We have seen (pp. 208-209) that two ruled surfaces can be tangent along a ruling if and only if they have the same striction along this line. If this condition is satisfied, the surfaces must be put together in such a way that their points of striction on these straight lines coincide. Throughout the contact motion the axodes must continue to satisfy this condition and to assume the relative positions just specified. If the angles between the lines of striction and the rulings at corresponding points of the two surfaces are always equal, then the contact motion is a pure rolling without any sliding. If, on the other hand, the angles differ, then the surfaces slide along their common rule during the motion.[1]

---

[1] The necessary and sufficient conditions for two ruled surfaces to be axodes of a motion in space cannot be explained without the help of analytical methods. First of all, it is necessary that it be possible to set up a correspondence between the lines of striction of the two surfaces in such a way that they have equal striction at corresponding points. If, then, α and α' are the angles between the line of striction and the rulings at the corresponding points and if s and s' are corresponding arc lengths on the two lines of striction, the equation

$$\frac{ds'}{ds} = \frac{\sin \alpha}{\sin \alpha'}$$

has to be satisfied.

In the first, more special, case the contact motion may be regarded as being composed of infinitesimal rotations and the axodes are two mutually developable surfaces.

As a particularly simple example, we shall consider the case where the axodes are two hyperboloids of revolution of one sheet. Here the lines of striction are the smallest circles of latitude of these surfaces. Because of the rotational symmetry of the surfaces, their striction is a constant that depends only on the shape and size of the generating hyperbola.

It is easy to find an analytical characterization for the condition that two hyperboloids be of equal striction. Let the equations of the generating hyperbolas in a system of rectangular coordinates, x, y, be

$$\frac{x^2}{a^2} - \frac{y^2}{b^2} = 1$$

and

$$\frac{x^2}{A^2} - \frac{y^2}{B^2} = 1 \text{ ,}$$

the y-axis being used as axis of rotation. Then equality of striction between the two hyperboloids thus generated is equivalent to the simple equation $b = B$. Fig. 268 exhibits two such hyperbolas together with their foci.

During the contact motion the *relative* position of the two hyperboloids remains unchanged. If therefore one hyperboloid is kept in a fixed position, the axis of rotation of the second hyperboloid performs a rotation D about the axis of rotation of the first. The motion is simplified considerably if the first surface is subjected to the rotation, about its own axis, that is the inverse of D. Then the axis of the second hyperboloid remains fixed in space (and the axis of the first hyperboloid obviously remains fixed as well). Thus the contact motion of these two surfaces can be produced by putting them together in such a way that they are tangent along a straight line and then revolving them both about their axes with velocities having a suitable ratio.

This furnishes a practical method of cogwheel transmission of motion between two skew axes. Since sliding is harmful to the material of the machine, we are limited to the case of congruent hyperboloids. Fig. 269 depicts a transmission of this type.

CHAPTER VI

TOPOLOGY

In the study of projective geometry we have already witnessed phenomena that can be described without any comparison of lengths and angles but that possess nonetheless a precise geometrical character. In topology we are concerned with geometrical facts that do not even involve the concepts of straight line or plane but only the continuous connectedness between the points of a figure. Let us imagine a figure made of a material that can be distorted as much as we please but that cannot be torn or cemented. We shall encounter properties that remain unchanged when such a figure is distorted at will. Thus, for example, the sphere shares all its topological properties with the ellipsoid, the cube, and the tetrahedron. On the other hand, the sphere is topologically different from the torus, for it is clear by looking at them that a sphere cannot be deformed into a torus without tearing or gluing.

It is natural that topological problems should have made their appearance still later in the development of the science of geometry than projective problems. And topological problems were indeed not studied until the 18th Century. More recently, the theorems of topology have been found to be connected, despite their apparent indefiniteness, with *the* most precise quantitative results in mathematics, that is, with the results of the algebra of complex numbers, the theory of functions of a complex variable, and the theory of groups. Today topology ranks among the most fertile and successful branches of mathematical endeavor.

We shall have to limit our discussion to a few problems from the topology of surfaces in three-space.[1] We begin with those surfaces that are the easiest to study topologically—the polyhedra.

---

[1] For a further introduction into the fundamental concepts of topology the reader is referred to the little book *Einfachste Grundbegriffe der Topologie* by Alexandroff.

§ 44. Polyhedra

By a *polyhedron* we mean any system of polygons arranged in such a way that (1) exactly two polygons meet (at an angle) at every edge, and (2) it is possible to get from every polygon to every other polygon by crossing edges of the polyhedron.

The simplest and most important polyhedra are the so-called *simple* polyhedra. This term applies to all polyhedra that can be continuously deformed into spheres. Examples of simple polyhedra are the regular polyhedra (§ 14). We shall soon see that there are numerous polyhedra that are not simple, i.e. that can not be continuously deformed into spheres. As we saw in § 14, the regular polyhedra have the additional property that they have no re-entrant edges. From this it follows that the regular polyhedra are convex, for we apply the term "convex" to every polyhedron that is entirely on one side of each of its faces, so that it can be set on a flat table top with any face down. Convexity is not a topological property, for we can change a convex polyhedron into one that is not convex by a topologically neutral transformation. But the convexity of a polyhedron *implies* a topological property, for, an easy argument shows that every convex polyhedron is of necessity simple.[1]

There is an important relation between the number of vertices, edges, and faces of a simple polyhedron. It is called *Euler's Formula for Polyhedra*, after its discoverer. Let V be the number of vertices, E the number of edges, and F the number of faces, of the polyhedron. Then Euler's formula states that the number $V - E + F$ is equal to 2 for all simple polyhedra:

$$V - E + F = 2.$$

Let us test this surprising theorem on some regular polyhedra:

Tetrahedron: $V - E + F = 4 - 6 + 4 = 2$.
Cube: $\qquad\qquad\qquad\ \ 8 - 12 + 6 = 2$.
Octahedron: $\qquad\qquad\ \ 6 - 12 + 8 = 2$.

---

[1] There is a peculiar difference between the convex and the non-convex polyhedra: whereas every closed convex polyhedron is rigid, there are closed non-convex polyhedra whose faces can be moved relative to each other. The rigidity of the convex polyhedra is analogous to the rigidity, mentioned on page 230, of closed convex surfaces. But it has not been found possible so far to deduce the rigidity of the closed convex surfaces directly from that of polyhedra by a limiting process.

To prove Euler's formula, we construct in the plane an image of the simple polyhedron, which we shall call the *planar net* of the polyhedron. To this end, we remove any face of the polyhedron and deform the other faces until they are in a common plane. This can be done in such a way that the faces remain polygons bounded by straight lines and retaining their original number of vertices. (However, the polygons in the plane can not of course all be congruent to the original polygons.) We call our system of polygons in the plane the planar net of the polyhedron. Figs. 153 to 157, page 146, may be considered as planar nets of the regular polyhedra.

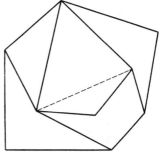

FIG. 270

The planar net has as many vertices and edges as the polyhedron, but one face less. We proceed to apply a series of transformations to the net which simplify its structure without changing the value of $V - E + F$. To begin with, if the net has a polygon with more than three sides, we draw a diagonal. Thus we add one face and one edge but do not change the number of vertices, and $V - E + F$ remains unchanged (see Fig. 270). We continue this process until we have a net consisting exclusively of triangular faces.

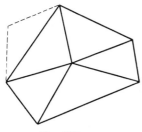

FIG. 271

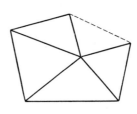

FIG. 272

If we add another triangle to such a triangular net in such a way that an edge of the new triangle coincides with an edge on the boundary of the net (see Fig. 271), the number of vertices and the number of faces are each increased by one, while the number of edges is increased by two, and the expression $V - E + F$ again remains unchanged. It remains unchanged also if we add a new triangle by connecting two vertices at a concave portion of the circumference by a new edge (see Fig. 272), for here we add one edge and one face but do not change the number of vertices.

It is easy to see that any net of triangles can be obtained from a single triangle by repeated application of the two operations just described. Hence the value of $V - E + F$ for every triangular net and, therefore, for every planar net whatsover, is the same as it is for a single triangle: $V - E + F = 3 - 3 + 1 = 1$. But since the net has exactly as many vertices and edges as the simple polyhedron, but one face less, the equation[2]

$$V - E + F = 2$$

must hold for the simple polyhedron.

Euler's formula furnishes a new and simple proof for the fact that there are only five regular polyhedra (cf. pp. 89, 90). In the regular polyhedron under consideration, let n faces, and accordingly, n edges also, meet at every vertex. If V, E, and F have the same meaning now as before, then the number of edges emanating from any of the vertices is nV, except that every edge is counted twice because each edge connects two vertices. Hence

$$nV = 2E.$$

Let every face of our polyhedron be bounded by r edges. Then there are altogether rF edges, counted as boundary segments of the faces. But here we have again counted the edges twice, since every edge forms a boundary segment of two faces. Hence

$$rF = 2E.$$

By substituting these two equations into Euler's formula we obtain

$$\frac{2E}{n} - E + \frac{2E}{r} = 2$$

which may also be written

$$\frac{1}{n} + \frac{1}{r} = \frac{1}{2} + \frac{1}{E}.$$

---

[2] Poincaré generalized Euler's formula to n-dimensional space. Instead of points, edges, and faces, we then have 0-, 1-, 2-, ..., $n-1$-dimensional entities. Let the number of these entities be $N_0, N_1, N_2, \ldots, N_{n-1}$, respectively. Then the equation

$$N_0 - N_1 + N_2 - \ldots = 1 - (-1)^n$$

applies to the manifolds corresponding to the simple polyhedra. For $n = 3$ this reduces to Euler's formula.

From the meaning of n and r it is clear that each of these numbers must be 3 at least. On the other hand, they cannot both be greater than 3 for in that event we would have

$$\frac{1}{E} = \frac{1}{n} + \frac{1}{r} - \frac{1}{2} \leqq \frac{1}{4} + \frac{1}{4} - \frac{1}{2} = 0 \,.$$

which is impossible. Now let $n = 3$. Then

$$\frac{1}{E} = \frac{1}{r} - \frac{1}{6} \,.$$

Hence, for $n = 3$, r can have only the values 3, 4, and 5, making E equal to 6, 12, and 30, respectively. But the equations are symmetrical with respect to n and r. Hence we get corresponding values of n for $r = 3$. We have thus found all the possible cases: there are six of them, but two, where $n = 3$ and $r = 3$, are identical. This

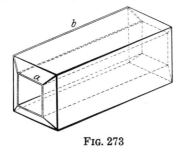

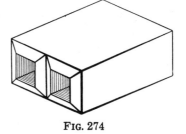

FIG. 273   FIG. 274

leaves five different possible types of polyhedra, and they are in fact realized in the regular polyhedra.[3]

What is special about this proof, as compared with the proof given before (p. 89), is the fact that it does not use the assumption that all the faces are regular polygons. The only assumption required here was that all the faces be bounded by the same number of edges and that the number of edges meeting in each of the vertices be the same. Accordingly, the number of "topologically regular" polyhedra is no greater than the number of "metrically regular" polyhedra, provided we consider only simple polyhedra.

We shall now turn to the non-simple polyhedra. We cite, as an example, the prismatic block (Fig. 273). This consists of a rectangular parallelepiped with a hole having the form of a smaller parallelepiped with its sides parallel to the outer faces of the block. The two ends that are common to the parallelepipeds are bevelled

---

[3] Similarly, Poincaré's generalization of Euler's formula furnishes a determination of the regular polytopes in higher-dimensional spaces.

off as illustrated in the diagram. The prismatic block is a polyhedron that can not be deformed into a sphere but can be deformed into a torus.[4] Other types can be obtained by removing several pieces from the inside of the block (see Fig. 274).

In order to get a general perspective of this variety of polyhedra, we assign a definite number h, the so-called connectivity number, to every polyhedron. Let us consider the closed, non-selfintersecting polygons consisting of edges of the polyhedron under consideration. If the surface of a polyhedron is divided into two separate parts by every such closed chain of edges, we assign the connectivity $h = 1$ to the polyhedron. Clearly, all simple polyhedra have connectivity 1, since the surface of the sphere is divided into two parts by every closed curve lying on it. Conversely, it is readily seen that all polyhedra with connectivity 1 can be continuously deformed into a sphere. Hence the simple polyhedra are also called *simply connected*.

On the other hand, there is a closed chain of edges (e.g. the square a in Fig. 273) on the prismatic block which does not divide the block in two. We assign a connectivity greater than 1 to any polyhedron having this property. In each case, we fix the value of the connectivity n by considering, along with a given chain of edges, all other (not necessarily closed) chains of edges that connect two points of the given chain.

If every such pair of chains divides the surface in two, we assign the connectivity $h = 2$ to this polyhedron. Otherwise, we continue the process. For the general case we have the following definition:

A polyhedron is said to have connectivity h (or to be h-tuply connected) if $h - 1$, but not h, chains of edges can be found on it in a certain order that do not cut the surface in two,[6] where it is stipulated that the first chain is closed and that every subsequent chain connects two points lying on the preceding chains.[7]

On the prismatic block there is a set of two such chains that do not cut the surface in two (the square a and the trapezoid b), as can be seen from Fig. 273. Thus this polyhedron is at least

---

[4] The prismatic block is also topologically regular.

[6] I.e., it must be possible to connect every pair of points on the polyhedron by a curve on the polyhedron that does not intersect any of the chains.

[7] Frequently the term connectivity is used in the literature to denote the greatest number of chains that do not cut the surface in two, viz., $h - 1$. [*Trans.*]

triply connected. We shall presently see that its connectivity is exactly 3.

The question arises whether Euler's formula, which we have proved for simply connected polyhedra, can be extended to polyhedra of any connectivity h. We can not expect the theorem to remain valid without modification, for we have made use, in the proof, of the planar net, and this can evidently be constructed only for simply connected polyhedra. But it can be shown that the formula

$$V - E + F = 3 - h$$

is valid in the general case. For $h = 1$, this gives the equation that we proved before. Another example is furnished by the prismatic block. It evidently has sixteen vertices, thirty-two edges, and sixteen faces, and we get the equation

$$16 - 32 + 16 = 3 - 3 = 0.$$

It follows that the connectivity of the prismatic block is exactly 3. Euler's formula can be used in the same way in the general case as a convenient means of determining the connectivity of any polyhedron. It is sufficient to count the vertices, edges, and faces, without having to follow the course of the chains of edges.

§ 45. Surfaces

We have seen that the simple polyhedra can be deformed into the sphere and that the prismatic block can be deformed into the torus. In a similar way, the more complicated topological structures can also be replaced by figures of a type similar to polyhedra. In this way, the theory of these topological structures is reduced to a study of figures that can be constructed from simple components by a process that is easy to describe. Moreover, this approach, known as *combinatorial topology*, has the great advantage that it can be immediately extended to the case of more than three dimensions; for, the structure of every polyhedron can be completely described by a schematic rule of combination without the aid of one's powers of visualization.

On the other hand, our intuitive understanding deals more readily with the curved surfaces as such. Thus the sphere is a simpler structure than the simple polyhedra, and the torus is simpler than the prismatic block. We shall therefore proceed to broaden the concept of the connectivity of polyhedra to apply to arbitrary surfaces.

We must set $h = 1$ for the sphere and $h = 3$ for the torus. Surfaces of higher connectivity can be constructed by flattening a sphere made of a plastic material and cutting holes into it (see Fig. 275). We shall call such surfaces *pretzels*. It can be proved that a pretzel with p holes must have connectivity $h = 2p + 1$. The figure shows pretzels of various connectivities with systems of curves lying on them that do not cut the surfaces in two. The curves number 0, 2, 4, and 6 for pretzels of connectivity 1, 3, 5, and 7, respectively. It is readily seen that every additional curve connecting two points on such a system of curves will cut the surface in two.

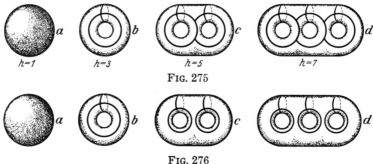

$h=1$ $h=3$ $h=5$ $h=7$

FIG. 275

FIG. 276

On a general surface, the curves can be chosen more freely than on polyhedra, where we restricted the choice to chains of edges. Hence various other definitions can be given for the connectivity of surfaces; for example, the following:

On a closed surface of connectivity h, we can draw $h - 1$ *closed* curves without cutting the surface in two, but every system of h closed curves cuts the surface into at least two separate parts.

Fig. 276 exhibits such curves for $h = 1, 3, 5,$ and 7.

We may impose the further condition that all the curves pass through some arbitrarily chosen point on the surface. Then we get the *canonical section* of the surface, which is found convenient for some purposes. Figs. 285, 286, and 287 on pages 300 and 301 illustrate three examples of such a section.

On the other hand, the result is changed if it is required that the curves shall not intersect each other. For, the following statement can be proved for surfaces whose connectivities are odd numbers.

On a closed surface of connectivity $h = 2p + 1$ there are p closed, mutually non-intersecting, curves—and no more than p—that do not cut the surface in two.

The reader may convince himself of the truth of this theorem by referring to Fig. 276.

We have so far considered only finite closed surfaces. The concept of connectivity can also be extended to other cases. First of all, let us consider surfaces that are finite but have a number of closed boundary curves. Let us assume that these boundaries do not intersect themselves or each other. Fig. 277 illustrates some surfaces of the class we are considering. Still other types of surfaces of this class can be obtained from the closed surfaces of

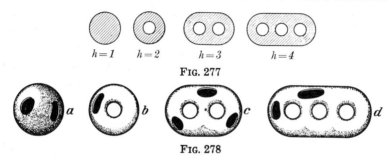

$h=1$ $h=2$ $h=3$ $h=4$

FIG. 277

FIG. 278

Figs. 275 and 276 if we consider them to be hollow and then imagine any number of holes cut into them (see Fig. 278)[1]. On the finite bounded surfaces we use the same definition of connectivity by systems of curves as before, with one modification: the first curve, instead of being closed, shall connect two points of the boundary, and every additional curve of the system may also begin and end on boundary points as well as points of previous curves of the system. According to this definition, the surfaces of Fig. 278 have connectivities 2, 3, 7, and 8, in that order.

The definition of connectivity by closed curves can not be directly extended to surfaces having boundaries.

Let us now consider a surface—with or without boundaries—that extends to infinity. The topological structure of such a surface will depend on whether we imagine it situated in metric or in

---

[1] In contrast to the surfaces shown in Fig. 277, those of Figs. 278b, c, and d can not be obtained by any amount of deformation from a sheet of paper with holes cut into it. This difference is of significance in the geometric theory of functions (simple and non-simple domains).

projective space. In the first case, our attention is confined to the
finite points of the surface; we may regard space as being, so to
speak, confined within a very large sphere, and we can replace our
surface by that portion of it that is inside the sphere. Then we
are dealing with a finite bounded surface, and the theory developed
above may be applied to it.[2]

In projective space, the conditions are entirely different. Here
we consider every straight line as a closed curve with a single
point at infinity where the two branches meet. Furthermore, this
point is common to all lines that are parallel to the first. With this
convention, the projective space taken as a whole is also connected
at its ideal points. A surface contains a given ideal point if there
is a path along the surface that keeps getting closer to some straight
line to which this ideal point belongs.
Here it is by no means necessary that
the surface also approach a line parallel
to the above in the opposite direction.
If the surface does approach two parallel
straight lines in opposite directions, it
is considered to be connected at their
common ideal point; if the surface
approaches a straight line along a certain path without approaching a parallel line in the opposite direction, the ideal point of the
straight line is a boundary point. Furthermore, if the surface has
a boundary curve that extends to infinity, then this curve must
be closed at infinity; i.e. the curve must either approach two
parallel straight lines asymptotically in the same or opposite
directions or must contain part of the line at infinity. For,
an open curve cannot form the boundary of a surface. For
example, the part of a plane in projective space which is marked
off by one straight line and two half-lines is not separated from

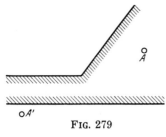

FIG. 279

---

[2] It is necessary to assume that the sphere can be chosen to be so large that
any further enlargement would leave the topological structure of the portion
of surface inside the sphere unchanged. It is easy to find examples of surfaces
that do not satisfy this condition. One example is obtained by drawing small
circles without common points about the points of a plane square latice. If we
remove the interiors of all the circles from the plane we obtain a certain surface.
The part of this surface that is inside any given sphere has a certain connectivity
which is easy to compute. But the connectivity obviously increases indefinitely
if we keep enlarging the sphere while keeping its center fixed.

the rest of the plane (see Fig. 279), for we can move, say from A to A', by way of infinity. In metric space, on the other hand, the same surface would behave as though it had a closed boundary.

Corresponding remarks apply to the plane as a whole. The metric plane has the line at infinity as a closed boundary and is thus topologically equivalent to a circular disk. On the other hand, the projective plane is a closed surface. We can also obtain a simpler topo-logical model for the projective plane. To this end, we begin with a construction that was treated in an earlier chapter (pp. 237, 238, 241). There we

FIG. 280

established a one-to-one mapping of the projective plane onto a hemispherical surface by identifying pairs of opposite points on the great circle that bounds the hemisphere. We could just as well have used a circular disk in place of the hemisphere, since the disk can always be continuously deformed into the hemisphere. Let us now deform the circular disk into the plane area bounded by a square. Then we see that the projective plane is topologically equivalent to a square (see Fig. 280), provided that we identify every pair of points of the boundary

FIG. 281

which can be connected by a straight line through the center of the square (e.g. $A = A'$, etc. in Fig. 280). Corresponding to closed curves of the projective plane, we have not only the closed curves on the square but also all those curves that in our model connect a pair of boundary points that are identi-fied with each other (e. g. the line-segment AA' in Fig. 280).

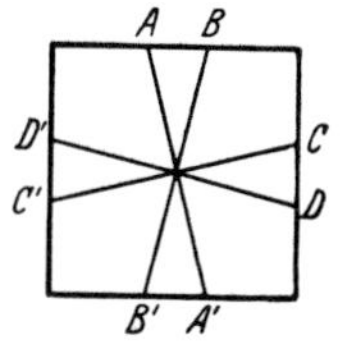

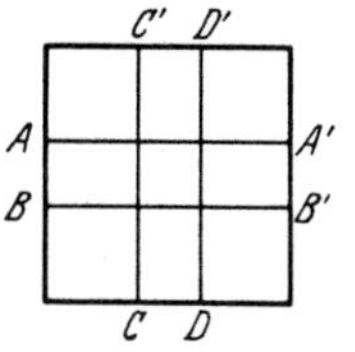

We shall interrupt our topological in-

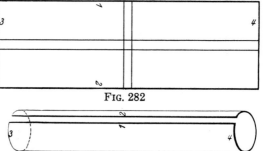

FIG. 282

FIG. 283

vestigation of the projective plane and take it up later (pp. 309ff.). However, we shall now consider other, similar, constructions to which the procedure of Fig. 280 leads directly. First of all, we shall again begin with the square or rectangle but we shall now identify pairs of boundary points according to the scheme indicated in Fig. 281. Once again, we obtain a model of a closed surface; but this time it is easy to reconstruct from the model the surface it

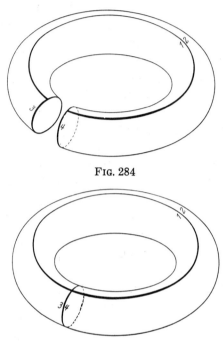

FIG. 284

represents. To begin with, we bend the rectangle into the form of a circular cylinder (see Figs. 282 and 283) and fasten the sides 1 and 2 together so that identified pairs of points on these sides are actually brought into coincidence. Meanwhile, the sides 3 and 4 have become circles, and by bending the cylinder (see Fig. 284), we can bring them together as prescribed by the identification. Finally, we arrive at the surface of a torus, and the boundary of our rectangle has become a canonical section on the torus, with each of the curves corresponding to two sides of the rectangle (see Figs. 285

FIG. 285

and 275b). Conversely, we can begin with a torus and obtain a figure that is topologically equivalent to a rectangle with its sides

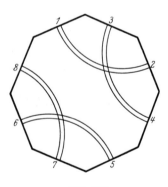

FIG. 286a

properly identified in pairs, by slitting the torus along the curves of a canonical section. This procedure can be generalized to all pretzels. For a pretzel of connectivity $2p + 1$, the canonical system consists of $2p$ curves, and cutting along these curves results in a $4p$-sided polygon with pairs of sides identified according to a definite rule. Figs. 286 and 287 illustrate the construction for the cases $h = 5$ and $h = 7$ (i.e. $p = 2$ and $p = 3$), respectively.

The mapping of pretzels into $4p$-sided polygons plays an important part both in the theory of continuous maps (cf. p. 322) and

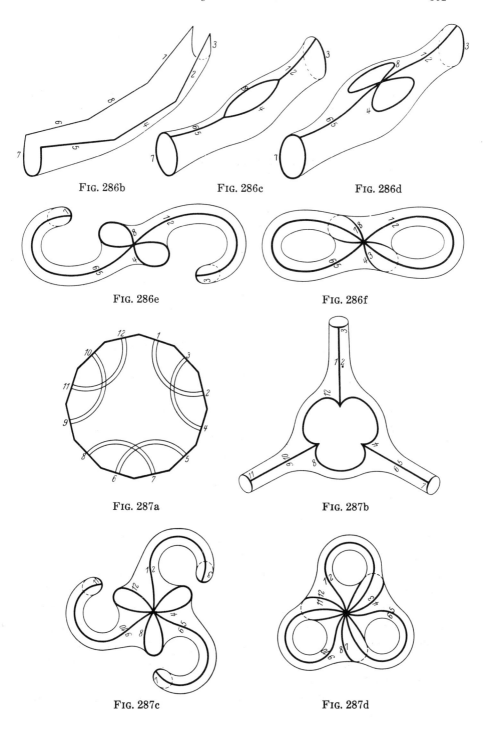

FIG. 286b

FIG. 286c

FIG. 286d

FIG. 286e

FIG. 286f

FIG. 287a

FIG. 287b

FIG. 287c

FIG. 287d

in the theory of functions (p. 333). Both applications are based on the fact that each of the regular $4p$-sided polygons generates a regular tiling of the hyperbolic plane (or, in the special case $p = 1$, of the Euclidean plane), as we have seen on page 259.

By pairing off the sides of our polygon differently, we can obtain many other surfaces besides the pretzels. We shall consider some of these surfaces in the sequel.

§ 46. One-Sided Surfaces

All the polyhedra and closed surfaces we have considered thus far had odd connectivity numbers. Thus the question arises whether

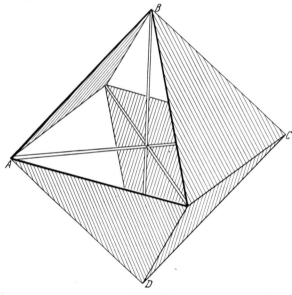

Fig. 288

there are any closed surfaces at all with even connectivities, i.e. whether there are surfaces whose topological behavior is midway between that of a sphere and that of a torus, or between that of two pretzels.

The answer is in the affirmative. Indeed, we shall now construct a polyhedron, the heptahedron, whose connectivity according to Euler's formula is 2. To this end, we begin with the eight triangular faces of a regular octahedron and add the three squares in the planes spanned by the diagonals (e.g. $ABCD$ in Fig. 288). The eleven faces obtained in this way do not constitute a polyhedron as defined earlier, for the number of faces meeting at each edge is three instead of two. We proceed to remove four triangles: from the front half of the figure (in the position shown in Fig. 288) we remove the upper left-hand triangle and the lower right-hand triangle, and from the part at the rear of the figure we remove the lower left-hand triangle and the upper right-hand triangle. Then only the four triangles shaded in the diagram remain. Thus we have obtained a figure consisting of four triangles and three squares. Its edges and vertices are the edges and vertices of the octahedron. The diagonals of the octahedron are not edges of our figure but are lines in which it intersects itself. It is clear that exactly two faces meet at every edge and that we can travel from any face to any other by crossing edges. Thus the figure is a polyhedron; and since it has seven faces, it is called a *heptahedron*. Like the octahedron, the heptahedron has twelve edges and six vertices. Thus the generalized form of Euler's formula gives the equation

FIG. 289b

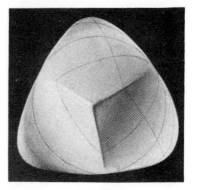

FIG. 289a

$$V - E + F =$$
$$6 - 12 + 7 = 1 = 3 - h,$$

whence the connectivity number for the heptahedron is $h = 2$. Just as the simple polyhedra can be continuously deformed into the sphere, so there is a simple closed surface into which the heptahedron can be

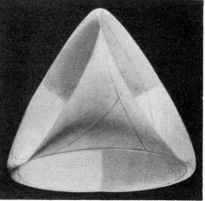

FIG. 289c

deformed. This is the *Roman* surface (see Fig. 289) investigated
by Steiner. Like the heptahedron, this surface intersects itself in
three mutually perpendicular straight-line segments. Its equation
in rectangular coordinates is

$$y^2 z^2 + z^2 x^2 + x^2 y^2 + xyz = 0.$$

Thus it is a surface of the fourth order.

In addition to its even connectivity number and its lines of self-
intersection, the heptahedron has another important property dif-
ferentiating it from the surfaces we have studied thus far. Let us

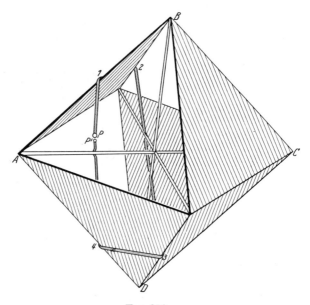

FIG. 290

imagine the surface realized by means of a membrane and follow
some creature, such as a beetle, which is taking a walk on the surface starting at a fixed point P. Directly opposite P, on the other
side of the thin membrane, there is a point P' that coincides with P
if the membrane is replaced by the original surface. Now it might
easily be thought that the beetle cannot get from P to P' without
boring a hole somewhere in the membrane. For the sphere and for
all the pretzels we have thus far studied, this is true. But it is not
true without qualification for the heptahedron. Let us start at a
point P that is on the square face in the plane of the paper on the

side facing the observer (see Fig. 290). Consider a path on the heptahedron which begins at P, crosses the edges 1, 2, 3, and 4, and then continues on the original square. Clearly, the beetle who follows this path starting on the front side of the square face arrives at the back of the same face after crossing the edge marked 4. It is true that it is necessary to bore through the membrane that forms the heptahedron, in three places, but in each case the face that is pierced is one that blocks the path at a place where the heptahedron intersects itself, not the face on which the beetle is travelling.

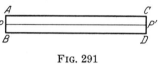

Fig. 291

For this reason, the heptahedron is called a *one-sided* surface, while the sphere and the pretzels considered thus far are called *two-sided*. This distinction can also be applied to bounded surfaces. We think of the surface as being embodied by a membrane and try to determine whether there is a path on it which leads from one side of the surface to the other without crossing the boundary and without piercing the membrane at a point that is just being traversed by the path. If such a path exists, the surface is called one-sided, otherwise we call it two-sided. All of the bounded surfaces we have considered up till now—such as the circular disk—are two-sided. But there is an example of a bounded surface which is one-sided and is much simpler than the heptahedron; this is the Möbius strip. We can make it from a long rectangular strip of paper such as the one illustrated in Fig. 291. If we put the ends AB and CD together in such a way that A meets C and B meets D,

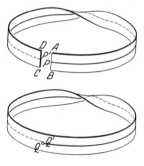

Fig. 292

we get a cylindrical strip, as we have already seen. This is a two-sided bounded surface. But if, before putting the ends together, we twist one end of the paper strip through an angle of 180° relative to the other and then join the ends, with A meeting D and B meeting C, we get a model of the Möbius strip (see Fig. 292). It is easy to see that this surface is one-sided. For example, we may draw the straight line PP' parallel to the long edges of the strip before putting the ends together. After the ends are put together, the line becomes a path QQ' that leads from one side of the strip to the other.[1]

The one-sided surfaces may also be characterized by means of another important topological concept which can be formulated without considering a membrane substituted for the surface. Imagine every point of any given surface (with the exception of boundary points, if any) to be enclosed in a small closed curve that lies entirely on the surface. We then try to fix a certain sense on each of these closed curves in such a way that any two curves that are sufficiently close together have the same sense. If such a determination of sense of traversal is possible in this way, we call it an *orientation* of the surface and call the surface *orientable*. We shall prove that a one-sided surface cannot be orientable. Let us consider one of the closed paths the existence of which is equivalent to the one-sidedness of the surface. Choosing, for example, the path QQ' on the Möbius strip, where Q and Q' are again regarded as identical, let us assign a sense to the point Q and preserve the sense continuously along the path QQ'; then the sense associated with the moving point when the point $Q' = Q$ is reached again is necessarily the reverse of the original sense. This phenomenon could not occur if the Möbius strip were orientable. The behavior of all other one-sided surfaces is analogous to that of the Möbius strip. And conversely, it can be demonstrated that all two-sided surfaces are orientable. Thus the classification of surfaces into two-sided and one-sided surfaces is identical with the classification into orientable and non-orientable surfaces.

It is easy to see that a surface is non-orientable if and only if there exists on the surface some closed curve s which is such that a small oriented circle whose center traverses the curve continuously will arrive at its starting point with its orientation reversed (e.g. the curve QQ' of Fig. 292). If on such a surface we move along one side of the curve s, we arrive on the other side of the curve although we have never crossed it. For this reason, we call s a curve with one bank. While all the curves on an orientable surface have

---

[1] The two following properties also illustrate the difference between the Möbius strip and the cylindrical strip. First, the boundary of the Möbius strip consists of a single closed curve, while the cylindrical strip is bounded by two separate closed curves. Second, the Möbius strip, unlike the cylindrical strip, when cut along the curve QQ', does not fall apart, but remains connected.

two banks, the existence of a closed curve with one bank is characteristic of the non-orientable surfaces. The one-sidedness of a surface and the presence on it of a curve with one bank are equivalent. The former property has reference to the position of a surface in space, the latter to the position of a curve on the surface.

Unlike the Möbius strip, the heptahedron has lines along which it intersects itself. It would seem to be a reasonable conjecture that every one-sided closed surface must intersect itself. For since it has only one side, such a surface cannot divide the space into two parts of which one is "inside" and the other "outside," and this is inconceivable in the case of a closed surface without self-intersections. The conjecture is true: all one-sided closed surfaces have self-intersections. But the proof would have to be conducted along quite different lines.

Not every self-intersection is a topological singularity. Consider,

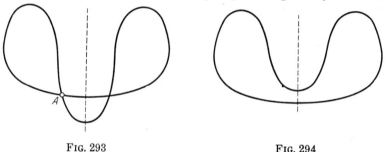

Fig. 293   Fig. 294

for example, the surface of revolution formed when the curve shown in Fig. 293 is rotated about the straight line as axis. The surface intersects itself along the circle generated by the point A. But a continuous deformation transforms the surface into the surface of revolution generated by the curve shown in Fig. 294. Clearly this curve has no self-intersections and is topologically equivalent to the sphere. Conversely, the sphere can be transformed into the first surface of revolution by a deformation. Hence the presence of curves of self-intersection need not represent a topological property. In the example we have just given, the points of self-intersection form a closed curve. On the heptahedron, on the other hand, the curves of self-intersection have six end-points in all, namely the vertices of the heptahedron. Now these points really have to be treated as singular points. For, the neighborhood of any regular point on a surface can be deformed into a circular disk, but for the neighborhood of a vertex of the heptahedron (Fig. 288) this is not possible. Accordingly, the heptahedron has six singular points. This raises the question of whether there is any one-sided closed surface at all that has no singular points.

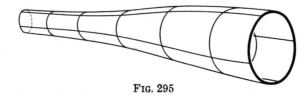

FIG. 295

Such a surface was first constructed by Felix Klein. We begin with an open tube (see Fig. 295). We earlier obtained the torus from such a tube by bending the tube until the ends met and then cementing the boundary circles together. This time we shall put

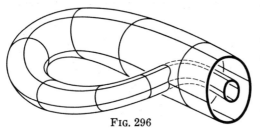

FIG. 296

the ends together in a different way. Taking a tube with one end a little thinner than the other, we bend the thin end over and push it through the wall of the tube into the position shown in Fig. 296, where the two circles at the ends of the tube have concentric positions. We now expand the smaller circle and contract the larger one a little until they meet, and then join them together. This does not create any singular points. This construction gives

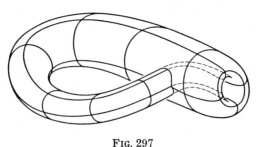

FIG. 297

us Klein's surface, also known as the Klein bottle, illustrated in Fig. 297. It is clear that the surface is one-sided and intersects itself along a closed curve where the narrow end was pushed through the wall of the tube.

Our first example of a closed one-sided surface, the heptahedron, differed from the two-sided closed surfaces we have studied thus far also in that it had an even connectivity number. Hence we might expect that the connectivity of the Klein bottle would likewise be even. But this is not the case. For, its connectivity number is 3, like that of the torus. Furthermore, we can choose the canonical section in the same way as on the torus: As the first closed curve of the system, we choose the seam along which the ends of the tube are fastened together. As the second curve, we choose one of the curves that become generating segments when the surface is transformed back into its cylindrical shape after cutting it open along the first curve. By being cut along these two curves, the Klein bottle, like the torus, is changed into a rectangle. Every additional curve connecting two boundary points of the rectangle divides it into two

	plane annulus	two boundary curves	$h = 2$	two-sided
	Möbius strip	one boundary curve	$h = 2$	one-sided
	torus	closed surface	$h = 3$	two-sided
	Klein bottle	closed surface	$h = 3$	one-sided
	projective plane	closed surface	$h = 2$	one-sided

parts. Applying the general definition of connectivity to the Klein bottle, we therefore have $h - 1 = 2$, $h = 3$, as was to be proved.

By this time, we have obtained five different surfaces from the rectangle (or square) by identifying pairs of edges in different ways.[2] The table above lists the five surfaces, together with relevant data. The data given for the projective plane will be justified later.

The table shows that the model of the Möbius strip is obtained from that of the Klein surface on cancelling the identification of

---

[2] In projective space, the hyperboloid of one sheet is to be considered as a closed surface, being connected at infinity. The reader will be able to decide by reference to the table whether the hyperboloid of one sheet, considered from this point of view, is topologically equivalent to the Klein bottle or to the torus.

one of the two pairs of sides. Hence it must be possible to convert the Klein bottle into a Möbius strip by cutting it open along a suitably chosen closed curve. It is left to the reader as an exercise to try this out on a model. Fig. 298 shows a different way of cutting open the Klein bottle which results in *two* Möbius strips. The reader is urged to find the corresponding modification which converts one of the square models in the table into the other.

Among the closed one-sided surfaces we saw examples both of

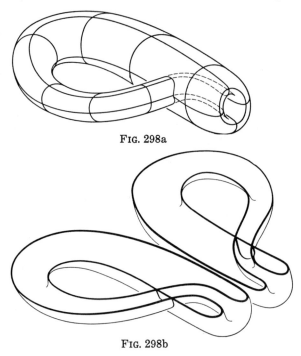

Fig. 298a

Fig. 298b

surfaces with even connectivities (e.g. the heptahedron) and of surfaces with odd connectivities (e.g. the Klein bottle). On the other hand, all the closed two-sided surfaces mentioned thus far have had odd connectivity numbers. And it can be shown, moreover, that there are no closed two-sided surfaces with even connectivity numbers.

Like the square, all the other regular $4p$-sided polygons can also be made to serve, by identifying pairs of edges in various ways, as models for a great many surfaces, including closed and bounded ones, and one-sided and two-sided ones. If AB and CD in Fig. 299 are to be two identified edges of the $4p$-gon, there are two possible ways of identifying them, as follows: (1) the two straight lines connecting associated end-points do not intersect, or (2) they intersect. An example of the first case is obtained by identifying A with C and B with D in Fig. 299; an example of the second case is obtained by identifying A with D and B with C. We shall prove the following: If any two sides of the $4p$-gon are associated in the second way, then the surface represented by the polygon is one-sided, irrespective of the way the other associations are set up.

We shall prove this by showing that the surface represented is not orientable, using the method sketched on page 306. Let P and P' be two points associated under the identification and lying on AB and CD respectively (see Fig. 299). Then the straight-line segment PP' represents a closed path on the surface. A point traversing this path on the surface is represented by a point R travelling on PP' first to the point P and then from P' back to its original position. Let us give the point of the surface represented by R a certain sense of orientation which is not to undergo any discontinuous change as the point moves; thus we have to draw a small circle about R with an arrow indicating a sense, and move the circle continu-

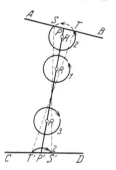

Fig. 299

ously along with R. As long as the whole circle lies inside the $4p$-gon, it is the image of a closed curve on the surface that the polygon represents. When R is near P, only the arc $\overrightarrow{ST}$ of the circle remains inside the $4p$-gon. To preserve the image of a closed curve on the surface, we have to make use of the points S' and T' on CD which are associated with S and T. Since the identification of AB and CD is of the second kind, S and S' lie on opposite sides of the line PP', and so do T and T'. Hence the closed curve, with its sense of traversal, is represented by the two directed arcs $\overrightarrow{ST}$ and $\overrightarrow{T'S'}$. This figure does not undergo any discontinuous change when R reaches P and then continues from P' towards its initial position. As the distance between the moving point and P' increases, the arc ST gradually disappears, while $S'T'$ is transformed into a full circle. But the sense of traversal of the new circle is opposite to the sense of traversal of the initial circle, which proves that the surface is not orientable.

As a special case of this theorem, we get the result that the projective plane is one-sided. For, in its model, both the identifications of pairs of sides are of the second kind.

The converse of our theorem—that the model always represents a two-sided surface if all the identifications are of the first kind—can also be proved without difficulty.

We obtained the model of the projective plane from the surface of the sphere. On the other hand, the Klein bottle and the torus were seen to be related, though not by the same relation as are the sphere and the projective plane. We shall now show that the same correspondence as exists between the two first-named surfaces can actually be set up also between the Klein bottle and the torus, and more generally, that there is a two-sided surface corresponding in the same way to every one-sided surface.

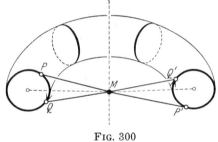

FIG. 300

In order to obtain the projective plane from the sphere, we had to identify every pair of diametrically opposite points (see pp. 237 and 299). We now apply the analogous construction to the torus. Let us designate as the center of the torus the point M at which the perpendicular from the center of one of the generating circles meets the axis (see Fig. 300). Now if P is any point on the torus, then the point P' which is the reflection of P in M lies on the torus as well. All pairs of points on the torus that are symmetrical with respect to M will be called diametrical. By treating every diametrical pair of points as a single point, we transform the torus into a new surface F. We shall prove that F is the Klein bottle.

Consider a generating circle of the torus. This is associated with a second generating circle, as shown in Fig. 300. The two circles divide the torus into two halves. Now the surface F is obtained by omission of one half of the torus and identification of the boundary circles of the remaining half in the manner prescribed; analogously, we were able to use a hemisphere instead of the full sphere in the construction of the projective plane. Now it becomes evident, from a consideration of the sense of traversal of the two identified circles, that the half-torus is converted into a Klein bottle by the identification.

Furthermore, it is evident that the second half of the torus can be superimposed on the first in such a way that every pair of points that originally was diametrical now coincides. It is necessary here, however, to turn the second half-torus inside out like a glove. If the two halves are subsequently stuck together, the torus finally acquires the form of a Klein bottle doubly covered.[3] For this reason, the torus may be referred to as a *two-sheeted covering surface* of the Klein bottle. Likewise, the sphere is called a two-sheeted covering surface of the projective plane. Quite generally, it can be proved that every one-sided surface has a two-sided surface as a two-sheeted covering surface.

§ 47. The Projective Plane as a Closed Surface

In order to determine the connectivity of the projective plane, we shall apply Euler's formula to the square model. Through the center M of the square (Fig. 301) we draw the straight lines PQ and RS parallel to the sides of the square, thus dividing the square into the smaller squares 1, 2, 3, and 4. But because of the way the edges are identified, the squares 1 and 3 represent a single polygon in the projective plane, and so do the squares 2 and 4. Furthermore, the two segments

Fig. 301

PM and QM must be regarded as a single edge, because P and Q represent the same point; and RM and SM are a single edge, because R and S represent the same point. There are no vertices other than M. In Euler's formula, we must therefore set

$$V = 1, \quad E = 2, \quad F = 2.$$

From Euler's formula we therefore get $V - E + F = 1 = 3 - h$, so that the connectivity of the projective plane is 2, as indicated in the table on page 309.

In analytic projective geometry, we encounter a different partition of the projective plane, resulting from the introduction of trilinear coordinates. This partition is shown in Fig. 302, where a circle, rather than a square, serves as model of the projective

---

[3] It might at first be assumed that the transformation can be effected by a mere deformation of the torus. This is not the case. On the contrary, it is necessary to cut the torus apart to make it possible to turn one half inside out.

plane.   Three arcs that do not all pass through a common point
divide the circle into seven regions.   If each arc meets the circumference in two diametrically opposite points, the regions 2 and 5
represent a single triangle; so do 3 and 6; and so do 4 and 7.   It can
be seen that any three straight lines without a common point divide
the projective plane in this way
into four parts.[1]   Here we have

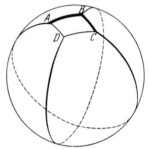

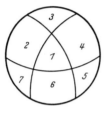

FIG. 302.   FIG. 303.

$V = 3$, $E = 6$, and $F = 4$, from which we get $h = 2$, as before.

We shall now apply the same procedure to the square model of
the projective plane as we used in constructing the torus and the
Klein bottle from their square models, i.e., we shall bring the identified edges together and join them.   First, we distort the square

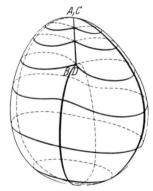

FIG. 304   FIG. 305

into a sphere with a small quadrilateral $ABCD$ removed (Fig. 303).
Now AB has to be attached to CD, and DA to BC.   This can be
accomplished by raising A and C and lowering B and D and then
drawing each of these two pairs of points together (see Fig. 304).
The final result is a closed surface intersecting itself in a line seg-

---

[1] The partitions of the projective plane illustrated in Figs. 301 and 302 were
obtained on pages 148 and 149 as projections of the octahedron.

ment (see Fig. 305). This surface is topologically equivalent to the projective plane.

There is an algebraic surface of this form (Fig. 306). Its equation is

$$(k_1 x^2 + k_2 y^2)(x^2 + y^2 + z^2) - 2z(x^2 + y^2) = 0.$$

This surface is connected with a construction in differential geom-

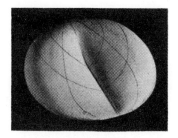

Fig. 306a

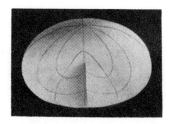

Fig. 306b

etry. On any surface F, we begin with a point P at which the curvature of F is positive. Then we construct all the circles of normal curvature at P (cf. pp. 183, 184). This family of circles sweeps out the very same surface that is shown in Fig. 306, where

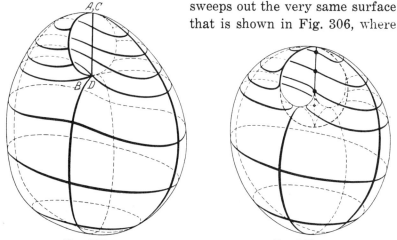

Fig. 307   Fig. 308

the line of self-intersection is a segment of the normal to the surface F at P. The equation given above is referred to the rectangular coordinate system with P as origin and with the principal directions of F at the point P as x-axis and y-axis. k_1 and k_2 are the principal curvatures of F at the point P.

If we once more start with Fig. 304 but now only put the pair
AB and CD together—but not DA and BC—we get a surface that
is topologically equivalent with the Möbius strip. For, this identi-

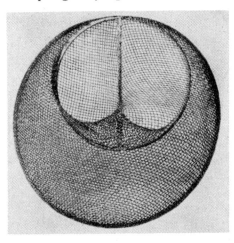

fication of sides is the same
identification which, by definition, transforms the square
into a Möbius strip. The
boundary of the new surface
is derived from the arcs DA
and BC, and since A and B
are attached to C and D respectively, it is a closed curve.
Thus we may, for example,
give the boundary the form
of a circle (as in Fig. 307).
Obviously, the surface is not
self-intersecting. At the two
points arising from A, C and

Fig. 309

B, D respectively, the curvature of the surface is discontinuous.
But by an additional deformation in the neighborhood of these
points, we can get a surface with continuous curvature everywhere. Figs. 308 and 309 give an indication of its form.

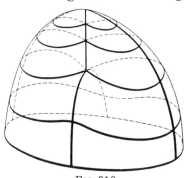

Although its boundary is circular,
our surface can not be used as a container: being one-sided, it does not
separate the interior from the rest
of space.

By closing the surface by the in-
sertion of a circular disk, we get our
model of the projective plane again,
as can easily be seen from Figs. 307
and 305. Conversely, it follows that
the removal of a circular disk from

Fig. 310

the model of the projective plane results in a model of the Möbius
strip. Here it is immaterial where the hole is made in the surface
of Fig. 305; for, since all diametrical pairs of points on the sphere
are alike, no point of the projective plane is distinguishable from
another. If, in particular, we choose to remove the bottom from
the surface of Fig. 305, we get an especially clear picture of the

residual surface, as illustrated in Fig. 310. This surface is called the cross-cap. It is another of the models of the Möbius strip that have a circle as boundary. Despite the fact that it has only one side, the cross-cap can obviously be used as a lid for a container. This is made possible by the presence of a line of self-intersection.

If the cross-cap is cut open along its line of self-intersection, the resulting surface can be deformed into a circular disk with a hole in the form of a quadrilateral or a circle: this is merely reversing the transformation outlined in Figs. 303 to 305. Accordingly, we can get a model of the Möbius strip from the region between two concentric circles by identifying all the diametrically opposite pairs of points of the smaller circle (see Fig. 311). At first sight it certainly would not appear that this figure represents the same surface as the

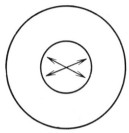

FIG. 311

square model in the table on page 309. However, the square model can be obtained from Fig. 311 by cutting the ring into two halves (Fig. 312), deforming the parts (Fig. 313), turning one half over (so as to interchange the positions of e and b' in Fig. 313), and finally physically re-uniting some of the pairs of edges that originally belonged together while abstractly identifying the rest (Fig. 314).

In our model of the projective plane, two points—the extremities

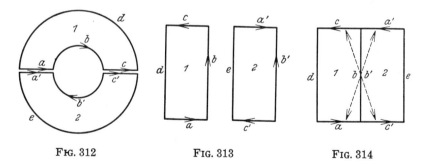

FIG. 312   FIG. 313   FIG. 314

of the line of self-intersection—are singular points. W. Boy succeeded in constructing a model of the projective plane that has no singular points and no points at which the curvature is discontinuous.

In constructing Boy's surface, we do not begin with a square but with a hexagon. Diametrically opposite points on the boundary of the hexagon are again treated as identical. A deformation

converts the hexagon into a sphere with a hole having the form
of a regular spherical hexagon. Like the original hexagon, the
new figure can be divided into three congruent parts arranged symmetrically about an axis (see Fig. 315). Next, we separate the

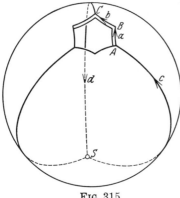

three parts and subject each of
them to a deformation that we
shall describe presently. Thus we
obtain three congruent pieces of
a certain shape, which we shall
finally join together to get Boy's
surface; it, too, will have a three-
fold axis of symmetry. Of course,
the method aims at finding a way
to join together the pairs of opposite points on the edge of the
hexagonal hole.

FIG. 315

Hence we start by bringing into coincidence, at N (Fig. 316),
the points A, B, C of the piece $ScAaBbCdS$ (Fig. 315) but without considering them as identical, since this would not be in accord
with the original scheme for identifying points. Then we move
the closed edge a up (Fig. 317) and over into the position shown in

Fig. 318, while the points S
and N and the edges b, c,
and d remain fixed. In this
operation, the part of the
surface between c and a is
distended considerably until
it is almost plane. Now we
move the loop b (in Fig. 318)
up towards the right until it
assumes the position shown
in Fig. 319, bordering from
behind on the part of the

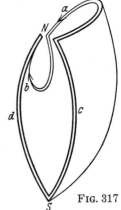

FIG. 316

FIG. 317

surface mentioned just before. In this final position, the arcs c and d
should be congruent, the loops a and b should be congruent, and all
should be so situated that a rotation about the axis SN through an
angle $2\pi/3$ as indicated by the arrows moves c into d and b into a
(see Fig. 319). To the surface we have thus constructed we add
another that is congruent to it and whose corresponding elements

we shall label a', S', etc., putting the surfaces together in such a way that d' coincides with c (S' coinciding with S, and N' with N). Then a' and b will automatically coincide and can thus be glued

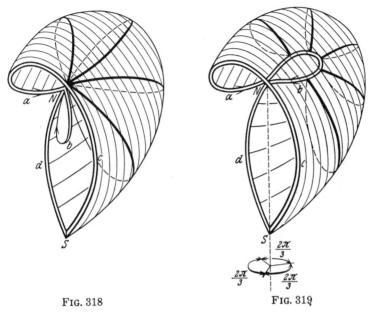

FIG. 318   FIG. 319

together. Now the curve along which the two surfaces are attached becomes a line of self-intersection for the new surface, as may be seen from Fig. 319. The boundary of the new surface consists of c', a, b', and d; this follows by going back to the hexagon with which we started (see Fig. 320). Evidently, we can attach a third replica to this boundary, so that d is in contact with c'', a with b'', b' with a'', and c' with d'' (where the meaning of the notation is obvious). This completes the construction of Boy's surface. It is clear from Fig. 320 that Boy's surface is equivalent to the projective plane. Fig. 321 shows a model made of wire

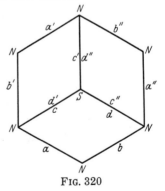

FIG. 320

netting. The curve in which the surface intersects itself consists of three loops which pass through the point N and which, like the whole surface, are symmetrically arranged about the axis SN. A study of Fig. 320 shows that three sheets of the surface pass through N. A necessary and sufficient condition for the continuity of the tangent planes of these three sheets at N is that the six end-points of the loops meeting at N be tangential to three mutually perpendicular straight lines at that point. Any creases or discon-

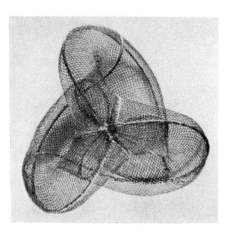

Fig. 321a

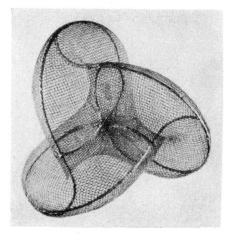

Fig. 321b

tinuities of curvature that may occur along the other seams at which the parts of the surface are joined, can be removed simply by smoothing the surface. In the model of Fig. 321, the line of self-intersection is accentuated by the use of heavier wire. The

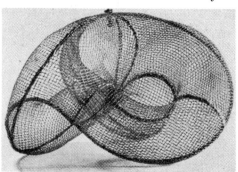

Fig. 321c

only purpose of the other heavy wires is to give support to the structure. The model is held together by a screw at the point S. The way in which the model is related to our construction should be particularly clear from Fig. 321b.

It follows from the foregoing discussion that the spherical image of Boy's surface is everywhere continuous. Unfortunately, the way in which it is distributed over the sphere has not yet been studied. Suppose we begin the construction of the image with an arbitrary normal vector and then follow the image continuously; it is certain, because of the one-sidedness of the surface, that we shall eventually reach also the opposite normal vector of the starting point.

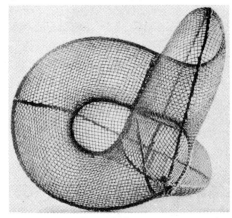

Thus the spherical representation assigns a pair of diametrically opposite points on the sphere to every point of Boy's surface. But since this identification transforms the sphere back into the projective plane, we see that the spherical representation of Boy's surface produces a mapping of the projective plane onto itself, although this is

FIG. 321d

not bi-unique, owing to the fact that several points of Boy's surface correspond to one pair of points on the sphere.

§ 48. Standard Forms for the Surfaces of Finite Connectivity

We define a class of surfaces as consisting of all those surfaces that can be transformed into each other by a topological mapping. The following are necessary conditions for two surfaces with finite connectivity numbers to belong to the same class:

1. Both surfaces are either closed or else have the same number of boundary curves.

2. Either both surfaces are orientable or both are non-orientable.

3. The connectivity numbers of the two surfaces are equal.

The necessity of the first condition is obvious. The proposition that the second condition is necessary may be reformulated as follows: Every surface F that can be topologically mapped onto an orientable surface G is itself orientable. In this form, the proposition is easily proved. For in the topological mapping, an orientation of G gives rise to an orientation of F. Similarity, we can derive the necessity of the third condition: The connectivity number of a surface determines the existence of a section on it which under a topological mapping becomes a section having the same structure on the image surface.

A more detailed study shows that the three conditions are also sufficient to ensure that two surfaces be related by a topological mapping. For if a given surface is known to be orientable and if the number of its boundary curves and its connectivity number are known, then we can follow a procedure similar to that used for the torus and the orientable closed surfaces of connectivities 5 and 7 and illustrated in Figs. 282 to 287 (pp. 299-301) : By dissection along a suitable system of curves, the surface can always be transformed into a polygon with some, or all, of its sides identified in pairs; the structure of the section as well as the number of sides of the polygon and the rule for identifying sides are uniquely determined by the three items of information mentioned. Therefore any two surfaces that are alike with respect to these three criteria can be mapped topologically onto the same polygon and therefore also onto each other.

As a result of the dissection, the closed orientable surfaces of genus p become $4p$-gons with pairs of sides identified in the manner

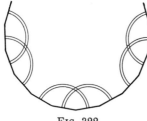

illustrated in Fig. 322. These $4p$-gons constitute a set of standard forms representing *all* the closed orientable surfaces, since the connectivity of every surface of this kind is an odd number $h = 2p + 1$. Another complete set of standard forms has already been given: The sphere, the torus, and the pretzels with p holes.

FIG. 322

Some of the Riemann surfaces encountered in the theory of functions are included in this classification, although their geometrical appearance would not lead us to suspect this. These surfaces, like the spherical images of most minimal surfaces (see p. 271), cover the sphere in several layers connected at branch points. All of these surfaces are orientable, since every orientation of the surface of the sphere is carried over to the layer next to it. A Riemann surface is closed if and only if the function associated with it is algebraic; all transcendental functions give rise to open Riemann surfaces. We shall not discuss this topic in further detail.

In the case of the *bounded* surfaces, we can also find a set of polygons which are such that every surface of finite connectivity whose boundary consists of a finite number of curves can be mapped topologically onto just one of these polygons. Two examples of such polygons are the square models for the plane annulus and the

Möbius strip. For the *orientable* bounded surfaces we can get even clearer standard types by taking the sphere, the torus, and the pretzels and cutting various numbers of holes into them (as in Fig. 278, p. 297). In order to construct similar standard types for the *non-orientable* surfaces as well, we can make use of the cross-cap, the surface we constructed on page 316 as a model for the Möbius strip. We take a sphere, cut a number of holes into it, and then seal some of them with cross-caps. Every non-orientable surface of finite connectivity is equivalent to a surface constructed in this way. The number of cross-caps and of open holes is uniquely determined by the number of boundary curves and the connectivity of the surface represented.

The cross-cap has a line of self-intersection and two singular points. The Klein bottle and Boy's surface furnish examples of one-sided surfaces not having singular points. The question of whether all the other closed non-orientable surfaces can be realized in space in a form free of singularities does not seem to have been investigated yet. Certainly, none of them can be freed from self-intersections, as has already been mentioned.

In four-dimensional space, however, all non-orientable surfaces can be represented in a form free of singularities or self-intersections. We shall use the notation R_4 for the four-dimensional space and R_3 for the three-dimensional space. We can think of the R_3 as being imbedded in R_4 in the same way as a plane is imbedded in R_3. Now we begin by constructing a cross-cap having no self-intersections and singularities in R_4. To this end, we take a cross-cap in R_3 and think of it as being imbedded in R_4. Then we choose a circular disc e on the cross-cap which has the line of self-intersection as a diameter (cf. Fig. 307, p. 315). In R_3, we can keep the circumference of any circular disc fixed while curving out the rest of the disc in such a way that none of its points remains in the plane of the circumference. Likewise, we can take the disc e in R_4 and deform it into a surface f in such a way that the circumference remains fixed on the cross-cap in the R_3 while the interior of f juts out of the R_3. But by this deformation, the cross-cap becomes a surface F in R_4 which is obviously devoid of self-intersections and singular points. If we now imbed into R_4 a sphere having a number of holes, and cover some of the holes not with cross-caps but with surfaces like F, we get standard types free of self-intersections and singularities, to represent all the non-orientable surfaces of finite connectivity.

Another problem is the representation of surfaces of a given topological structure by algebraic equations of lowest possible degree. Thus, for example, we mentioned that Steiner's surface is a model which represents the projective plane. The question of whether there are any algebraic surfaces representing Boy's surface has not yet been investigated. The projective plane can be realized in a surface in R_4 that is given by very simple equations and has no self-intersections or singularities. The derivation is given in an appendix to this chapter.

The problem of topological equivalence has been extended from surfaces to three-dimensional and higher-dimensional structures. This led to the study of *Betti groups*. In the theory of Betti groups, the concepts of connectivity number and orientability of a surface are treated from a much more general point of view. The reader is referred to the books mentioned in the footnote on page 289.

§ 49. Topological Mappings of a Surface onto Itself. Fixed Points. Classes of Mappings. The Universal Covering Surface of the Torus

The simplest topological mapping of a surface onto itself consists of a continuous distortion which is such as to transform the surface as a whole into itself. This type of mapping is called a deformation. The motions of the plane into itself are deformations. The reflection of the plane in a straight line, on the other hand, is an example of a topological mapping that is not a deformation. For, a reflection reverses the sense of traversal of every circle, whereas deformations cannot reverse the sense of traversal.

A point that is mapped onto itself under a mapping is called a *fixed point* of the mapping. We shall prove that every continuous mapping of a circular disk (with the points of the circumference included) onto itself has at least one fixed point. Let us begin by supposing the contrary, i.e. by supposing that there is a continuous mapping e of the disk onto itself in which no point is fixed. Then we can attach an arrow to every point P of e pointing in the direction of the image of P (as this would fail to be possible only at a fixed point). Since, by assumption, the mapping is continuous, the change in direction of the arrows from point to point must be continuous. Now consider the arrow attached to a point on the

circumference, and let the point move once around the circumference clockwise; obviously, the tangent to the circle at the point
will make one full clockwise turn at the same time. We can show
that the arrow attached to the point must also make exactly one
clockwise turn in the process: First of all, the arrow has to make
an integral number of turns (which may conceivably be zero),
because it returns to its original position. Now, since the arrow
at a point of the circumference is always directed into the interior
of the circle, the angle between the tangent and the arrow can never
equal zero or any multiple of π. Yet if the number of turns made
by the arrow in the course of the motion differed from the number
of turns made by the tangent, it would have to happen at least
once on the circumference that the two directions are either equal
or opposite. Next, we consider the number of turns of the arrow
on any interior circle k concentric with the circumference, using
a similar argument. Here too, the arrow makes just one clockwise
turn during the course of one clockwise run of the point around
the circle, for otherwise there would have to be at least one discontinuous change in the number of turns of the arrow as the circle
is shrunk continuously from the circumference.to the position k,
and this would contradict the continuity of the distribution of the
arrows. On the other hand, if k is continuously shrunk towards
the center M of the disk, the directions of the arrows for all the
points on k have to get closer and closer to one single direction,
viz. the direction of the arrow at M. For sufficiently small circles,
the number of turns would therefore have to be zero. This is a
contradiction. Consequently, there is no continuous mapping without fixed points of a circular disk onto itself.

Similarly, we can prove that every continuous mapping of the
surface of a sphere onto itself necessarily has either a fixed point
or a point that is mapped onto the diametrically opposite point.
Otherwise, every point would uniquely define an arc of a great
circle connecting the point with its image. This would create a
distribution of arrows that has to be continuous over the whole
surface of the sphere, and by consideration of the number of rotations of the arrows, we can prove that such a distribution cannot
exist. We therefore cannot place signposts at all points on the
earth in such a way that the directions in which they point always
vary continuously from one place to the next.

If we interpret the sphere with diametrically opposite pairs of points identified, as a model of the projective plane, we get, as a consequence of the theorem about the mapping of a sphere, that every continuous mapping of the projective plane onto itself has a fixed point.

In order to get a better perspective of the topological mappings of a given surface onto itself, we shall divide all these mappings into classes. Two mappings are put into the same class if they differ only by a deformation; the deformations themselves consti-   ·
tute the class of the identity. An example of a mapping on the sphere which does not belong to this class is obtained by mapping every point onto the diametrically opposite point; for, it is intuitively obvious that this mapping reverses the sense of traversal on small circles. Thus we have found two classes, so far, of mappings of the sphere. It can be shown, by a more detailed investigation which would lead us too far afield here, that there are no further classes of mappings of the sphere. It follows that all the topological mappings of the projective plane are deformations.

On the torus, however, there is an infinity of classes. In order to get a picture of some of these classes, we imagine the torus cut open along a meridian and then bent into the shape of a circular cylinder with two boundary circles. We then keep one of the circles fixed and twist the cylinder in such a way that the cylinder is transformed into itself, while the second boundary circle makes k turns about the axis; this changes every generating line of the cylinder into a helix which makes k turns about the axis of the cylinder. If the cylinder is subsequently bent back into the form of the torus and the end circles are stuck together, the result is a topological mapping of the torus onto itself under which all the points of the identified boundary circles are fixed points. The mapping of all the other points is determined by the mapping of the cylinder: the generators of the cylinder correspond to the circles of latitude of the torus, and by extending the correspondence between the two surfaces to apply to the three-dimensional regions bounded by them, we can make the axis of the cylinder correspond to the "core" of the torus, i.e. to the path traced out by the center of the generating circle of the torus. Then the mapping of the torus onto itself thus constructed transforms the circles of latitude into closed curves on the torus that turn, screw-like, k times around the core. No subsequent deformation of the torus can change the number k associated with such a curve. Hence two mappings of the torus having different values of k cannot possibly belong to the same class.

It would be a mistake to infer that an analogous argument could be used to prove that on the Klein bottle there exist infinitely many classes of mappings. The closed curves on the Klein bottle that correspond to the helical images of the generators of the cylinder for different values of k, can be transformed into each other by deformation. We can shed some light on the way in which the Klein bottle differs in this respect from the torus by referring to the square models. As a matter of fact, the Klein bottle has only a finite number of classes of mappings.

The above method by no means exhausts the totality of classes of mappings on the torus. We may get a complete picture of this totality with the help of the *universal covering surface* of the torus. In order to get an idea of what this surface looks like, we wrap the Euclidean plane around a circular cylinder of infinite length; of course, the cylinder is covered infinitely many times in the process. We have several times before bent a finite cylinder, bounded by two circles, into the form of a torus. In the same way, we can convert the infinite cylinder into a torus. In this operation, the cylinder appears to slide into itself infinitely often, while its axis makes infinitely many turns about the core of the torus. In this manner, the Euclidean plane is mapped topologically onto a surface that covers the torus in infinitely many layers without any folds or branch points. This surface is the universal covering surface of the torus.

Every turn around a meridian or circle of latitude of the torus takes us from one layer of the covering surface into another layer. Let us draw a canonical section (consisting of a meridian and a circle of latitude) on the torus; we know that this converts the torus into a rectangle with a definite identification of opposite sides. Suppose we mark out all the points on the covering surface which cover the curves of the section, and then convert the covering back into a plane. Then the points we have drawn will mark out a system of lines that divides the plane into infinitely many rectangles arranged like the unit cells of the crystallographic group of plane translations (see Fig. 72, p. 70), and each rectangle corresponds to one layer of the covering. We shall demonstrate this by using a different construction of the universal covering surface. Let us represent the torus by a square with pairs of opposite sides identified. Proceeding as in the construction of the square lattice in the plane (cf. p. 32), we put such squares together to form a plane strip S that extends to infinity on both sides and has two parallel straight lines a and b as its boundary. By a suitable bending which brings a and b together, S is transformed into a circular cylinder C of infinite length. The boundary lines separating the squares of S divide C into regions bounded by circles. We can get from such a region back to the torus by identifying the two circles that constitute its boundary. If we therefore pull the cylinder over the torus in the manner described above, the regions will come to lie one on top of the other, with each region covering the whole torus just once, and all the boundary lines coinciding with a canonical section of the torus. We now continue as in the construction of the square lattice: we cover the whole plane with adjacent strips like S. If the plane is wrapped infinitely often around C in such a way that S is transformed into C as before, then all of the strips, like S, which fill out the plane, obviously become superimposed on S, and the subdivisions into squares of all those strips coincide with the subdivisions of S. On pulling C over the torus again, all the squares of the plane become superimposed on one another and all the boundaries fall on a canonical section of the torus, which is what we set out to prove.

This second construction gives a particularly simple mapping of the universal covering surface U of the torus onto the plane E. For if all those points of U which cover the same point of the torus are called equivalent, then every system of equivalent points of U is represented by a square point lattice on E. Let us now define the *fundamental group* (f) of the torus as the group of all those topological mappings of U onto itself that map every point into an equivalent point. Then the mapping $U \to E$ clearly transforms (f) into the group of translations that move the square lattice into itself.

Let g be any other topological mapping of U *onto itself* that, although it need not map every point into a point equivalent to it, maps equivalent pairs of points into equivalent pairs of points. Then g corresponds to a definite topological mapping h *of the torus onto itself*. To see this, we note that every point P of the torus is occupied by a certain infinite set of equivalent points (Q) of U. But by definition of g, all the images (Q') of the points (Q) cover a single point P' on the torus. Hence g defines the topological mapping $P \to P'$ of the torus onto itself, which we call h. The converse can also be proved; for any given mapping h of the torus we can find a mapping g of the covering surface that is related to h as described above. Then g is defined only to within an arbitrary mapping of the group (f).

By use of this result, we can get a complete survey of the classes of mappings of the torus onto itself. We shall state the result without proof. Let every mapping g be replaced by the mapping γ of E obtained from g by the mapping $U \to E$. Let $ABCD$ be a square unit cell of the translation group (t) in E that corresponds to (f). Let $A'B'C'D'$ be the images of $ABCD$ under the mapping γ; then the parallelogram $A'B'C'D'$ must be a unit cell of (t). Now the mapping h of the torus is a deformation if and only if $ABCD$ can be brought into coincidence with $A'B'C'D'$ by a *translation*. The other classes of mappings of the torus correspond to the other forms that can be assumed by a generating parallelogram of the lattice (cf. Fig. 39, p. 33), as well as to the rotations and reflections that map the square $ABCD$ onto itself.[1]

The concept of universal covering surface can be defined for all surfaces. For the closed orientable surfaces we get the universal covering surfaces by putting $4p$-gons together and setting up a correspondence among them, in much the same way as we did with the squares in the case of the torus. For $p > 1$ the fundamental group cannot, however, be represented by a Euclidean translation group; but it *can* be represented by a hyperbolic translation group in which are $4p$-gons are the unit cells (cf. Fig. 249, p. 259 for the case $p = 2$). Surfaces with boundaries lead to groups of Euclidean or hyperbolic translations with open unit cells. In the case of non-orientable surfaces, the metrical realization of the fundamental group calls for the consideration of Euclidean and hyperbolic glide-reflections in addition to Euclidean and hyperbolic translations.

---

[1] If the lattice is defined as the set of all points whose Cartesian coordinates are integers and if A' is moved to the origin by a translation, then the parallelogram $A'B'C'D'$ is fixed by the coordinates a, b of B' and c, d of C'. In order to get all the classes of mappings of the torus, we have to give a, b, c, d all integral values satisfying the condition $ad - bc = +1$ or -1.

§ 50. Conformal Mapping of the Torus

In § 39 we raised the question of whether—and if so, in how many ways—a surface can be mapped conformally onto itself or onto another surface. We confined our attention there to surfaces topologically equivalent either to the interior of a circle, or to a circular disk including its circumference, or to a sphere. The concept of universal covering surface enables us to attack this problem for other surfaces as well. Let us limit ourselves to the task of finding all the conformal mappings of a *torus* onto itself or onto another torus. We shall content ourselves with this because the methods we shall use for the torus apply to all the other surfaces as well, although they are most easily visualized in the case of the torus. In the sequel, we shall use the word torus to apply not only to the surface of revolution formed by the rotation of a circle about an axis lying in the plane of the circle but not intersecting it, but also to every surface that is topologically equivalent to this surface of revolution.

By the "either-or" theorem mentioned in § 39, every surface that is topologically equivalent to the interior of a circle, or, what amounts to the same, to the Euclidean plane, can be mapped conformally either onto the hyperbolic plane or onto the Euclidean plane. We shall apply this theorem to the universal covering surface U of a torus T, noting that U satisfies the conditions of the theorem. Accordingly, let U be mapped conformally onto a plane E, and let it be left open for the time being whether E is the Euclidean plane or the hyperbolic plane.

Now, the fundamental group (f) is certainly a group of *conformal* mappings of U onto itself, since the images of every region of U under the mappings of (f) are even congruent to that region. In the conformal representation $U \to E$, the group (f) is therefore transformed into a group (t) of conformal mappings of E onto itself. But all the conformal mappings of the plane onto itself are known: they are the hyperbolic rigid motions if E is the hyperbolic plane, the Euclidean rigid motions and similarity transformations if E is the Euclidean plane (cf. pp. 265 and 267). Furthermore, we know that the group (t) has a certain kinship to a crystallographic translation group in the Euclidean plane: all the mappings in (t), with the exception of the identity, are free of fixed points, and the unit cell of the group has four sides. If E were the hyperbolic plane, then (t) would have to be a discontinuous group of hyperbolic translations with a finite unit cell. But on pages 258-259 we have mentioned, and tried to make plausible, that the unit cells of such groups have at least eight sides. The only remaining alternative is that E is the Euclidean plane. It can be proved by elementary methods that every Euclidean similarity transformation other than a rigid motion has a fixed point. Hence the group (t) can only contain, besides the identity, the rigid motions without fixed points, i.e. translations. Since, in addition, (t) is discontinuous and has a finite unit cell, (t) must be a crystallographic translation group of the type discussed on pages 70-71.

Now let the same argument be carried through for any other torus T': Let U' be the universal covering surface of T'; let the conformal representation $U' \rightarrow E$ transform the fundamental group of T' into the crystallographic translation group (t') of E. We have already mentioned that every mapping of a torus onto itself can be extended to a mapping of the covering surface. Similarly, every conformal mapping $T \rightarrow T'$ can be matched by a conformal mapping $U \rightarrow U'$ that is such that corresponding points of U' and U' always cover corresponding points of T and T'. The mappings $U \rightarrow E$ and $U' \rightarrow E$ transform $U \rightarrow U'$ into a conformal mapping a of E onto itself. a must be a Euclidean rigid motion or similarity transformation. Furthermore, a has to carry the translation group (t) into (t').

We have thus shown that there is a conformal mapping of T onto T' only if the group (t) can be carried into (t') by a rigid motion or a similarity transformation. This condition can be expressed in convenient geometrical form as follows. Let t_1 be a shortest translation in the group (t). Let t_2 be a shortest translation from among those translations of (t) that are not parallel to t_1. Let m be the quotient of the lengths of t_2 and t_1, so that $m \geqq 1$. Let a be the angle between the directions of these translations; in order to fix a uniquely, it is sufficient to impose the condition $0 < a \leqq \pi/2$. Let m' and a' be the corresponding quantities for the group (t'). Then a necessary and sufficient condition for the existence of a similarity transformation carrying (t) into (t') is that $m = m'$ and $a = a'$. (The proof is elementary and is left as an exercise for the reader.) Consequently, we can associate with every torus T two numbers m and a which are such that T can be mapped conformally only onto those toruses for which these two numbers are the same as they are for T. These two numbers (or another pair of numbers related to them by a one-to-one correspondence) are called the *moduli* of the torus.

But for the existence of a conformal mapping of a torus T onto a torus T', the equality of the moduli is not only necessary but also sufficient. For if it is satisfied, then there is a similarity transformation or a rigid motion a of E into itself that transforms (t) into (t') ; and it is easy to see that the conformal mapping $U \to U'$ belonging to a determines a conformal mapping $T \to T'$, because our mapping $U \to U'$ transforms equivalent points of U—and them only—into equivalent points of U'. Summarizing our result, we may say that the toruses constitute a two-parameter family with respect to conformal mapping.

If the spatial form of a torus does not display any particular regularity, then the values of the moduli for this torus cannot be deduced directly from its geometrical appearance. But if the torus T is a surface of revolution, then (t) must have a rectangular unit cell, so that $a = \pi/2$. For, in this case, the mapping $U \to E$ can be given explicitly: It transforms the orthogonal net of meridians and circles of latitude into two orthogonal families of parallel straight lines of E. In the particular case in which T is the surface of revolution of a circle, the ratio m between the sides of the rectangular unit cells of (t) cannot depend on anything other than the ratio between the radius of the meridian circle and that of the core. Hence two toruses generated by circles can be mapped conformally onto each other if and only if they are similar.

In four-dimensional space we can find a torus whose covering surface U can even be mapped *isometrically* onto the Euclidean plane (see Appendix 2).

Now we can easily get a picture of the various ways in which any given torus T can be mapped conformally onto itself. The group (k) of these mappings must correspond to the group (l) of rigid motions and of similarity transformations of E that leave (t) invariant. Clearly, (l) contains all the translations of E into itself. In general, these exhaust (l) ; but if (t) exhibits any special properties of regularity, such as a square unit cell, then (l) may also contain rotations and reflections.

The procedure we have followed in the case of the torus can also be adapted to apply to all the other classes of surfaces. But in the majority of cases the image plane in the conformal mapping of the covering surface is not Euclidean, as it was in the case of the torus, but hyperbolic. This applies, for example, to all closed orientable surfaces of genus $p > 1$. These surfaces give rise to hyperbolic translation groups, and two such surfaces can be mapped conformally onto each other only if their translation groups can be transformed into each other by a hyperbolic rigid motion. It is found in hyperbolic geometry that $6p - 6$ constants determine a group of hyperbolic translations with a $4p$-sided finite unit cell to within a hyperbolic rigid motion. Hence every closed orientable surface of genus $p > 1$ has $6p - 6$ moduli.

In the theory of functions, this method is applied chiefly to the Riemann surfaces of the algebraic functions. For $p = 1$, the mapping $U \to E$ leads to the elliptic functions; for $p > 1$, to the automorphic functions of Klein and Poincare.

The open surfaces give rise to groups with infinite unit cells. In the theory of functions, such groups are encountered, for instance, in the study of the exponential function and the elliptic modular functions.

§ 51. The Problem of Contiguous Regions, The Thread Problem, and the Color Problem

In conclusion, we shall discuss three problems, intimately related with each other, that arise when a surface is partitioned into regions. In the plane, we find an example of such a partition in ordinary geographical maps. Furthermore, in combinatorial topology, partitionings of arbitrary surfaces are encountered whenever a curved surface is replaced by a topologically equivalent polyhedron. To obtain the faces of the polyhedron, we must first partition the curved surface into regions.

The problem of contiguous regions is the problem of finding the greatest number of regions on a given surface which are such that each of them borders on every other along a curve.[1] Let us begin by examining this problem for the plane. Let us choose two contiguous regions 1 and 2 in the plane bordering on each other along

---

[1] It is not required that the regions cover the whole surface.

a curve. If a third region is chosen which surrounds the first two
completely, then it is impossible to find a fourth region bordering
on each of the first three (see Fig. 323). But if we choose the third
region in the manner illustrated in Fig. 324, then it is easy to find
a fourth. But no matter how the fourth region is chosen, one of
the remaining regions will be completely surrounded by the others,
so that it is impossible to find a fifth region that borders on each
of the first four along a curve. Try as we may, we can not get the
number of such regions in the plane to exceed four. The fact that
the maximal number of contiguous regions in the plane is four can
also be proved rigorously.   Fig. 325 shows a particularly symmetrical arrangement of four such regions.

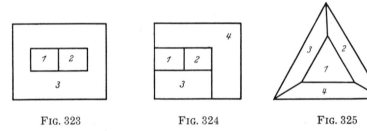

FIG. 323   FIG. 324   FIG. 325

The thread problem is the dual converse of the problem of contiguous regions (where duality is to be understood in the sense of
a topological generalization of the principle of duality in *space* of
projective geometry). The thread problem is concerned with the
greatest number of points on a surface having the following property: Each point can be joined to any other by a curve on the
surface in such a way that no two of these curves intersect. The
following simple argument shows that this maximal number is
equal to the maximal number of contiguous regions on the same
surface. Choose one point from each of the contiguous regions.
Since any two contiguous regions border on each other along a
curve, any two of these points can be connected by a curve lying
wholly inside the two regions containing the points. Furthermore,
the curves thus obtained can be chosen in such a way that the
portions lying in any one given region do not intersect, for in this
region we need only connect one interior point with a number of
points on the boundary. Thus every arrangement of n contiguous
regions yields a solution of the thread problem for n points. Therefore the maximal number of points in the thread problem is at

least equal to the maximal number of contiguous regions. But conversely, every solution of the thread problem for n points also gives rise to an arrangement of n contiguous regions. To obtain such an arrangement, we divide into two parts each of the curves connecting a pair of points and make a two-dimensional region out of the portion of the curve emanating from each point by adjoining the surrounding points of the surface. In this way, we obtain n star-shaped regions each of which borders on every other one. Hence the maximal number of adjacent regions is at least equal to the maximal number of points satisfying the condition of the thread problem. And since we have already proved the converse inequality, it follows that the two maximal numbers are equal.

These maximal numbers have also been determined for surfaces of connectivity other than 1. For the projective plane and the

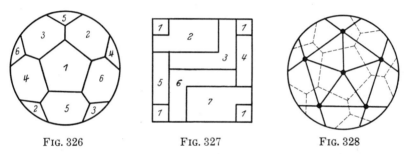

FIG. 326   FIG. 327   FIG. 328

torus, the numbers are 6 and 7 respectively. Figs. 326 and 327 exemplify such arrangements of adjacent regions. The projective plane is represented by a circular disk with opposite points of the circumference identified, the torus by a square with the usual identification of pairs of sides. Fig. 326 is essentially the same as Fig. 167 on page 149 which represents a projection of the dodecahedron. Fig. 328 illustrates a solution of the thread problem in the projective plane; it corresponds dually to the partition of Fig. 326.

A problem that is closely related to the problem of contiguous regions is the color problem. This can be presented as a problem of practical cartography, as follows. Let a number of regions be drawn on a surface. Each region has to be filled in with a certain color in such a way that no two regions that border on each other along a curve have the same color. (If two regions meet at isolated points only, they are permitted to have the same color.) The problem is to find the smallest number of colors that will suffice to color

the regions in every conceivable partition of the surface without
violating the above rule.

The number of colors must be at least equal to the greatest
number of contiguous regions possible on the surface. For, each
one of a set of contiguous regions must have a different color.
Conversely, it would seem to be a plausible assumption that this
maximal number of contiguous regions is also sufficient. In the
case of the projective plane and of the torus this has been proved
to be correct: In the projective plane six colors are sufficient for
the proper coloring of any map, and seven colors are sufficient on
the torus. On the other hand, it is still an unproved conjecture
that four colors will do on the plane and on the sphere.[2]

Let us begin with some examples of partitions in the plane. The
three neighboring areas of Fig. 329a have to be colored with three

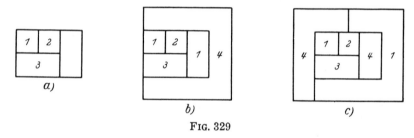

Fig. 329

different colors, 1, 2, and 3. The fourth region, bordering on 2
and 3, may be given the color 4 or the color 1. If 4 is used, then
four colors will not suffice to fill in the regions of Fig. 329b.
Hence we have to use the color 1 for the fourth region in this
case. But this would get us into difficulty in coloring the regions
of Fig. 329c: here the fourth area has to have the color 4. This
example shows that the arrangement of the other regions has an
influence on the way the first four can be colored. Whenever a
new region is added, we may have to change the colors on the
regions already colored. This fact is at the root of the difficulty
in our problem.

We shall now follow a procedure that will lead to solutions of
the color problem for a number of closed surfaces. We begin by
distorting the surface in such a way that it becomes a polyhedron and that the individual regions become the faces of the

---

[2] The problems for the sphere and the plane are essentially the same.

polyhedron.[3] Then it is clear that it is sufficient to solve the problem for all polyhedra having the same connectivity as the given surface.

First of all, we prove the following result: Every polyhedron of connectivity h can be colored with at most n colors if n satisfies the inequality

$$nF > 6(F + h - 3)$$

for all integers $F > n$. Subsequently we shall determine, for any given $h > 0$, the smallest number n_h for which the inequality is satisfied. As a result, we shall have proved that every partitioning of a closed surface of connectivity h can be filled in with n_h colors.

Now let h be a fixed number and let any number n be given satisfying the above condition for this h. Let us classify the polyhedra of connectivity h according to the number F of faces. We shall prove our result by induction on F. For all $F \leq n$, the result is trivially true, for then we can simply give each face of the polyhedron a different color. Now let us assume that the

FIG. 330

theorem is already proved for all $F \leq F_0$ and let us prove it for $F = F_0 + 1$. From the preceding remarks it follows that we need only consider the case $F > n$. We assume, then, that this number F satisfies the inequality.

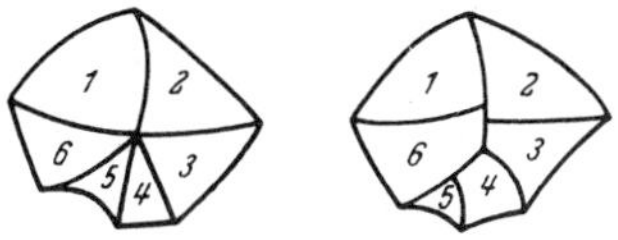

$$nF > 6(F + h - 3).$$

We shall make use of Euler's formula:[4] $V - E + F = 3 - h$, or $F + h - 3 = E - V$. By a deformation, which does not change the number F or the connectivity h, we can get the polyhedron into such a form that only three faces meet at every vertex, so that there will also be only three edges meeting at each vertex (see Fig. 330). Hence $3V$ edges altogether meet at the V vertices, and since each edge is here counted twice, we have $3V = 2E$, so that

$$6(F + h - 3) = 6E - 6V = 6E - 4E = 2E.$$

---

[3] As may be seen from the examples of Figs. 326 and 327, this deformation will in general be possible only if it is permitted that some of the faces be curved. This will not affect the proof to be given here.

[4] In originally deriving this formula, we made certain assumptions about the arrangement of the faces, which may not be satisfied in the present case. It may be seen, however, that the formula also applies under the present conditions.

Hence the inequality for the number n takes on the form

$$nF > 2E.$$

From this inequality we may deduce that at least one face of the polyhedron is bounded by less than n edges. For otherwise, the F faces of the polyhedron would be bounded by at least nF edges in all, and, allowing for the fact that every edge was counted twice, we would get $nF \leq 2E$. This argument is the core of our proof.

Now consider one of those faces that border on less than n other faces. We remove this face for the time being and fill the resulting gap by extending the neighboring faces into it. This gives another closed polyhedron. The transformation has left the connectivity number unchanged but has diminished the number of faces by one. By our assumption, we can therefore fill in the new polyhedron with n colors. Let us do this and then reverse the deformation. We then get the old polyhedron with all its faces, excepting the one we removed, filled in with our n colors. But since only $n - 1$ faces, at most, have an edge in common with the exceptional face, this may also be colored without recourse to a new color. It may have been necessary to alter the original polyhedron to get it into a form where only three edges meet at every vertex. But this alteration may now be reversed without changing the coloring system, as the reverse transformation does not create any new boundary lines.

The next step is to find out which numbers n satisfy the condition we have imposed. We shall write it in the form

$$n > 6\,[1 + (h - 3)\,/F],$$

where F has to take all integral values exceeding n. If h is equal to 1 or 2, the right-hand side of the inequality approaches 6 with increasing F and always remains smaller than this value. In these two cases, therefore, $n_h = 6$ is the smallest integer satisfying our assumption. For $h = 3$, the right-hand side has the fixed value 6, so that $n_h = 7$. For $h > 3$, the right-hand side decreases as F increases, and it is therefore sufficient to substitute the smallest admissible value $n + 1$ for F. This gives for $n > 3$ the inequality

$$n > 6\left(1 + \frac{h - 3}{n + 1}\right),$$

which may be written

$$n\,(n + 1) > 6\,n + 6 + 6\,h - 18, \qquad n^2 - 5\,n > 6\,h - 12,$$

or

$$n > \tfrac{5}{2} + \tfrac{1}{2}\sqrt{24h - 23}.$$

If $[x]$ denotes the largest integer contained in x, we therefore get, for $h > 3$,

$$n_h = \left[\tfrac{7}{2} + \tfrac{1}{2}\sqrt{24h - 23}\right].$$

It happens that this formula also leads to the correct values, $n_h = 6$ and $n_h = 7$, for $h = 2$ and $h = 3$, although it is not applicable to these cases. But for $h = 1$, the formula would give us 4 instead of the value 6 obtained above. Although a proof has not been found to date, it is highly probable that 4 is the correct value for the minimal number of colors, since nobody has been able to construct a set of regions in the plane that can not be filled in with four colors. The following table lists the values of n_h for $h = 1$ to $h = 13$:

$h =$	$n_h =$	$h =$	$n_h =$
1	6 ([4.000] = 4)	8	[10.000] = 10
2	6 ([6.000] = 6)	9	[10.447] = 10
3	7 ([7.000] = 7)	10	[10.866] = 10
4	[7.775] = 7	11	[11.264] = 11
5	[8.425] = 8	12	[11.640] = 11
6	[9.000] = 9	13	[12.000] = 12
7	[9.522] = 9		

So far, we have only proved that the numbers in the table represent sufficient numbers of colors. It is conceivable that there are surfaces of connectivity h on which every combination of regions can be filled in with fewer than n_h colors. For the cases $h = 2, 3, 5, 7, 9, 11, 13$, however, it has been proved that exactly n_h contiguous areas can be constructed. On these surfaces, any number of colors less than n_h is therefore insufficient; hence the solution of the color problem is complete for these surfaces. For all other surfaces, the numbers n_h represent upper bounds for the numbers of adjacent regions.

A particularly conspicuous feature of the color problem is the absence, so far, of any proof for the theorem in the case of the plane, where the result seems intuitively to be particularly obvious. This type of difficulty is encountered frequently in mathematics if one wants to achieve a purely logical understanding, based on numerical concepts, of theorems that are intuitively plausible. We may cite, as an additional example, the theorem that any closed curve without double points divides the plane into two parts or the theorem that the sphere contains the maximum volume for a given surface area. Both theorems require fairly difficult and involved proofs. But by far the most characteristic example of this kind is the four-color problem, because there is no apparent reason why just the case that is visually the simplest should offer such difficulties while much more complicated cases admit of a solution.

Appendices to Chapter VI

1. The Projective Plane in Four-Dimensional Space

We shall construct an algebraic surface in Euclidean four-space E_4 which is topologically equivalent to the projective plane but which, unlike Boy's surface, has no self-intersections or singularities of any kind. We begin with the spherical surface

$$(1) \qquad u^2 + v^2 + w^2 = 1$$

and consider the figure that is given in the four-dimensional Cartesian coordinates x, y, z, t by the equations

$$(2) \qquad x = u^2 - v^2, \quad y = uv, \quad z = uw, \quad t = vw,$$

where the values of the parameters u, v, and w are subject to the condition (1). Since x, y, z, t are homogeneous quadratic functions of u, v, and w, every diametrically opposite pair of points on the sphere (1) is represented by a single point (2) of E_4. We proceed to show that any two points of (1) that are not diametrically opposite are represented by two distinct points in (2). To begin with, let us consider a point P of the sphere for which none of the coordinates u, v, w vanishes. The corresponding values of y, z, and t are different from zero and define the proportion $u:v:w$ uniquely. Hence the point of (2) associated with P does not represent any points of the sphere other than P and the point opposite P. If w vanishes, the values of u^2 and v^2 are uniquely determined by the equations $u^2 + v^2 = 1$, $u^2 - v^2 = x$, and the corresponding point in (2) can only take on the four positions $(u, v, 0)$, $(u, -v, 0)$, $(-u, v, 0)$, and $(-u, -v, 0)$. If, in addition, we have $u = 0$ or $v = 0$, these four points are reduced to a single pair of diametrically opposite points, so that there is nothing left to prove in this case. If $u \neq 0$ and $v \neq 0$, we have to use the remaining equation, $y = uv$; this selects one diametrically opposite pair from the four points. The only cases that remain to be considered are those in which w differs from zero while one of the variables u and v vanishes, in other words, either $u = 0$, $v \neq 0$, $w \neq 0$, or $u \neq 0$, $v = 0$, $w \neq 0$, or finally $u = v = 0$, $w = +1$ or -1. In the first case, we have $x = -v^2$, $-x + w^2 = 1$, $vw = t$; whence v^2, w^2, and vw are known. Analogously, u^2, w^2, and uw are known in the second case. In both cases, it follows, as in the case $w = 0$, that the corresponding point of (2) represents only one pair of opposite points of (1). The third case only applies to two diametrically opposite points of the sphere (1) anyway, so that there is nothing left to prove in this case. Thus we have demonstrated that (2) together with the auxiliary condition (1) is a one-to-one representation of a sphere with pairs of opposite points identified, i.e. of a projective plane.

It is easy to eliminate u, v, and w from the equations defining the model. From the last three equations of (2) we get

$$yz/t = u^2, \quad yt/z = v^2, \quad zt/y = w^2.$$

Consequently, the first equation of (2) becomes

(3) $$y(z^2 - t^2) = xzt,$$

and (1) is transformed into

(4) $$y^2 z^2 + y^2 t^2 + z^2 t^2 = yzt.$$

Thus our model is the intersection of the hypersurfaces (3) and (4).

The fact that the model is free of singularities, i.e. that its tangent plane is everywhere continuous, is readily verified by expressing the variables u, v, w of the sphere (1) as functions of two independent parameters and then, by means of (2), expressing x, y, z, t in terms of the new parameters.

2. The Euclidean Plane in Four-Dimensional Space

In E_3, all the surfaces that are isometric with the Euclidean plane must extend to infinity, since they are necessarily ruled surfaces. In E_4, on the other hand, there are surfaces that are isometric with the Euclidean plane in the small but are not ruled. We shall present such a surface F. It is confined to a finite part of the space and is topologically equivalent to the torus. F is defined by the simple parametric equations

$$x_1 = \cos u, \qquad\qquad x_3 = \cos v,$$
$$x_2 = \sin u, \qquad\qquad x_4 = \sin v.$$

The line element of F is

$$ds^2 = dx_1^2 + dx_2^2 + dx_3^2 + dx_4^2$$
$$= \sin^2 u\, du^2 + \cos^2 u\, du^2 + \sin^2 v\, dv^2 + \cos^2 v\, dv^2 = du^2 + dv^2.$$

Thus F is indeed isometric with the plane having the rectangular coordinates u, v. The surface is finite, because all the coordinates of its points lie between $+1$ and -1. F may also be thought of as the intersection of the two three-dimensional hypercylinders $x_1^2 + x_2^2 = 1$ and $x_3^2 + x_4^2 = 1$. We get all the points of F by letting the point (u, v) in the Cartesian (u, v)-plane traverse all the points of a square whose sides are parallel to the axes and equal in length to 2π. Any two distinct points of the interior of the square give rise to two distinct points of F; on the other hand, two points of the circumference represent the same point of F if they lie on a common straight line $u = \text{const.}$ or $v = \text{const.}$ and on opposite sides of the square. Hence F is a torus, and the (u, v)-plane is its universal covering surface.

We might attempt to realize Euclidean geometry on closed surfaces other than the torus. It is found, however, that the Klein bottle is the only other closed surface on which this is possible. Hyperbolic geometry, however, can be realized on closed surfaces of connectivity $h > 3$, and on such surfaces only. Elliptic geometry can not be realized on any closed surface other than the sphere and the projective plane. These theorems may be deduced from the formula, due to O. Bonnet, for the surface integral of the geodesic curvature (*curvatura integra*).

INDEX

INDEX

CHELSEA

SCIENTIFIC

BOOKS

THÉORIE DES OPÉRATIONS LINÉAIRES

By S. BANACH

—1933. xii + 250 pp. 5¼x8¼.   **$3.95**

THEORIE DER FUNKTIONEN MEHRERER KOMPLEXER VERÄNDERLICHEN

By H. BEHNKE and P. THULLEN

—(Ergeb. der Math.) 1934. vii+115 pp. 5½x8½.   **$3.25**

LEHRBUCH DER FUNKTIONENTHEORIE

By L. BIEBERBACH

"One of the best introductions to the theory of functions of a complex variable. . . . scores of new problems, methods and results. **Indispensable for anyone interested in modern developments.**"
—*Bulletin of the A. M. S.*

"Students of physics, engineering and related fields . . . will profit by a thorough study of these volumes."—*Journal of Applied Physics.*

—Vol. I Fourth (latest) ed. xiv+322 pp. Vol. 2, Second (latest) ed. vi+370 pp. 5½x8½. Originally $14.80.
Two vol. set **$9.00**

CONFORMAL MAPPING

By L. BIEBERBACH

"The first book in English to give an elementary, readable account of the Riemann Mapping Theorem and the distortion theorems and uniformisation problem with which it is connected. . . . The fourth presented in very attractive and readable form."
—*Math. Gazette.*

Engineers will profitably use this book for its accurate exposition."—*Appl. Mechanics Reviews.*

—1952. vi + 234 pp. 4½x6½.   **$2.50**

KREIS UND KUGEL

By W. BLASCHKE

Isoperimetric properties of the circle and sphere, the (Brunn-Minkowski) theory of convex bodies, and differential-geometric properties (in the large) of convex bodies. A standard work.

—x + 169 pp. 5½x8½.   Cloth **$3.50**
                               Paper **$1.50**

VORLESUNGEN ÜBER INTEGRAL-GEOMETRIE. Vols. I and II

By W. BLASCHKE

AND

EINFÜHRUNG IN DIE THEORIE DER SYSTEME VON DIFFERENTIALGLEI-CHUNGEN

By E. KÄHLER

—222 pp. 5½x8½.   Three Vols. in One **$4.50**

VORLESUNGEN ÜBER FOURIERSCHE INTEGRALE

By S. BOCHNER

"A readable account of those parts of the subject useful for applications to problems of mathematical physics or pure analysis."
—*Bulletin of the A. M. S.*

—1932. 237 pp. 5½x8½. Orig. publ. at $6.40.   **$4.50**

ALMOST PERIODIC FUNCTIONS
By H. BOHR
Translated by H. COHN. From the famous series *Ergebnisse der Mathematik und ihrer Grenzgebiete*, a beautiful exposition of the theory of Almost Periodic Functions written by the creator of that theory.

—1951. 120 pp. 6x9. Lithotyped. German edition was $4.50.
$2.50

THEORIE DER KONVEXEN KÖRPER
By T. BONNESEN and W. FENCHEL
"Remarkable monograph."
—*J. D. Tamarkin, Bulletin of the A. M. S.*
—1934. 171 pp. 5½x8½. Orig. publ. at $7.50 Cloth, **$3.95**

THEORY OF FUNCTIONS
By C. CARATHÉODORY
Translated by F. STEINHARDT. The recent, and already famous textbook, *Funktionentheorie*.

Partial Contents: **Part One.** Chap. I. Algebra of Complex Numbers II. Geometry of Complex Numbers. III. Euclidean, Spherical, and Non-Euclidean Geometry. **Part Two.** Theorems from Point Set Theory and Topology. Chap. I. Sequences and Continuous Complex Functions. II. Curves and Regions. III. Line Integrals. **Part Three.** Analytic Functions. Chap. I. Foundations. II. The Maximum-modulus principle. III. Poisson Integral and Harmonic Functions. IV. Meromorphic Functions. **Part Four.** Generation of Analytic Functions by Limiting Processes. Chap. I. Uniform Convergence. II. Normal Families of Meromorphic Functions. III. Power Series. IV. Partial Fraction Decomposition and the Calculus of Residues. **Part Five.** Special Functions. Chap. I. The Exponential Function and the Trigonometric Functions. II. Logarithmic Function. III. Bernoulli Numbers and the Gamma Function.

Vol. II.: **Part Six.** Foundations of Geometric Function Theory. Chap. I. Bounded Functions. II. Conformal Mapping. III. The Mapping of the Boundary. **Part Seven.** The Triangle Function and Picard's Theorem. Chap. I. Functions of Several Complex Variables. II. Conformal Mapping of Circular-Arc Triangles. III. The Schwarz Triangle Functions and the Modular Function. IV. Essential Singularities and Picard's Theorems.

"A book by a master . . . Carathéodory himself regarded [it] as his finest achievement . . . written from a catholic point of view."—*Bulletin of A.M.S.*
—Vol. I. 1954. 310 pp. 6x9.   **$4.95**
—Vol. II. 1954. 220 pp. 6x9.   **$4.95**

MEASURE AND INTEGRAL
By C. CARATHÉODORY
—About 360 pp. Translated from the German.   **In prep.**

VORLESUNGEN ÜBER REELLE FUNKTIONEN
By C. CARATHÉODORY
This great classic is at once a book for the beginner, a reference work for the advanced scholar and a source of inspiration for the research worker.
—2nd, latest complete, ed. 728 pp. 5½x8½. Orig. publ. at $11.60.   **$8.00**

REELLE FUNKTIONEN
By C. CARATHÉODORY
—1939. 190 pp. 5¼x8.   **$3.50**

ELECTRIC CIRCUIT THEORY and the OPERATIONAL CALCULUS

By J. R. CARSON

"A rigorous and logical exposition and treatment of the Heaviside operational calculus and its applications to electrical problems . . . will be enjoyed and studied by mathematicians, engineers and scientists."—*Electrical World*.

—2nd ed. 206 pp. 5¼x8.   Cloth   **$3.95**
                               Paper   **$1.88**

THEORY OF LIE GROUPS

—1946. x + 217 pp. 5¼x8¼. (Winter, 1955). **In prep.**

TEXTBOOK OF ALGEBRA

By G. CHRYSTAL

The usefulness, both as a textbook and as a work of reference, of this charming classic is attested to by the number of editions it has run through—the present being the sixth. Its richness of content can be only appreciated by an examination of the twelve-hundred-page book itself. **Thousands of valuable exercises (with solutions)**.

6th ed. 2 Vols. 1235 pages. 5⅜x8.   Two vol. set **$8.00**

EIGENWERTPROBLEME UND IHRE NUMERISCHE BEHANDLUNG

By L. COLLATZ

"**Part I** presents an interesting and valuable collection of PRACTICAL APPLICATIONS.
    "**Part II** deals with the MATHEMATICAL THEORY.
    "**Part III** takes up various methods of NUMERICAL SOLUTION of boundary value problems. These include step-by-step approximations, graphical integration, the Rayleigh-Ritz method and methods depending on finite differences. **Here, as throughout the book, the theory is kept in close touch with practice by numerous specific examples.**"
               —*Mathematical Reviews*.

—1945. 350 pp. 5½x8½. Orig. pub. at $8.80.   **$4.95**

ALGEBREN

By M. DEURING

—(Ergeb. der Math.) 1935. v+143 pp. 5½x8½. Orig. pub. at $6.60.   **$3.95**

HISTORY OF THE THEORY OF NUMBERS

By L. E. DICKSON

"**A monumental work** . . . Dickson always has in mind the needs of the investigator . . . The author has [often] expressed in a nut-shell the main results of a long and involved paper *in a much clearer way than the writer of the article did himself*. The ability to reduce complicated mathematical arguments to simple and elementary terms is highly developed in Dickson."—*Bulletin of A. M. S.*

—Vol. I (Divisibility and Primality) xii+486 pp. Vol. II (Diophantine Analysis) xxv+803 pp. Vol. III (Quadratic and Higher Forms) v+313 pp   Three vol. set **$19.50**

THE INTEGRAL CALCULUS
By J. W. EDWARDS

A leisurely, immensely detailed, textbook of over 1,900 pages, rich in illustrative examples and manipulative techniques and containing much interesting material that must of necessity be omitted from less comprehensive works.

There are forty large chapters in all. The earlier cover a leisurely and a more-than-usually-detailed treatment of all the elementary standard topics. Later chapters include: Jacobian Elliptic Functions, Weierstrassian Elliptic Functions, Evaluation of Definite Integrals, Harmonic Analysis, Calculus of Variations, etc. Every chapter contains many exercises (with solutions).

—2 vols. 1,922 pp. 5x8. Originally published at $31.50 the set.
Each volume **$6.50**

AUTOMORPHIC FUNCTIONS
By L. R. FORD

—2nd ed. (Cor. repr. of 1st ed.) x+333 pp. 5⅜x8. **$4.95**

THEORY OF DIFFERENTIAL EQUATIONS
By A. R. FORSYTH

Professor Forsyth's six-volume treatise deals with Exact Equations and Pfaff's Problem (Vol. I), Non-Linear Differential Equations (Vols. II and III), Ordinary Linear Differential Equations (Vol. IV), and Partial Differential Equations (Vols. V and VI). The volume on Linear Equations (Vol. IV) is independent of the preceding volumes.

—Vol. I (Exact Equations and Pfaff's Problem), Vol.II (Non-Linear Equations), Vol. III (same) 1,112 pp. (bound as one) (Winter, '56 or Spring '57) **In prep.**

—Vol. IV (Ordinary Linear Differential Equations) xiv + 534 pp. (Winter '56 or Spring '57) **In prep.**

—Vol. V (Partial Differential Equations), Vol. VI (same) xxx + 1,074 pp. (bound as one) **In prep.**

RUSSIAN MATHEMATICAL BIBLIOGRAPHY
By G. E. FORSYTHE

A bibliography of Russian Mathematics Books for the quarter century ending in 1955. Supplements may be issued. Added subject index.

—1956. 120 pp. 5¼x8¼. (Sept., 1956). Probable price **$3.95**

LES INTÉGRALES DE STIELTJES ET LEURS APPLICATIONS AUX PROBLÈMES DE LA PHYSIQUE MATHÉMATIQUE
By N. GUNTHER

—1932. 498 pp. 5½x8 in. **$5.95**

LEÇONS SUR LA PROPAGATION DES ONDES ET LES EQUATIONS DE L'HYDRODYNAMIQUE
By J. HADAMARD

"[Hadamard's] unusual analytic proficiency enables him to connect in a wonderful manner the physical problem of propagation of waves and the mathematical problem of Cauchy concerning the characteristics of partial differential equations of the second order."—*Bulletin of the A. M. S.*

—viii+375 pp. 5½x8½. **$4.95**

REELLE FUNKTIONEN. Punktfunktionen
By H. HAHN

—426 pp. 5½x8½. Orig. pub. at $12.80. **$5.50**

INTRODUCTION TO HILBERT SPACE AND THE THEORY OF SPECTRAL MULTIPLICITY
By P. R. HALMOS

Prof. Halmos' latest book gives a clear, readable introductory treatment of Hilbert Space. The multiplicity theory of continuous spectra is treated, for the first time in English, in full generality.

—1957. 2nd. ed. (c. repr. of 1st ed.). 120 pp. 6x9. **$3.25**

GRUNDZÜGE DER MENGENLEHRE
By F. HAUSDORFF

Some of the topics in the Grundzüge omitted from later editions:

Symmetric Sets—Principle of Duality—most of the "Algebra" of Sets—most of the "Ordered Sets"—Partially Ordered Sets—Arbitrary Sets of Complexes—Normal Types—Initial and Final Ordering—Complexes of Real Numbers—General Topological Spaces—Euclidean Spaces —the Special Methods Applicable in the Euclidean plane—Jordan's separation Theorem—The Theory of Content and Measure—The Theory of the Lebesgue Integral.

—First edition. 484 pp. 5½x8¼. **$4.95**

SET THEORY
By F. HAUSDORFF

A translation of the third German edition of the classic.

—Third edition. About 320 pp. **In prep.**

VORLESUNGEN ÜBER DIE THEORIE DER ALGEBRAISCHEN ZAHLEN
By E. HECKE

"An elegant and comprehensive account of the modern theory of algebraic numbers."
—*Bulletin of the A. M. S.*
"A classic."—*Mathematical Gazette.*

—1923. 264 pp. 5½x8½. **$3.95**

INTEGRALGLEICHUNGEN UND GLEICHUNGEN MIT UNENDLICHVIELEN UNBEKANNTEN
By E. HELLINGER and O. TOEPLITZ

"Indispensable to anybody who desires to penetrate deeply into this subject."—*Bulletin of A.M.S.*

—With a preface by E. Hilb. 1928. 286 pp. 5¼x8. **$4.50**

Grundzüge Einer Allgemeinen Theorie der LINEAREN INTEGRALGLEICHUNGEN
By D. HILBERT

—306 pp. 5½x8¼. **$4.50**

PRINCIPLES OF MATHEMATICAL LOGIC

By D. HILBERT and W. ACKERMANN

The famous *Grundzüge der Theoretischen Logik* translated into English, with added notes and revisions by PROF. R. E. LUCE.

"The best textbook in a Western European language for a student wishing a fairly thorough treatment."—*Bulletin of the A. M. S.*

—1950. xii + 172 pp. 6x9. **$3.75**

GEOMETRY AND THE IMAGINATION

By D. HILBERT and S. COHN-VOSSEN

The theme of this book is *insight*. Not merely proofs, but proofs that offer *insight*—intuitive understanding—into *why they are true*. Not merely properties of the hyperboloid or of Pascal's hexagon, but *insight* into *why they have these properties*. In this wide-ranging survey, one of the world's greatest and most original mathematicians uses *insight* as both his technique and his aim. Both the beginner and the mature mathematician will learn much from this fascinating treatise.

Translated from the German by P. NEMENYI.

CHAPTER HEADINGS: I. The Simplest Curves and surfaces. II. Regular Systems of Points. III. Projective Configurations. IV. Differential Geometry. V. Kinematics. VI. Topology.

"A mathematical classic . . . The purpose is to make the reader *see* and *feel* the proofs."—*Science.*

" A fascinating tour of the 20th-century mathematical zoo."—*Scientific American.*

"Students . . . will experience the sensation of being taken into the friendly confidence of a great mathematician and being shown the **real significance** of things."—*Science Progress.*

"A glance down the index (*twenty-five columns of it*) reveal the breadth of range:—

"Annulus; Atomic structure; Automorphic functions; Bubble, soap; Caustic Curve; Color problem; Density of packing, of circles; Four-dimensional space; Gears, hyperboloidal; Graphite; Lattices; Mapping; "Monkey Saddle"; Table salt; Zinc.

"These are but a few of the topics . . . The title evokes the imagination and the text must surely capture it."—Math. Gazette.

—1952. 358 pp. 6x9. **$6.00**

SQUARING THE CIRCLE, and other Monographs

By HOBSON et al.

SQUARING THE CIRCLE, by Hobson. A fascinating and scholarly history of the number π.

RULER AND COMPASSES, by *Hudson.* "An analytical and geometrical investigation of how far Euclidean constructions can take us. It is as thoroughgoing as it is constructive."—*Sci. Monthly.*

THE THEORY AND CONSTRUCTION OF NON-DIFFERENTIABLE FUNCTIONS, by *Singh.* I. Functions Defined by Series. II. Functions Defined Geometrically. III. Functions Defined Arithmetically. IV. Properties of Non-Differentiable Functions.

HOW TO DRAW A STRAIGHT LINE, by *Kempe.* An intriguing monograph on linkages. Describes, among other things, a linkage that will trisect any angle.

"Intriguing, meaty."—*Scientific American.*

—388 pp. 4½x7½. Four vols. in one **$3.25**

SPHERICAL AND ELLIPSOIDAL HARMONICS
By E. W. HOBSON

"A comprehensive treatise . . . an up-to-date hand-book of spherical harmonics . . . and the standard reference in its field."—*Bulletin of the A. M. S.*
—1930. 512 pp. 5⅜x8. Orig. pub. at $13.50   **$6.00**

DIE METHODEN ZUR ANGENÄHERTEN LOSUNG VON EIGENWERTPROBLEMEN IN DER ELASTOKINETIK
By K. HOHENEMSER

—(Ergeb. der Math.) 1932. 89 pp. 5½x8½. Orig. pub. at $4.25.   **$2.75**

ERGODENTHEORIE
By E. HOPF

—(Ergeb. der Math.) 1937. 89 pp. 5½x8½.   **$2.75**

HUDSON, "Ruler and Compasses," *see* Hobson

THE CALCULUS OF FINITE DIFFERENCES
By CHARLES JORDAN

". . . destined to remain the classic treatment of the subject . . . for many years to come."—*Harry C. Carver, Founder and formerly Editor of the* ANNALS OF MATHEMATICAL STATISTICS.
—1947. Second edition. xxi+652 pp. 5½x8¼. Orig. pub. at $8.00.   **$6.00**

THEORIE DER ORTHOGONALREIHEN
By S. KACZMARZ and H. STEINHAUS

The theory of general orthogonal functions. *Monografje Matematyczne*, Vol. VI.
—304 pp. 6x9.   **$4.95**

KAHLER, See Blaschke

DIFFERENTIALGLEICHUNGEN: LOESUNGSMETHODEN UND LOESUNGEN
By E. KAMKE

Everything possible that can be of use when one has a given differential equation to solve, or when one wishes to investigate that solution thoroughly.

PART A: General Methods of Solution and the Properties of the Solutions.

PART B: Boundary and Characteristic Value Problems.

PART C: Dictionary of some 1600 Equations in Lexicographical Order, with solution, techniques for solving, and references.

"A reference work of outstanding importance which should be in every mathematical library."
—*Mathematical Gazette.*
—3rd ed. 1944. 692 pp. 6x9. Orig. publ. at $15.00   **$9.50**

KEMPE, "How to Draw a Straight Line," *see* Hobson

ASYMPTOTISCHE GESETZE DER WAHRSCHEINLICHKEITSRECHNUNG
By A. A. KHINTCHINE

—1933. 82 pp. (Ergeb. der Math.) 5½x8½. Orig. pub. at $3.85. Paper.   **$2.00**

ENTWICKLUNG DER MATHEMATIK IM 19. JAHRHUNDERT

By F. KLEIN

Vol. I deals with general Advanced **Mathematics** of the prolific 19th century. Vol. II deals with the mathematics of Relativity Theory.

—616 pp. 5¼x8¼. Orig. $14.40   2 Vols. in one **$7.50**

VORLESUNGEN ÜBER HOHERE GEOMETRIE

By FELIX KLEIN

—Third ed. 413 pp. 5½x8. Orig. publ. at $10.80.   **$4.95**

FAMOUS PROBLEMS, and other monographs

By KLEIN et al.

FAMOUS PROBLEMS OF ELEMENTARY GEOMETRY, by *Klein*. A fascinating little book. A simple, easily understandable, account of the famous problems of Geometry—The Duplication of the Cube, Trisection of the Angle, Squaring of the Circle—and the proofs that these cannot be solved by ruler and compass—presentable, say, before an undergraduate math club (no calculus required). Also, the modern problems about transcendental numbers, the existence of such numbers, and proofs of the transcendence of e.

FROM DETERMINANT TO TENSOR, by *Sheppard*. A novel and charming introduction. Written with the utmost simplicity. PT I. Origin of Determinants. II. Properties of Determinants. III. Solution of Simultaneous Equations. IV. Properties. V. Tensor Notation. PT II. VI. Sets. VII. Cogredience, etc. VIII. Examples from Statistics. IX. Tensors in Theory of Relativity.

INTRODUCTION TO COMBINATORY ANALYSIS, by *MacMahon*. A concise introduction to this field. Written as introduction to the author's two-volume work.

THREE LECTURES ON FERMAT'S LAST THEOREM, by *Mordell*. These lectures on what is perhaps the most celebrated conjecture in Mathematics are intended for those without training in Number Theory. I. History, Early Proofs. II. Kummer's Treatment and Recent Results. III. Libri's and Germain's Methods.

—350 pp. 5¼x8¼.   Four vols. in one. **$3.25**

THEORIE DER ENDLICHEN UND UNENDLICHEN GRAPHEN

By D. KÖNIG

"Elegant applications to Matrix Theory . . . Abstract Set Theory . . . Linear Forms . . . Electricity . . . Basis Problems . . . Logic, Theory of Games, Group Theory."—*L. Kalmar, Acta Szeged.*

—1936. 269 pp. 5¼x8¼. Orig. publ. at $7.20   **$4.50**

DIOPHANTISCHE APPROXIMATIONEN

By J. F. KOKSMA

—(Ergeb. der Math.) 1936. 165 pp. 5½x8½. Orig. publ. at $7.25.   **$3.50**

FOUNDATIONS OF THE THEORY OF PROBABILITY
By A. KOLMOGOROV

Translation edited by N. MORRISON. With a bibliography and notes by A. T. BHARUCHA-REID.

Almost indispensable for anyone who wishes a thorough understanding of modern statistics, this basic tract develops probability theory on a postulational basis.

—2nd. ed. 1956. viii + 84 pp. 6x9.　　　**$2.50**

EINFÜHRUNG IN DIE THEORIE DER KONTINUIERLICHEN GRUPPEN
By G. KOWALEWSKI

—406 pp. 5¼x8¼. Orig. publ. at $10.20.　　　**$4.95**

DETERMINANTENTHEORIE EINSCHLIESSLICH DER FREDHOLMSCHEN DETERMINANTEN
By G. KOWALEWSKI

"A classic in its field."—*Bulletin of the A. M. S.*
—Third edition. 1942. 328 pp. 5½x8.　　　**$4.95**

IDEALTHEORIE
By W. KRULL

—(Ergeb. der Math.) 1935. 159 pp. 5½x8½. Orig. publ. (paper bound) at $7.00.　　　Cloth, **$3.95**

GROUP THEORY
By A. KUROSH

Translated from the second Russian edition and with added notes by PROF. K. A. HIRSCH.

A complete rewriting of the first, and already famous, Russian edition.

Partial Contents: PART ONE: The Elements of Group Theory. Chap. I. Definition. II. Subgroups (Systems, Cyclic Groups, Ascending Sequences of Groups). III. Normal Subgroups. IV. Endomorphisms and Automorphisms. Groups with Operators. V. Series of Subgroups. Direct Products. Defining Relations, etc. PART TWO: Abelian Groups. VI. Foundations of the Theory of Abelian Groups (Finite Abelian Groups, Rings of Endomorphisms, Abelian Groups with Operators). VII. Primary and Mixed Abelian Groups. VIII. Torsion-Free Abelian Groups. Editor's Notes. Bibliography.

Vol. II. PART THREE: Group-Theoretical Constructions. IX. Free Products and Free Groups (Free Products with Amalgamated Subgroup, Fully Invariant Subgroups). X. Finitely Generated Groups. XI. Direct Products. Lattices (Modular, Complete Modular, etc.). XII. Extensions of Groups (of Abelian Groups, of Non-commutative Groups, Cohomology Groups). PART FOUR: Solvable and Nilpotent Groups. XIII. Finiteness Conditions, Sylow Subgroups, etc. XIV. Solvable Groups (Solvable and Generalized Solvable Groups, Local Theorems). XV. Nilpotent Groups (Generalized, Complete, Locally Nilpotent Torsion-Free, etc.). Editor's Notes. Bibliography.

—Vol. I. 1955. 271 pp. 6x9.　　　**$4.95**
—Vol. II. 1956. 308 pp. 6x9.　　　**$4.95**

DIFFERENTIAL AND INTEGRAL CALCULUS
By E. LANDAU

Landau's sparkling *Einführung* in English translation. Completely rigorous, completely self-contained, borrowing not even the fundamental theorem of algebra (of which it gives a rigorous elementary proof), it develops the entire calculus including Fourier series, starting only with the properties of the number system. A masterpiece of rigor and clarity.

—1950. 372 pp. 6x9.   **$5.00**

HANDBUCH DER LEHRE VON DER VERTEILUNG DER PRIMZAHLEN
By E. LANDAU

To Landau's monumental work on prime-number theory there has been added, in this edition, two of Landau's papers and an up-to-date guide to the work: an Appendix by Prof. Paul T. Bateman.

—2nd ed. 1953. 1,028 pp. 5½x8½.   Two vol. set **$17.50**

ELEMENTARE ZAHLENTHEORIE
By E. LANDAU

"Interest is enlisted at once and sustained by the accuracy, skill, and enthusiasm with which Landau marshals . . . facts and simplifies . . . details."
—*G. D. Birkhoff, Bulletin of the A. M. S.*

—1927. vii+180+iv pp. 5½x8¼.   **$3.50**

FOUNDATIONS OF ANALYSIS
By E. LANDAU

"Certainly no clearer treatment of the foundations of the number system can be offered. . . . One can only be thankful to the author for this fundamental piece of exposition which is alive with his vitality and genius."—*J. F. Ritt, Amer. Math. Monthly.*

—1950. 6x9.   **$3.50**

VORLESUNGEN ÜBER ZAHLENTHEORIE
By E. LANDAU

The various sections of this important work (Additive, Analytic, Geometric, and Algebraic Number Theory) can be read independently of one another.

—Vol. I, Pt. 2. ✱(Additive Number Theory) xii + 180 pp. Vol. II. (Analytical Number Theory and Geometrical Number Theory) viii + 308 pp. Vol. III. (Algebraic Number Theory and Fermat's Last Theorem) viii + 341 pp. 5¼x8¼. ✱(Vol I, Pt. 1 is issued as **Elementary Number Theory.**)   Originally publ. at **$26.40**
Three vols. in one **$12.00**

ELEMENTARY NUMBER THEORY
By E. LANDAU
—About 200 pp.   **In prep.**

GRUNDLAGEN DER ANALYSIS
By E. LANDAU

The student who wishes to learn mathematical German will find this book ideally suited to his needs. *Less than fifty German words* will enable him to read the entire book with only an occasional glance at the vocabulary! [A *complete* German-English vocabulary has been added.]

—Orig. publ. at $4.00.   **$2.95**

DARSTELLUNG UND BEGRÜNDUNG EINIGER NEUERER ERGEBNISSE DER FUNKTIONENTHEORIE

By E. LANDAU

—2nd ed. 1929. 122 pp. 5¼x8. Orig. publ. at $4.00.　**$3.25**

EINFÜHRUNG IN DIE ELEMENTARE UND ANALYTISCHE THEORIE DER ALGEBRAISCHEN ZAHLEN UND DER IDEALE

By E. LANDAU

—2nd ed. vii+147 pp. 5½x8.　**$2.95**

MÉMOIRES SUR LA THEORIE DES SYSTÈMES DES EQUATIONS DIFFERENTIELLES LINÉAIRES, Vols. I, II, III

By J. A. LAPPO-DANILEVSKY

Some of the chapter titles are: General theory of functions of matrices; Analytic theory of matrices; Problem of Poincaré; Systems of equations in neighborhood of a pole; Analytic continuation; Integral equations and their application to the theory of linear differential equations; Riemann's problem; etc.

—Vol. I. xiv + 253 pp. Vol. II. viii+ 208 pp. Vol. III. iv+204 pp. 5¼x8¼.　　Three vols. in one. **$10.00**

TOPOLOGY

By S. LEFSCHETZ

—2nd. ed. (Corr. repr. of 1st. ed.) x + 410 pp. 5¼x8¼.
$4.95

ELEMENTS OF ALGEBRA

By HOWARD LEVI

"This book is addressed to beginning students of mathematics. . . . The level of the book, however, is so unusually high, mathematically as well as pedagogically, that it merits the attention of professional mathematicians (as well as of professional pedagogues) interested in the wider dissemination of their subject among cultured people . . . a closer approximation to the right way to teach mathematics to beginners than anything else now in existence."—*Bulletin of the A. M. S.*

—2nd. ed. 1956 vi + 160 pp. 5¼x8¼.　**$3.25**

LE CALCUL DES RÉSIDUS

By E. LINDELOF

Important applications in a striking diversity of mathematical fields: statistics, number theory, the theory of Fourier series, the calculus of finite differences, mathematical physics and advanced calculus, as well as function theory itself.

—151 pp. 5½x8½.　**$3.25**

THE THEORY OF MATRICES

By C. C. MacDUFFEE

"No mathematical library can afford to be without this book."—*Bulletin of the A. M. S.*

—(Ergeb. der Math.) 2nd edition. 116 pp. 6x9. Orig. publ. at $5.20　**$2.95**

MACMAHON, "Introduction . . ." *see Klein*

COMBINATORY ANALYSIS

By P. A. MACMAHON

—Vol. I. xix + 300 pp. Vol. II. xix + 340 pp. 5¼x8¼. 2 Vols. in one. **In prep.**

FORMULAS AND THEOREMS FOR THE FUNCTIONS OF MATHEMATICAL PHYSICS

By W. MAGNUS and F. OBERHETTINGER

Gathered into a compact, handy and well-arranged reference work are thousands of results on the many important functions needed by the physicist, engineer and applied mathematician.

Translated by J. WERMER.

—1954. 182 pp. 6x9. German edition was $7.00.   **$3.90**

GEOMETRIE DER ZAHLEN

By H. MINKOWSKI

—viii+256 pp. 5½x8¼.   **$4.50**

DIOPHANTISCHE APPROXIMATIONEN

By H. MINKOWSKI

"Since the author has given an elementary, entertaining, account, both in geometric and arithmetic language, of some important original results as well as the salient features of a classic theory, but presented in a novel manner, his work is deserving of the attention of the very widest circle of readers."—*L. E. Dickson.*

—viii + 235 pp. 5¼x8¼.   **In prep.**

MORDELL, "Fermat's Last Theorem," see Klein

INVERSIVE GEOMETRY

By F. MORLEY and F. V. MORLEY

CHAPTER HEADINGS: I. Operations of Elementary Geometry. II. Algebra. III. The Euclidean Group. IV. Inversions. V. Quadratics. VI. The Inversive Group of the Plane. VII. Finite Inversive Groups. VIII. Parabolic, Hyperbolic, and Elliptic Geometries. IX. Celestial Sphere. X. Flow. XI. Differential Geometry. XII. The Line and the Circle. XIII. Regular Polygons. XIV. Motions. XV. The Triangle. XVI. Invariants under Homologies. XVII. Rational Curves. XVIII. Conics. XIX. Cardioid and Deltoid. XX. Cremona Transformations. XXI. The n-Line.

—xi + 273 pp. 5¼x8¼.   **$3.95**

VORLESUNGEN ÜBER DIFFERENZENRECHNUNG

By N. H. NÖRLUND

—ix+551pp. 5x8. Orig. publ. at $11.50.   **$5.95**

DIE LEHRE VON DEN KETTENBRUECHEN

By O. PERRON

Both the Arithmetic Theory and the Analytic Theory are treated fully.

"An indispensable work . . . Perron remains the best guide for the novice. The style is simple and precise and presents no difficulties."

—*Mathematical Gazette.*

—2nd ed. 536 pp. 5¼x8.   **$5.95**

IRRATIONALZAHLEN

By O. PERRON

Methods of introducing irrational numbers (Cauchy, Bolzano, Weierstrass, Dedekind, Cantor, Méray, Bachman, etc.) *Systematic fractions, continued fractions, Cantor's series and algorithm, Lüroth's and Engel's series, Cantor's products.* Approximations, *Kronecker theorem, Algebraic and transcendental numbers (including transcendency proofs for e and π; Liouville numbers, etc.)*

—2nd. ed. 1939. 207 pp. 5¼x8¼.   Cloth **$3.25**
                                                   Paper **$1.50**

SUBHARMONIC FUNCTIONS

By T. RADO

—(Ergeb. der Math.) 1937. iv+56 pp. 5½x8½.   **$2.00**

THE PROBLEM OF PLATEAU

By T. RADO

—(Ergeb. der Math.) 1933. 113 pp. 5½x8. Orig. publ. (in paper binding) at $5.10   Cloth, **$2.95**

EINFÜHRUNG IN DIE KOMBINATORISCHE TOPOLOGIE

By K. REIDEMEISTER

—221 pp. 5½x8¼.   **$3.50**

KNOTENTHEORIE

By K. REIDEMEISTER

—(Ergeb. der Math.) 1932. 78 pp. 5½x8½.   **$2.25**

FOURIER SERIES

By W. ROGOSINSKI

Translated by H. COHN. Designed for beginners with no more background than a year of calculus, this text covers, nevertheless, an amazing amount of ground. It is suitable for self-study courses as well as classroom use.

"The field covered is extensive and the treatment is thoroughly modern in outlook . . . An admirable guide to the theory."—*Mathematical Gazette.*

—1950. 182 pp. 4½x6½. (English translation).   **$2.25**

CONIC SECTIONS

By G. SALMON

"The classic book on the subject, covering the whole ground and full of touches of genius."
                    —*Mathematical Association.*

—6th. ed. xv + 400 pp. 5¼x8¼.   Cloth **$3.25**
                                                   Paper **$1.94**

ANALYTIC GEOMETRY OF THREE DIMENSIONS

By G. SALMON

                                                   In prep.

INTRODUCTION TO MODERN ALGEBRA AND MATRIX THEORY

By O. SCHREIER and E. SPERNER

An English translation of the revolutionary work, *Einführung in die Analytische Geometrie und Algebra*. Chapter Headings: I. Affine Space. Linear Equations. (Vector Spaces). II. Euclidean Space. Theory of Determinants. III. The Theory of Fields. Fundamental Theorem of Algebra. IV. Elements of Group Theory. V. Matrices and Linear Transformations. **The treatment of matrices is especially extensive.**

"Outstanding . . . good introduction . . . well suited for use as a text . . . Self-contained and each topic is painstakingly developed."
—*Mathematics Teacher.*

—viii + 378 pp. 6x9.   **$6.00**

PROJECTIVE GEOMETRY

By O. SCHREIER and E. SPERNER

Analytic Projective Geometry of n dimensions.
—(Being volume two of **Introduction to Modern Algebra.**)
In prep.

LEHRBUCH DER TOPOLOGIE

By H. SEIFERT and W. THRELFALL

This famous book is the only modern work on *combinatorial topology* addressed to the student as well as to the specialist. It is almost indispensable to the mathematician who wishes to gain a knowledge of this important field.

"The exposition proceeds by easy stages **with examples and illustrations at every turn.**"
—*Bulletin of the A. M. S.*

—1934. 360 pp. 5½x8½. Orig. publ. at $8.00.   **$4.95**

VARIATIONSRECHNUNG IM GROSSEN
(Theorie von Marston Morse)

By H. SEIFERT and W. THRELFALL

The brilliant expository talents of Professors Seifert and Threlfall—familiar to the many readers of their *Lehrbuch der Topologie*—are here devoted to an eminently readable account of the calculus of variations in the large.

—1938. 120 pp. 6x9.   **$2.95**

SHEPPARD, "From Determinant to Tensor," *see* Klein

HYPOTHÈSE DU CONTINU
By W. SIERPINSKI

—197 pp. 5¼x8¼. (Winter '56 or Spring '57)   **In prep.**

SINGH, "Non-Differentiable Functions," *see* Hobson

DIOPHANTISCHE GLEICHUNGEN
By T. SKOLEM

—(Ergeb. der Math.) 1938. ix+130 pp. 5½x8½. Cloth. Orig. publ. at $6.50.   **$3.50**

ALGEBRAISCHE THEORIE DER KOERPER
By E. STEINITZ
"Epoch-making."—*A. Haar, Acta Szeged.*
—177 pp. including two appendices. 5¼x8¼. **$3.25**

INTERPOLATION
By J. F. STEFFENSEN
"A landmark in the history of the subject.

"Starting from scratch, the author deals with formulae of interpolation, construction of tables, inverse interpolation, summation of formulae, the symbolic calculus, interpolation with several variables, in a clear, elegant and rigorous manner ... The student ... will be rewarded by a comprehensive view of the whole field. ... A classic account which no serious student can afford to neglect."—*Mathematical Gazette.*
—1950. 2nd ed. 256 pp. 5¼x8¼. Orig. publ. at $8.00. **$3.95**

A HISTORY OF THE MATHEMATICAL THEORY OF PROBABILITY
By I. TODHUNTER
Introduces the reader to *almost every process and every species of problem which the literature of the subject can furnish.* Hundreds of problems are solved in detail.
—640 pages. 5¼x8. Previously publ. at $8.00. **$4.95**

LECTURES ON THE GENERAL THEORY OF INTEGRAL FUNCTIONS
By G. VALIRON
—1923. xii+208 pp. 5¼x8. **$3.50**

GRUPPEN VON LINEAREN TRANSFORMATIONEN
By B. L. VAN DER WAERDEN
—(Ergeb. der Math.) 1935. 94 pp. 5½x8½. **$2.50**

ALGEBRAIC SURFACES
By O. ZARISKI
—(Ergeb. der Math.) 1935. 204 pp. 5½x8½. Orig. publ. at $9.20. **$4.50**

THE THEORY OF GROUPS
By H. ZASSENHAUS
Prof. Zassenhaus has revised and added considerable new material in this second English edition of his famous textbook. Lattice theory, subinvariant subgroups, semi-groups, and other topics that have come into prominence are treated and numerous exercises on the new material provided.
—2nd ed. Approx. viii+265 pp. 6x9. (Winter, '56.)
Prob. price **$5.95**

TRIGONOMETRIC SERIES
By A. ZYGMUND
"*The* book on Fourier Series."
—*Bulletin of the A. M. S.*
—2nd. ed. 324 pp. 6x9.
Cloth **$4.95**
Paper **$1.50**